BRIEF REVIEW in

Biology

BERTRAM COREN

Reviewed by
Mary P. Colvard
Biology Teacher
Golding High School
Cobleskill, New York

ORDER INFORMATION

Send orders to:

PRENTICE HALL SCHOOL DIVISION
CUSTOMER SERVICE CENTER
4350 Equity Drive
P.O. Box 2649
Columbus, OH 43272

or

CALL TOLL-FREE: 1-800-848-9500
(8:00 AM–4:30 PM)

- Orders processed with your call. Please include the ISBN number on the back cover when ordering.
- **Your price includes all shipping and handling.**

PRENTICE HALL Textbook Programs that help you meet the requirements of the Regents:

Biology: The Study of Life
Biology by Miller and Levine
Chemistry: The Study of Matter
Chemistry: Connections to Our Changing World
Physics: Its Methods and Meanings
Earth Science: A Study of a Changing Planet

Prentice Hall

Needham, Massachusetts   Upper Saddle River, New Jersey

ABOUT THIS BOOK

Brief Review in Biology provides a thorough review of the Regents Biology course and intensive preparation for the Regents Examination in Biology. The following are some of its noteworthy features:

1. It provides a clear, accurate, and concise presentation of the facts, vocabulary, and biological concepts required by the latest Regents syllabus. Numerous drawings, charts, and tables supplement the text.

2. There is a convenient arrangement of text and practice questions. Short sections of text are followed by Regents-type questions on the topics covered.

3. Extended Area material, which is tested only on Part II of the Regents Examination, is clearly identified.

4. In addition to the topically arranged questions, there are separate sections of Practice Tests for the Extended Areas tested on Part II of the Regents Examination and a separate practice section for the Laboratory Skills and Reading Comprehension tested on Part III. Several new questions have been added to this revised section. There are over 800 questions in all.

5. Important vocabulary terms are highlighted in bold type and clearly defined in the glossary.

6. Special emphasis is placed on the representative organisms selected by the syllabus. There are comparative diagrams of organ systems in Unit II and diagrams of the body structures of representative organisms on pages 252–253.

7. Several of the most recent Regents Examinations are included.

8. A College Board review section reviews topics usually given light coverage in biology courses and includes a practice College Board test.

Credits

Editorial   Julia A. Fellows, Natania Mlawer, Beth A. Norman, Thomas L. Messer
Marketing   Arthur C. Germano, Joel Gendler
Design   Alison Anholt-White, Jonathan Pollard
Production   David Graham, Robin Tiano
Manufacturing   Jackie Zidek Bedoya

Cover Design: Richard Hannus

PRENTICE HALL
A Viacom Company
Upper Saddle River, New Jersey 07458

CONTENTS

UNIT I   UNITY AND DIVERSITY AMONG LIVING THINGS

I-1. CONCEPT OF LIFE

A. DEFINITION OF LIFE. Scientists have not been able to agree upon a single, simple definition of life. Living organisms perform certain functions that are taken to be the characteristics of life.

B. THE LIFE FUNCTIONS. The following are the functions or activities carried on by living organisms.

  1. Nutrition includes the activities by which an organism obtains materials from its environment and prepares them for its use. In the case of animals, nutrition includes **ingestion** (the taking in of food), **digestion** (the breakdown of food molecules so that they can be absorbed into the organism), and **egestion** (the removal of indigestible or undigested food materials).

  2. Transport includes absorption of materials into the organism and distribution of the materials within the organism.

  3. Respiration includes the chemical processes by which an organism obtains energy from food materials in order to maintain its life functions.

  4. Excretion is the removal of waste products produced within the organism as a result of metabolic activities.

  5. Synthesis includes the chemical activities by which an organism builds large molecules from smaller ones.

  6. Regulation is the control and coordination of the various activities of an organism, including response to stimuli.

  7. Growth is the use of the products of synthesis to increase the cell size and/or the number of cells of an organism.

  8. Reproduction is the production of new individuals. Since individual organisms have a limited life span, reproduction is necessary for the survival of the type of organism, or species.

C. METABOLISM. The term **metabolism** refers to all the chemical processes by which an organism carries on its life functions and maintains its life.

D. HOMEOSTASIS. By means of the control and regulation of its metabolic activities, an organism maintains a stable, or fairly constant, internal environment, even though wide changes occur in the external environment. This maintenance of a stable internal environment is called **homeostasis.**

QUESTIONS

1. The process by which animals take in materials to be used for nourishment is called   (1) digestion   (2) ingestion   (3) egestion   (4) circulation

2. Some large, insoluble food molecules are reduced to small, soluble food molecules by the process of   (1) ingestion   (2) digestion   (3) assimilation   (4) excretion

3. Which life function includes the absorption and circulation of essential substances throughout an organism?   (1) transport   (2) excretion   (3) ingestion   (4) nutrition

4. The energy-releasing process in all plant and animal cells is known as   (1) secretion   (2) photosynthesis   (3) respiration   (4) circulation

5. The life activity known as synthesis is chiefly characterized by the (1) distribution of essential compounds throughout an organism (2) production of complex molecules from simple molecules   (3) elimination of waste products from the organism   (4) regulation of physiological activities

6. The process by which an organism maintains its stability through coordinated activity in a constantly changing environment is   (1) reproduction   (2) growth   (3) regulation   (4) synthesis

7. Which life activity is not essential for the maintenance of an individual organism?   (1) reproduction   (2) synthesis   (3) excretion (4) regulation

8. The concentration of glucose in the blood of a certain animal is always about the same. This is an example of   (1) digestion   (2) homeostasis   (3) synthesis   (4) excretion

I-2. THE DIVERSITY OF LIFE

A. NEED FOR CLASSIFICATION. All organisms are basically alike in the life functions they perform. This is referred to as the *unity of life*. However, there is great variety in the ways and means by which different organisms carry on these functions. This is referred to as the *diversity of life*. In order to study the variety of life in an organized and systematic manner, the different kinds of organisms are grouped, or **classified,** on the basis of certain common characteristics or relationships they share. Classification of organisms is based mainly on similarities of structure, supplemented by other evidence of relationships such as the fossil record, genetic makeup, life-cycle characteristics, embryonic development, and chemical similarities. Modern classification systems are based on the assumption that all present forms of life developed from earlier forms and have common ancestors. The grouping of organisms suggests relationships among them that may be the result of common ancestry.

B. MODERN CLASSIFICATION SYSTEMS. In classifying organisms, they are first separated into **kingdoms.** Biologists have not agreed upon the number of kingdoms to be used. All systems have a **plant** kingdom and an **animal** kingdom. The plants in general are multicellular and make their own food by photosynthesis. Animals are multicellular and ingest food from their environment. In one modern system, bacteria and certain unicellular organisms called blue-green algae are placed in a kingdom called the **Monera.** The cells of the Monera do not have a distinct nucleus surrounded by a membrane. All other single-celled, or unicellular, organisms and some of the simplest multicellular organisms are placed in a kingdom called the **Protista** (or protists). The cells of the Protista do have a distinct nucleus surrounded by a membrane. The **Fungi** make up a fifth kingdom. Some of the fungi (the yeasts) are unicellular, but most of them have a branched, multinucleated structure. They are not photosynthetic. They digest and absorb nutrients from the environment.

C. PHYLA. The organisms in each kingdom are separated into major groups called **phyla** (singular, **phylum**). Table 1-1 lists a few of the phyla in each kingdom, with their distinguishing characteristics and representative examples. The underlined examples are representative organisms studied in detail in the Regents biology course. (See *Body Structures of Representative Organisms* at the end of the book.)

D. NOMENCLATURE. Within each phylum, organisms are separated into smaller and smaller groups in which the members become increasingly alike. Each organism is named by the binomial system developed by Linnaeus. In this system, the first part of an organism's name is its **genus** (plural, *genera*). The second part of an organism's name is its **species** within the genus. Names are in Latin, usually *italicized,* with the genus name capitalized and the species name not capitalized. A species (the plural is also *species*) is a group of organisms that reproduce their own kind and if they mate with one another, produce offspring also capable of reproduction. Organisms in the same genus are very similar. Examples of different species within the same genus are *Felis domestica* (the domestic cat), *Felis leo* (the lion), and *Felis tigris* (the tiger). The genus name of these species is *Felis.* The binomial name of humans is *Homo sapiens.*

QUESTIONS

   1. The classification of plants and animals is based chiefly on (1) the chemical composition of living substance (2) evolutionary succession (3) similarity of life functions (4) structural and biochemical similarities

   2. The arrangement of plants and animals in taxonomic groups which show increasing complexity is mainly a reflection of (1) gradual change or evolution (2) the great diversity in the habitats of organisms (3) the importance of DNA in heredity (4) the great similarity in the structure of organisms

   3. In one commonly used modern system of classification, every organism is classified in one of five (1) phyla (2) kingdoms (3) genera (4) species

   4. According to the modern, five-kingdom system of classification, which two are classified as plants? (1) ferns and maple trees (2) fungi and slime molds (3) algae and fungi (4) lichens and pine trees

   5. Which organisms may be classified as protists? (1) bryophytes and tracheophytes (2) algae and protozoans (3) arthropods and chordates (4) protozoans and coelenterates

   6. Which is characteristic of all tracheophytes? (1) Conducting tissue is present. (2) Flowers are produced. (3) Seeds develop within fruits. (4) Seeds develop within cones.

TABLE 1-1. A FEW PHYLA IN THE FIVE-KINGDOM CLASSIFICATION.

Kingdom	Phylum	Distinguishing Characteristics	Examples
MONERA	Schizomycetes (bacteria)	primitive cell structure with no nuclear membrane, mitochondria, or endoplasmic reticulum; have cell wall; some are photosynthetic	*Escherichia coli* (lives in human intestine)
	Cyanophyta (blue-green algae)	cells larger than bacteria; all are photosynthetic; chlorophyll not enclosed in chloroplasts	
PROTISTS	Protozoa	unicellular or colonial; animal-like nutrition	<u>paramecium</u>, <u>ameba</u>
	Algae	unicellular or multicellular; plant-like nutrition (photosynthetic); cells have cell walls and chloroplasts	spirogyra, kelp
	Slime molds	usually consist of a mass of cytoplasm with many nuclei; move by amebalike motion; resemble both protozoa and fungi	
FUNGI		multicellular (except yeasts), with branched, multinucleated structure; not photosynthetic; absorb digested nutrients from environment	yeast, bread mold, mushrooms
PLANTS	Bryophytes	no conducting (vascular) tissue; no true roots, stems, or leaves	mosses
	Tracheophytes	have vascular tissue, true roots, stems, and leaves	ferns; evergreens (pines, hemlocks); flowering plants (beans, corn, geranium, coleus, trees)
ANIMALS	Coelenterates	body wall has two cell layers; hollow body cavity with one opening; radial symmetry	<u>hydra</u>, jellyfish
	Annelids	worms with segmented body; tube-within-a-tube body structure; openings at both ends	<u>earthworm</u>, leech, sandworm
	Arthropods	segmented body; jointed appendages; exoskeleton	<u>grasshopper</u>, lobster, spider
	Chordates	dorsal nerve cord	
	Subphylum Vertebrates	true backbone	fish, frog, snake, bird, humans

7. Which organisms contain vascular tissues? (1) algae (2) bread molds (3) apple trees (4) lichens

8. Which combination of traits would identify an animal as probably belonging to the phylum arthropods? (1) dorsal nerve cord, endoskeleton, closed circulatory system (2) nonsegmented body, ventral nerve cord (3) exoskeleton, segmented body, jointed appendages (4) ventrally located heart, unilaterally symmetrical body

9. The proper order for the classification of organisms is (1) kingdom, phylum, species, genus (2) kingdom, genus, phylum, species (3) phylum, kingdom, genus, species (4) kingdom, phylum, genus, species

10. In which group would there be the greatest similarity between members in terms of structure and function? (1) species (2) genus (3) kingdom (4) phylum

11. Which pair of organisms belongs to the same genus? (1) jellyfish and tuna (2) whale and shark (3) horse and cow (4) lion and tiger

Base your answers to questions 12 and 13 on the paragraph below:

> "Today scientists generally agree that a group of organisms should be considered a basic group if it consists of organisms which have certain similarities and which can mate with each other and produce fertile offspring."

12. The "basic group" referred to is a (1) genus (2) species (3) phylum (4) kingdom

13. The "certain similarities" referred to are similarities in (1) structure, evolutionary history, and embryological development (2) structure and evolutionary history, but not embryological development (3) structure and embryological development, but not evolutionary history (4) evolutionary history and embryological development, but not structure

I-3. THE STRUCTURE OF CELLS

A. THE CELL THEORY. The basic statements of the cell theory are:

1. *The cell is the unit of structure and function in living things.* This means that every organism is made up of one or more cells and that the life functions of the organism are performed by its cells working individually or together in tissues and organs.

2. *Cells come only from pre-existing cells.* This means that no cell today can arise from noncellular materials or structures. New cells are formed by division of existing cells.

B. HISTORICAL DEVELOPMENT OF THE CELL THEORY. The discovery of cells and their structure and function was made possible by the invention and gradual improvement of the microscope. The scientists who made major contributions to the development of the cell theory were:

1. Anton van Leeuwenhoek (1632-1723). Dutch. Using simple (one-lens) microscopes that he made himself, discovered one-celled organisms, sperm cells, and blood cells.

2. Robert Hooke (1635-1703). English. Examined slices of cork and other plant materials with the compound microscope. Saw structure of hollow spaces, which he named *cells*. He actually observed only the walls of the plant cells.

3. Robert Brown (1773-1858). English. Discovered the cell nucleus.

4. Matthias Jakob Schleiden (1804-1881). German. Stated that all plants were composed of cells.

5. Theodor Schwann (1810-1882). German. Stated that animal tissues were also composed of cells.

Schleiden and Schwann are considered to have established the cell theory of the structure of living things.

6. Rudolph Virchow (1821-1902). German. Stated that all cells arise from pre-existing cells, thus completing the cell theory in its modern form.

C. EXCEPTIONS TO THE CELL THEORY. Several biological facts are not explained by the cell theory:

1. Viruses, which consist of DNA or RNA in a protein capsule, reproduce themselves inside living cells, but are not cells themselves.

2. Certain parts of cells, such as mitochondria and chloroplasts, have their own DNA and apparently can duplicate themselves.

3. The first cells must have arisen from noncellular structures.

QUESTIONS

1. Which of the following statements is NOT considered to be generally true of living organisms? (1) The simplest organisms have no cells. (2) New cells can arise today only from existing cells. (3) Groups of cells work together to perform the functions of a complex organism. (4) Some organisms consist of a single cell.

For each phrase in questions 2 through 5 select the number of the name of the scientist, chosen from the list below, to whom the phrase best applies.

Scientists
(1) Robert Brown
(2) Robert Hooke
(3) Anton van Leeuwenhoek
(4) Rudolph Virchow

2. Gave the name *cells* to structures he saw in dead plant tissue.
3. First person to report seeing microscopic organisms.
4. Discovered the cell nucleus.
5. Stated that all cells arise from pre-existing cells.

6. The modern cell theory fails to account for (1) bacteria (2) reproduction (3) viruses (4) tissues

D. TECHNIQUES OF CELL STUDY. Improvements in the microscope and development of related techniques made possible our present knowledge of cell structures and functions.

1. The compound light microscope has two **lenses** or lens combinations: (a) the **objective** lens, which forms a magnified image of the specimen, and (b) the **ocular,** or **eyepiece** lens, which further magnifies the image. The specimen must usually be transparent. The main parts of a compound microscope are shown in Figure 1-1. The functions of these parts are:

Tube: Holds the lenses.

Nosepiece: Rotates to change objective lens from one power to another.

Stage: Platform on which specimen is mounted for observation. Specimen is usually on a glass slide.

Clips: Hold the slide in position.

Diaphragm: Controls diameter of light beam passing through the specimen. Smaller openings increase resolution, or amount of detail in image.

Mirror: Directs light from horizontal source up through diaphragm and specimen. May be replaced by **substage light source.**

Arm: Holds tube and stage; used for carrying the instrument.

Base: Supports the instrument.

Coarse adjustment: Used for preliminary focusing under low power (up to 100X) only; coarse adjustment must NEVER be used when high-power objective is in viewing position.

Fine adjustment: Used for focusing under high power and for final focusing under low power. Should never be turned more than one-half turn in either direction.

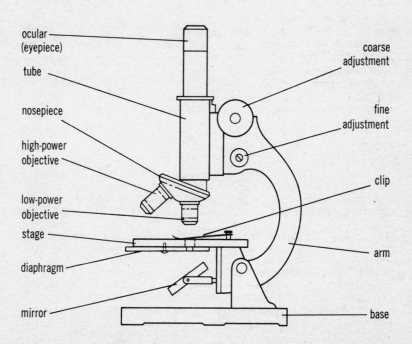

Figure 1-1. The compound microscope.

2. The **magnification,** or **magnifying power,** of a compound microscope is the product of the power of the objective multiplied by the power of the ocular. For example, if the objective is 43X and the ocular is 10X, the total power is 43 × 10 = 430X. Useful magnification of a light microscope is limited by its **resolving power** (ability to separate two objects close together). Properties of light place an upper limit on resolving power of any light microscope.

3. The **electron microscope** uses beams of electrons, rather than light waves, to produce magnified images. Focusing is accomplished with magnetic lenses. This microscope is capable of very high resolving power and useful magnification. Specimens must be extremely thin, specially fixed and treated, and mounted in high vacuum in order to be observed. Living specimens cannot be observed.

4. The **dissecting microscope** is a binocular, or twin-tube, microscope that presents a slightly different view of the specimen to each eye, producing an image with depth (three dimensions). It is useful for examining opaque objects and small organisms or body structures.

5. The **phase contrast microscope** can be used to observe unstained living cells in which structures could not be seen under ordinary microscope.

6. The **ultracentrifuge** is a device that can separate the parts of cells according to their different densities by whirling them in a test tube at very high speed.

7. Microdissection instruments can be used under the microscope for removal, addition, or transfer of cell parts.

8. Staining. Structures in cells can be made visible by treatment with solutions that color certain parts of cells and not others. This technique is called **staining.**

9. Measurement. Scientists use the **micrometer** (symbol, μm) as a unit of length in measurements of microscopic structures. One micrometer equals 1/1000 millimeter; 1000 micrometers equals one millimeter.

QUESTIONS

1. The lens of a compound microscope that is close to the specimen is called the   (1) diaphragm   (2) objective   (3) eyepiece   (4) low-power lens

2. A specimen being observed under high power of a compound microscope appears blurred and indistinct. The part of the microscope that should be manipulated to obtain a clearer image is the   (1) fine adjustment   (2) coarse adjustment   (3) mirror   (4) diaphragm

3. A microscope has a 10X eyepiece, and a 10X and a 40X objective. The magnifications that can be obtained with this microscope are (1) 10X and 40X   (2) 40X and 400X   (3) 10X, 100X, and 400X   (4) 100X and 400X

4. The useful magnification that can be obtained with a light microscope is limited by   (1) the length of its tube   (2) the diameter of its objective lens   (3) its resolution   (4) the amount of light

5. The internal structure of chloroplasts is best studied with the aid of which type of microscope? (1) simple (2) compound light (3) electron (4) phase contrast

6. Which would most probably be used to observe unstained, living tissues? (1) electron microscope (2) phase-contrast microscope (3) ultracentrifuge (4) microdissection instruments

7. Which would be used to collect mitochondria from cells of different organisms? (1) electron microscope (2) microdissection apparatus (3) microtome (4) ultracentrifuge

8. The width of a human hair is 0.1 millimeter. The width of this human hair in micrometers is (1) 1 (2) 10 (3) 100 (4) 1000

E. ORGANELLES OF CELLS. Various functions of cells occur in specialized structures called **organelles.** The chief organelles and their functions are:

1. Plasma (or cell) membrane: Thin, two-layered film that surrounds entire cell. Consists of lipid molecules in which protein molecules are embedded. It is described as **semipermeable, differentially permeable,** or **selectively permeable.** This means it permits the passage or transport of certain materials into and out of the cell, and prevents transport of other materials.

2. Cytoplasm: The fluid-like material inside the plasma membrane and outside the nucleus of the cell. Various organelles are present in the cytoplasm and many biochemical processes occur in it.

3. Nucleus: Structure containing the chromosomes and DNA of the cell, which carry hereditary information and direct the biochemical activities of the cell. Separated from the cytoplasm by the **nuclear membrane.**

4. Nucleolus: Structure within the nucleus that is involved in the synthesis of the RNA found in ribosomes.

5. Endoplasmic reticulum (ER): A network of channels in the cytoplasm that function in synthesizing, transporting, and storing substances made in the cell.

6. Ribosomes: Small structures that are the sites of protein synthesis. There are large numbers of ribosomes in the cell, which may be free in the cytoplasm or attached to the surface of the ER.

7. Mitochondria (singular, *mitochondrion*): Sites of aerobic cellular respiration. Most ATP of the cell is made in the mitochondria.

8. Golgi complex: Membrane-bound channels in which materials are synthesized or packaged.

9. Lysosomes: Structures that contain digestive enzymes and which take part in the digestion of food materials.

10. Vacuoles: Spaces in the cytoplasm enclosed by a membrane and containing water and other materials. Many one-celled organisms have **food vacuoles** in which ingested food is stored and digested, and **contractile vacuoles** that pump excess water out of the cell.

11. Centrioles: A pair of cylindrical structures found just outside the nuclear membrane in most animal cells. The centrioles are active during cell division.

12. Cell wall: A nonliving structure composed mainly of cellulose, which surrounds the cell and gives it strength and rigidity; usually present in plant cells. It has pores or openings that permit free passage of water and dissolved substances.

13. Chloroplasts: Structures, found in plant cells, algae, and some other protists, that contain the pigment chlorophyll and are the sites of photosynthesis.

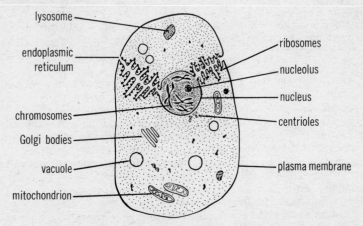

Figure 1-2. A generalized animal cell. This is a diagrammatic representation of the structures found in animal cells, not a drawing of any actual cell.

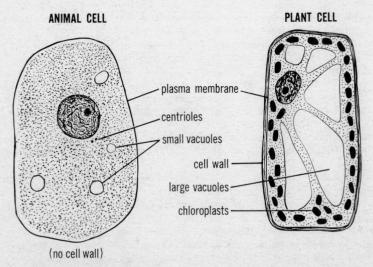

Figure 1-3. A comparison of typical animal and plant cells. The differences usually observed are illustrated.

QUESTIONS

1. Which structure is a boundary between the living cell and its environment? (1) endoplasmic reticulum (2) mitochondrial crista (3) cell membrane (4) vacuolar membrane

2. Which structure carries out a similar function in both plant and animal cells? (1) cell wall (2) chloroplast (3) anal pore (4) plasma membrane

3. Which are the main structural components of a cell membrane? (1) proteins and carbohydrates (2) lipids and cellulose (3) amino acids and proteins (4) proteins and lipids

4. An organelle differs from an organ in that an organelle (1) is a substructure of a cell (2) contains one specific type of tissue (3) is larger than an organ (4) cannot be stained

5. Under high power magnification of the electron microscope, which cell structure would resemble the one sketched?
(1) ribosome
(2) mitochondrion
(3) chloroplast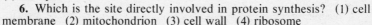
(4) endoplasmic reticulum

6. Which is the site directly involved in protein synthesis? (1) cell membrane (2) mitochondrion (3) cell wall (4) ribosome

7. With which function would structure X normally be associated?
(1) intracellular transport
(2) formation of ATP
(3) reproduction
(4) digestion

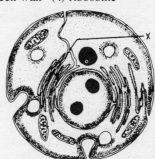

8. Which cell structure is nonliving? (1) endoplasmic reticulum (2) chloroplast (3) cell wall (4) centrosome

9. Which are common to most plant and animal cells? (1) cell wall and nucleus (2) vacuole and chloroplast (3) cytoplasm and cell membrane (4) centrosome and nucleolus

10. Which cellular structures are found in the epidermal cells of humans but not in the epidermal cells of leaves? (1) centrioles (2) mitochondria (3) cell membranes (4) chromosomes

I-4. THE CHEMISTRY OF LIFE

A. CHEMICAL ELEMENTS

1. Elements are single substances that cannot be broken down into simpler substances. 105 different elements are known.

2. Elements in living things. Four of the elements—carbon, hydrogen, oxygen, and nitrogen—are the most common in living things. Others present in smaller percentages include sulfur, phosphorus, magnesium, iron, iodine, calcium, sodium, chlorine, and potassium.

3. Symbols. Each element is represented by a **symbol,** which may be a single capital letter or two letters of which the first is capitalized. The symbols of the elements named above are given in Table 1-2.

TABLE 1-2. SYMBOLS OF SOME ELEMENTS FOUND IN LIVING ORGANISMS.

Name	Symbol	Name	Symbol
carbon	C	iron	Fe
hydrogen	H	iodine	I
oxygen	O	calcium	Ca
nitrogen	N	sodium	Na
sulfur	S	chlorine	Cl
phosphorus	P	potassium	K
magnesium	Mg		

4. Atoms. Each element is made up of particles called **atoms.** The atoms of a given element are alike, and different from the atoms of any other element.

5. Atomic structure. Each atom has a central region called the **nucleus,** which contains positively charged particles called **protons** and neutral (uncharged) particles called **neutrons.** Negatively charged particles called **electrons** are located in *shells* or *energy levels* around the nucleus. The atoms of each element have a specific number of electrons (different for each element) in a distinct arrangement by shells.

B. CHEMICAL COMPOUNDS

1. Compounds are chemical combinations of two or more elements.

2. Chemical bonding. Atoms combine to form compounds either by transferring electrons from one atom to another, or by sharing electrons between them. When electrons are *transferred,* the atoms acquire an electric charge and become **ions.** This process is called **ionic bonding,** and the compound forms an *ionic crystal.* When electrons are *shared,* the process is called **covalent bonding,** and the atoms that share electrons form **molecules.**

3. Formulas. The composition of a compound can be shown by a **formula.** An *empirical formula* shows the symbols of the elements in the compound followed by small subscript numbers showing the ratios of the atoms in the compound. A *structural formula* shows how atoms are joined by covalent bonds to form a molecule of the compound.

4. Inorganic compounds are compounds that do not contain both carbon and hydrogen. Inorganic compounds have relatively simple compositions. Inorganic compounds found in living things include water, salts (minerals), inorganic acids, and bases.

5. Organic compounds are compounds containing the elements carbon and hydrogen. They are formed in nature by the activities of living organisms (but they can also be synthesized in the laboratory). Organic compounds can be very complex because of the special bonding power of carbon. A carbon atom can form four covalent bonds with other atoms, while most of the other atoms can form only one or two bonds. As a result, carbon compounds can consist of long chains of atoms, or of closed rings of atoms with many side branches.

6. Importance of water. Of all the substances in living cells, water is by far the most abundant. In some cells the cytoplasm is over 90% water. Water is essential for the life functions of cells, mainly because it is a substance in which many other substances will dissolve. Most chemical reactions occur only in water solutions. Water is also important as a raw material for certain reactions, as the agent for hydrolysis (page 31), and as a transport medium.

C. KINDS OF ORGANIC COMPOUNDS. The major kinds of organic compounds in living things are *carbohydrates, lipids, proteins,* and *nucleic acids.*

1. Carbohydrates. Carbohydrates are made of the elements carbon, hydrogen, and oxygen. Hydrogen and oxygen atoms are usually present in a ratio of 2:1, the same as in water, H_2O. Examples of formulas of carbohydrates are: $C_6H_{12}O_6$; $C_{12}H_{22}O_{11}$; $C_5H_{10}O_5$.

a. Monosaccharides. Most carbohydrates are made up of units called **sugars.** The simple sugars are the smallest units and are called **monosaccharides.** The names of sugars usually end in *ose.* Glucose, fructose, and galactose are examples of monosaccharides. They have the molecular formula $C_6H_{12}O_6$.

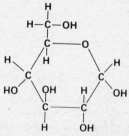

Figure 1-4. Structure of glucose, a monosaccharide.

b. Disaccharides. Carbohydrates made of two simple sugars joined together are called **disaccharides.** Maltose, sucrose, and lactose are examples of disaccharides. They have the molecular formula $C_{12}H_{22}O_{11}$.

c. Dehydration synthesis is a chemical process by which two molecules are joined to form a larger molecule (synthesis). In this process, a water molecule is removed (dehydration). The reaction by which two monosaccharide units are combined to form a disaccharide molecule by dehydration synthesis is represented in Figure 1-5.

d. Polysaccharides. Dehydration synthesis can link similar units into long chains called **polymers.** Carbohydrates made of many sugar units joined together into long chains are called **polysaccharides.** Starches and cellulose are polysaccharides.

Note: The monosaccharide units in a polysaccharide need not be alike.

e. Hydrolysis. Polymers can be broken down into simpler units by **hydrolysis,** which is the reverse of dehydration synthesis (see Human Digestion, page 67).

f. Uses of carbohydrates. In living things, sugars are used as sources of energy. Surplus sugars not immediately needed for energy are stored in the form of starches. Carbohydrates are also used to make cell structures, for example, the cellulose in cell walls.

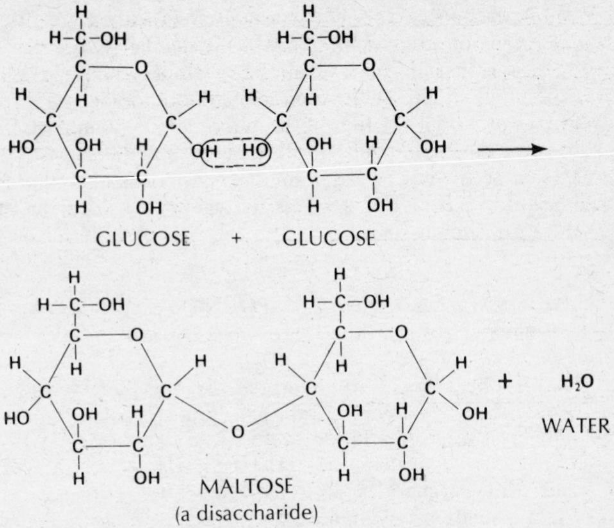

Figure 1-5. Dehydration synthesis of maltose.

2. Lipids, like carbohydrates, are made of the elements carbon, hydrogen, and oxygen. However, the ratio of hydrogen to oxygen is much greater than 2:1 and varies from one lipid to another. Lipids include *fats,* which are solids at room temperature, and *oils,* which are liquids. They are used in living organisms as sources of stored energy and as components of cell structures, for example, in cell membranes.

a. Chemical structure. A lipid molecule is a combination of three *fatty acid molecules* and one molecule of *glycerol* (see Figure 1-6).

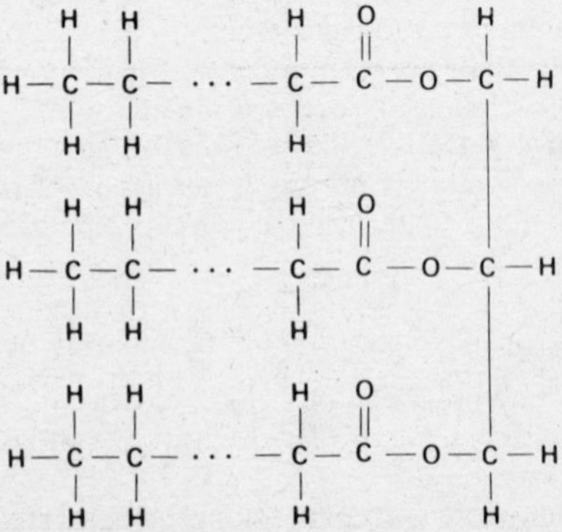

Figure 1-6. The chemical structure of a lipid.

b. Dehydration synthesis of a lipid. The formation of a lipid by dehydration synthesis is represented in Figure 1-8 (page 16).

3. Proteins contain the element nitrogen in addition to carbon, hydrogen, and oxygen. Many proteins also contain some sulfur. Thousands of different proteins are synthesized in living cells. They are used to make cell structures, such as cell membranes. All enzymes are proteins. Many hormones, such as insulin, are proteins, as well as many other important substances necessary for life functions, such as hemoglobin.

a. Chemical structure. A protein molecule is composed of molecular units called **amino acids.** Living organisms use twenty different amino acids to synthesize their proteins. Each amino acid molecule has an *amino group* at one end and a *carboxyl group* (acid group) at the other end. A variable group represented by the letter R is bonded to one of the carbon atoms. Each different amino acid has a different R group, but otherwise they are alike. The structure of an amino acid is represented in Figure 1-7.

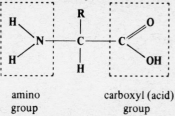

amino group

carboxyl (acid) group

Figure 1-7. Structure of an amino acid.

By continued dehydration synthesis, many amino acids can be joined to form a long chain called a **polypeptide** (see Figure 1-9).

A protein molecule consists of one or more polypeptide chains, which twist, coil, and fold to give the molecule a characteristic shape.

4. Nucleic acids are long chains of repeating units that carry hereditary, or genetic, information and control the life processes of cells. They are discussed more fully in Unit V (pages 134-138).

QUESTIONS

(Core Topics)

1. Which are the four most abundant elements in living cells? (1) carbon, oxygen, nitrogen, sulfur   (2) carbon, oxygen, hydrogen, nitrogen   (3) carbon, oxygen, sulfur, phosphorus   (4) carbon, sulfur, hydrogen, magnesium

2. Which pair of compounds can be classified as inorganic?   (1) nucleic acids and minerals   (2) proteins and water   (3) water and salts   (4) nucleic acids and proteins

3. Which chemical formula represents an organic compound? (1) H_2O (2) $NaCl$ (3) NH_3 (4) $C_6H_{12}O_6$

4. The most abundant compound in cytoplasm is   (1) fat   (2) water   (3) protein   (4) carbohydrates

5. One of the carbon compounds found in a cell has twice as many hydrogen atoms as oxygen atoms. This compound most likely belongs to the group of substances known as   (1) nucleic acids   (2) lipids   (3) proteins   (4) carbohydrates

████ EXTENDED AREA—BIOCHEMISTRY ████

FIGURE 1-8. DEHYDRATION SYNTHESIS OF A LIPID

FIGURE 1-9. DEHYDRATION SYNTHESIS OF A DIPEPTIDE

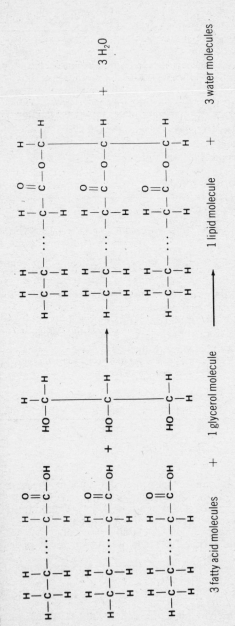

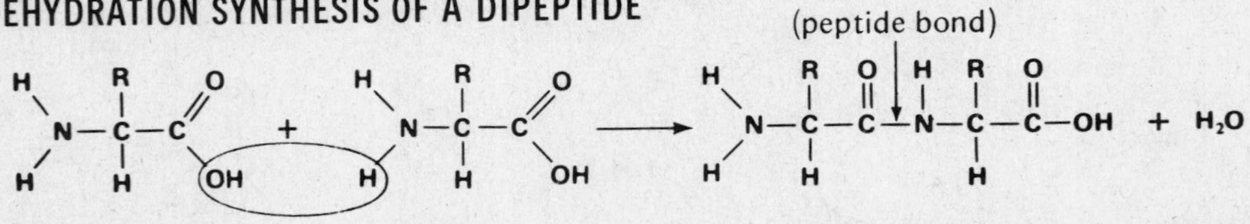

6. A compound whose chemical composition is most closely related to maltose is (1) starch (2) ATP (3) protein (4) RNA

7. Which general formula best represents a monosaccharide? (1) C_2O (2) C_2HO (3) CHO_2 (4) CH_2O

8. Water is produced as a waste product by the process of (1) dehydration synthesis (2) protein ingestion (3) carbohydrate digestion (4) absorption of minerals

9. What are the most common building blocks of fats? (1) alcohol and carbohydrates (2) alcohol and proteins (3) glycerol and amino acids (4) glycerol and fatty acids

10. Compared to carbohydrates, the ratio of hydrogen to oxygen in lipids is (1) the same (2) sometimes smaller (3) always smaller (4) always greater

11. As a class of compounds, lipids include (1) fats and oils (2) fats, carbohydrates, and proteins (3) alcohols and acids (4) sugars and starches

12. Fertilizers containing radioactive nitrogen compounds are used in growing experimental plants. In which molecules would these compounds be detected first? (1) sugar (2) starch (3) proteins (4) fats

13. Amino acids are required in the human diet principally for the synthesis of (1) proteins (2) sugars (3) starches (4) lipids

14. A sample of small, soluble, organic molecules was analyzed and found to contain the elements carbon, oxygen, hydrogen, and nitrogen. It is most likely that the molecules were (1) lipids (2) fatty acids (3) simple sugars (4) amino acids

15. The process by which amino acids are chemically joined together is called (1) pinocytosis (2) hydrolysis (3) nitrogen fixation (4) dehydration synthesis

16. Protein has a great potential for variation of structure because (1) many amino acids may combine in a number of ways (2) different types of amino acids may occur in pairs (3) fatty acids may vary (4) nucleotides may vary

17. Which substance is classified as a protein? (1) sucrose (2) glycerol (3) starch (4) hemoglobin

QUESTIONS

(Extended Area—Biochemistry)

1. The compound represented by this structural formula is a(n)
(1) amino acid
(2) lipid
(3) fatty acid
(4) monosaccharide

Questions 2 and 3 refer to the following chemical equation:

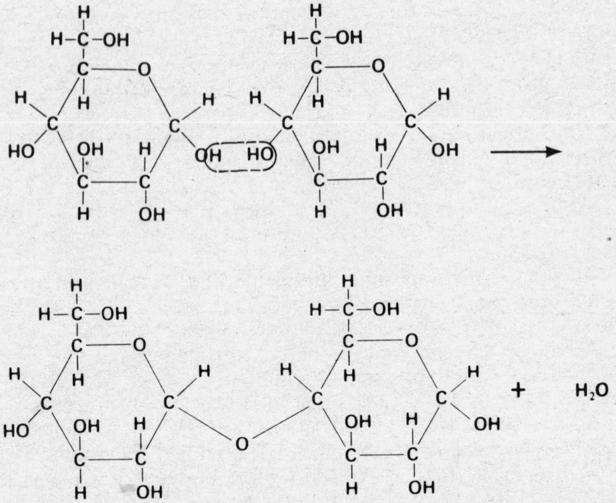

2. The reaction represented is an example of (1) protein synthesis (2) dehydration synthesis (3) hydrolysis (4) chemical digestion

3. One of the products of this reaction is a (1) polypeptide (2) disaccharide (3) simple sugar (4) lipid

4. Molecules made up of long chains of repeating units are called (1) polymers (2) enzymes (3) fatty acids (4) DNA

5. Which group of atoms is always a part of a fatty acid?

(1) —C(=O)—OH (2) H—N—C=O (3) $—HPO_3$ (4) —N(H)—H

6. The formula $C_{68}H_{103}O_{45}N_{17}S_2$ most likely represents a (1) lipid (2) polysaccharide (3) starch (4) protein

7. Which type of organic compound has molecules that include both an amino group and a carboxyl group? (1) alcohols (2) proteins (3) carbohydrates (4) lipids

8. Two side groups which are characteristic of all amino acids are (1) —OH and —COOH (2) $—CH_3$ and —OH (3) $—NH_2$ and —COOH (4) $—NH_2$ and $—CH_2OH$

9. Which represents a peptide bond?

(1) —C—C— (2) —O—O— (3) —C(=O)—N(H)— (4) —N=O

10. What occurs when a peptide bond forms between two amino acids? (1) Oxygen is released. (2) Water is released. (3) Oxygen is added. (4) Water is added.

Base your answers to questions 11 to 15 on the chemical equation below and on your knowledge of biology.

$$
\begin{array}{l}
\text{H\ H\ O} \\
| \ | \ \| \\
\text{H—N—C—C—OH}
\end{array}
+
\begin{array}{l}
\text{H\ H\ O} \\
| \ | \ \| \\
\text{H—N—C—C—OH} \\
| \\
\text{H—C—H} \\
| \\
\text{OH}
\end{array}
\rightarrow
\begin{array}{l}
\text{H\ \ H\ O\ H\ H\ O} \\
| \ \ | \ \| \ | \ | \ \| \\
\text{H—N—C—C—N—C—C—OH} \\
| \ \ \ \ \ \ \ \ \ \ | \\
\text{H\ \ \ \ \ \ \ H—C—H} \\
\ \ \ \ \ \ \ \ \ \ \ | \\
\ \ \ \ \ \ \ \ \ \ \ \text{OH}
\end{array}
+ \text{HOH}
$$

  (A)   (B)   (C)   (D)

11. How many organic molecules are shown in this equation?   (1) 1 (2) 2   (3) 3   (4) 4

12. Which molecule is most abundant in living cells?   (1) A   (2) B (3) C   (4) D

13. Which molecule contains the most energy?   (1) A   (2) B   (3) C (4) D

14. This reaction in cells will usually take place only in the presence of   (1) an enzyme   (2) a sugar   (3) a polymer   (4) a phosphate

15. Which type of chemical reaction is indicated by this equation? (1) oxidation   (2) hydrolysis   (3) dehydration synthesis   (4) decomposition

I-5. ENZYMES

A. IMPORTANCE OF ENZYMES. Thousands of chemical reactions occur in living cells. Each of these reactions requires and is controlled by a specific substance called an **enzyme.** Although enzymes are needed to cause reactions to occur in the cell, the enzymes are not changed by the reaction. They can be used over and over for the same type of reaction. Substances that affect the rate of a chemical reaction but are not changed by the reaction are called *catalysts.* Enzymes are organic catalysts.

B. STRUCTURE AND FUNCTION OF ENZYMES. Each organism synthesizes the enzymes it needs. Enzymes have the following characteristics.

1. Chemical nature. All enzymes are proteins. In order to function, an enzyme may also need a non-protein part called a **coenzyme.** Several vitamins function as coenzymes. The lack of a vitamin prevents the enzyme from performing its function and thus interferes with an organism's normal metabolism.

2. Active site. Enzyme molecules are usually much larger than the molecules they act upon. It is believed that only a small region of the enzyme molecule is involved in the enzyme action. This region is called the **active site** of the enzyme molecule. The active site is the result of the specific ways in which the polypeptide chains of the enzyme molecule twist and fold.

3. Enzyme-substrate complex. It is believed that an enzyme functions by forming a temporary association with the molecules of the substances whose reactions it controls. These substances are called the **substrates** of the enzyme. This association involves close contact at the active site and the temporary formation of an *enzyme-substrate complex*. Enzyme action takes place when the enzyme-substrate complex forms, causing a reaction to occur. After the reaction, the enzyme separates from the product or products of the reaction and can then act again on other molecules of substrate.

4. "Lock-and-key" model of enzyme action. According to the **lock-and-key model,** the shape of the active site of an enzyme molecule fits the shapes of its substrates only. It therefore can form a complex only with those substrates or possibly with a few similar substances. This is like a key whose shape fits only one lock, and therefore opens only that lock.

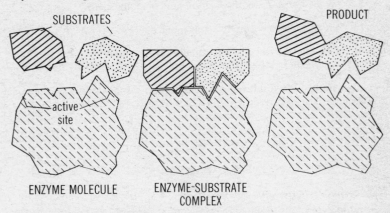

SUBSTRATES   PRODUCT

active site

ENZYME MOLECULE   ENZYME-SUBSTRATE COMPLEX

Figure 1-10. Lock-and-key model of enzyme action. In many cases, the same enzyme can catalyze the reverse reaction, breaking down the combined molecule into its original parts. In this case, the combined molecule is the substrate.

5. Replacement of enzymes. Although enzyme molecules can be reused many times, they are eventually decomposed in the cell. The organism must therefore synthesize new enzymes continuously to replace those that are destroyed.

6. Names of enzymes. The names of enzymes end in *ase* and are often derived from the name of their substrate. For example, maltase is the enzyme that breaks down maltose.

C. RATE OF ENZYME ACTION. The rate of enzyme action varies with conditions in the cellular environment. Factors that affect the rate of enzyme action include *pH* (degree of acidity or alkalinity), *temperature,* and *relative amounts* of enzyme and substrate present.

D. FACTORS AFFECTING ENZYME ACTION

1. Temperature. The rate of enzyme action is generally low at low temperatures, and increases as the temperature rises. At some particular

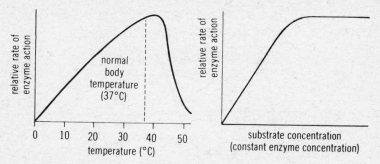

Figure 1-11. Effect of temperature and substrate concentration on the rate of enzyme action.

temperature, however, the enzyme suddenly loses effectiveness. This effect is called **denaturation.** It is believed that denaturation occurs at high temperatures because the shape of the enzyme is altered and its active site no longer fits its substrates. For many enzymes in the human body, denaturation occurs around 40°C, just above the normal body temperature of 37°C.

2. Relative amounts of enzyme and substrate. Starting with a given concentration of enzyme and a low concentration of substrate, the rate of enzyme action increases as the concentration of substrate increases. The rate of action increases up to a point and then levels off as more substrate is added. It is inferred that at this point all the enzyme molecules are working at their maximum rate so that an excess of substrate has no further effect on the rate of action.

3. pH

　　a. Meaning of pH. A solution may be acid, basic (alkaline), or neutral in its chemical properties. This characteristic of a solution depends on its *hydrogen ion* (H^+) *concentration*, and is measured by its **pH.** The pH scale extends from a pH of 0 (strongly acid) to a pH of 14 (strongly alkaline, or basic). A pH of 7 represents a **neutral** condition (neither acid nor basic). Pure water has a pH of 7. Acids have a pH less than 7. Bases have a pH greater than 7.

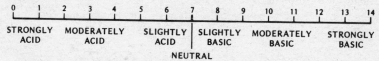

Figure 1-12. The pH scale. Each change of 1 unit on this scale is a change of 10 times in the degree of acidity. For example, a pH of 4 is 10 times as acid as a pH of 5.

　　b. Effect of pH on enzyme activity. Each enzyme acts most effectively within a certain pH range. For example, pepsin, the gastric protease secreted by the stomach, works best in a fairly acid environment (pH around 2); it is ineffective in a neutral or basic solution. Trypsin, the pancreatic protease in the small intestine, is most effective in a slightly basic environment (pH around 8).

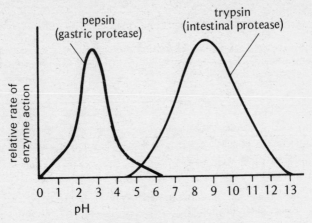

Figure 1-13. Effect of pH on enzyme activity.

QUESTIONS

(Core Topics)

1. Enzymes influence chemical reactions in living systems by (1) providing the substrate required for the reactions to occur (2) combining with excess hydrogen to form gaseous wastes (3) affecting the rate at which the reactions occur (4) absorbing water released when polymers are formed

2. Which group of organic compounds includes the enzymes? (1) proteins (2) carbohydrates (3) sugars (4) starches

3. Any substance that is acted upon by an enzyme is called a (1) coenzyme (2) vitamin (3) substrate (4) polypeptide

4. An enzyme that hydrolyzes starch usually will not act upon sucrose. This fact is an indication that enzymes are (1) specific (2) synthetic (3) hydrolytic (4) catalytic

Base your answers to questions 5 through 7 on the diagram below of an enzyme-controlled process which occurs in humans.

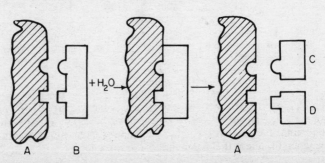

5. The process represented by the diagram is known as (1) photosynthesis (2) hydrolysis (3) dehydration synthesis (4) aerobic respiration
  6. The enzyme is represented by figure (1) A (2) B (3) C (4) D
  7. If figure B represents a disaccharide, figure D must represent a molecule of (1) a polysaccharide (2) a fatty acid (3) an amino acid (4) a simple sugar

QUESTIONS

(Extended Area—Biochemistry)

1. At what point on the graph shown below can the rate of enzyme activity be increased by increasing the concentration of substrate molecules? (1) 1 (2) 2 (3) 3 (4) 4

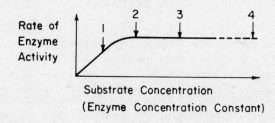

Rate of
Enzyme
Activity

Substrate Concentration

(Enzyme Concentration Constant)

2. Which statement best describes the information supplied by the graph below? (1) The rate of enzyme activity varies directly with the enzyme concentration. (2) The rate of enzyme activity becomes stabilized when a certain enzyme concentration is reached. (3) Enzyme concentrations have no effect upon the rate of enzyme activity. (4) As the enzyme concentration is increased, the enzyme activity increases constantly.

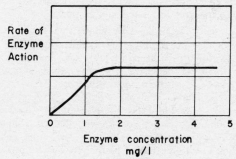

Rate of
Enzyme
Action

Enzyme concentration
mg/l

3. A solution with a pH of 9 is (1) acidic (2) basic (3) neutral (4) saline
  4. At high temperatures, the rate of enzyme action decreases because the increased heat (1) changes the pH of the system (2) neutralizes the acids and bases in the system (3) increases the concentration of the enzyme (4) alters the active site of the enzyme

UNIT II   ANIMAL AND PLANT MAINTENANCE

II-1. ADAPTATIONS

All organisms must perform the functions described on page 1 in order to maintain life. Organisms have various structures and behavior patterns that enable them to perform these functions efficiently in their environment. These structures and patterns are called **adaptations.**

II-2. NUTRITION

Nutrition includes all the activities by which organisms obtain and process foods for their use. Foods furnish the nutrients needed for energy, growth, repair, and regulation.

A. TYPES OF NUTRITION. There are two types of nutrition—*autotrophic* and *heterotrophic*. In **autotrophic nutrition** the organism manufactures organic compounds from inorganic raw materials. Such organisms are called **autotrophs.** Most plants and some monerans and protists (including all the algae) are autotrophs. *Photosynthesis* (discussed in Section B) is the most common type of autotrophic nutrition. *Chemosynthesis* (Section F) is another type.

In **heterotrophic nutrition,** the organism cannot make organic compounds from inorganic raw materials. It must obtain organic materials from other living organisms or their products. Such organisms are called **heterotrophs.** All animals and most fungi, protozoans, and bacteria are heterotrophs.

B. PHOTOSYNTHESIS
   1. Photosynthesis is the process by which the energy of light is converted to the chemical bond energy of organic compounds.
   2. Importance of photosynthesis. Most of the chemical bond energy in the food of organisms is the result of photosynthesis. Photosynthesis is also the source of most of the oxygen in the air.
   3. Photosynthetic pigments. Most cells that carry on photosynthesis have organelles called **chloroplasts.** Chloroplasts contain **pigments—** colored compounds that absorb certain wavelengths of light and reflect others. The color of pigments is due to the wavelengths they reflect. The most important photosynthetic pigments are compounds called **chlorophylls.** Chlorophylls are *green* because they absorb the red and blue wavelengths of light and reflect green. The pigments in chloroplasts can be separated and identified by a technique called *chromatography*.
   4. Chemical process. In photosynthesis, carbon dioxide and water are the raw materials. They are used to form glucose, a simple sugar, or monosaccharide. Oxygen is a by-product of photosynthesis. Energy absorbed from light by chlorophyll is converted to the chemical bond

energy of the glucose produced. Red and blue wavelengths of light are most effective for this energy conversion because these are the wavelengths strongly absorbed by chlorophyll. Wavelengths of green light are much less effective.

5. Equations of photosynthesis. The equation for photosynthesis in simple molecular form is:

$$6 \; CO_2 + 12 \; H_2O \longrightarrow C_6H_{12}O_6 + 6 \; H_2O + 6 \; O_2$$

6. Light and dark reactions. Note that water appears on both sides of the equation. It is both a raw material and a product of photosynthesis. The reason for this is that photosynthesis involves two sets of reactions—the **light reactions** and the **dark reactions.** In the light reactions, water is consumed. In the dark reactions, water is produced. During the light reactions, light energy is converted to chemical energy, and water is split into hydrogen and oxygen. During the dark reactions, carbohydrates are synthesized from carbon dioxide and hydrogen. All the oxygen released during photosynthesis comes from the water that is split during the light reactions.

7. Investigations of photosynthesis. Our present understanding of the reactions of photosynthesis has been obtained through the use of **isotopes** of oxygen and carbon. Isotopes are different forms of the same element. Isotopes act chemically in the same way, but have different physical properties. Many isotopes are **radioactive** and can be detected by the radiation they give off. These properties of isotopes make it possible to use them as "tracers" to follow the sequence of biochemical reactions.

QUESTIONS

1. An organism is classified as autotrophic rather than heterotrophic if it   (1) gives off carbon dioxide as a waste   (2) grows only in the daytime   (3) synthesizes nutrients from inorganic materials   (4) forms a spindle during cell division

2. Most free oxygen on the earth today is a result of the process of (1) respiration   (2) photosynthesis   (3) excretion   (4) chemosynthesis

3. In a green plant cell, the synthesis of organic compounds from inorganic raw materials occurs in the   (1) cell membrane   (2) chloroplasts   (3) nucleus   (4) mitochondria

4. Most bacteria and fungi are classified as heterotrophs because both of these forms of life   (1) carry on anaerobic respiration   (2) are unable to synthesize organic compounds from inorganic substances (3) carry on intracellular digestion in the absence of oxygen   (4) require large amounts of ATP to sustain life

5. In the leaves of green plants, CO_2 is utilized during the process of (1) regulation   (2) excretion   (3) photosynthesis   (4) respiration

6. Which color light is least important to a green plant during photosynthetic activities?   (1) green   (2) yellow   (3) blue   (4) orange

7. The wavelengths of light which can be used most effectively in photosynthesis by a bean plant are   (1) red and green   (2) red and blue (3) green and blue   (4) blue and yellow

8. Which wavelength of light will be reflected most when a beam of white light is directed at a solution of chlorophyll? (1) yellow (2) blue (3) white (4) green

9. Which occurs during the light reactions in photosynthesis? (1) Chlorophyll is produced. (2) Water is split to form hydrogen and oxygen. (3) Sugar is formed from carbon dioxide and water. (4) Carbon dioxide is given off as a waste product.

10. During the process of photosynthesis, the oxygen released as a byproduct is derived from the breakdown of molecules of (1) carbon dioxide (2) chlorophyll (3) glucose (4) water

11. The hydrogen atoms that are included within a molecule of sugar originally came from (1) chlorophyll (2) carbon dioxide (3) ATP (4) water

12. Bromthymol blue is a blue indicator that turns yellow in the presence of CO_2. A solution of yellow bromthymol blue and an Elodea plant were placed in two test tubes. Test tube I was kept in the dark and test tube II was kept in the light. What was probably observed after 24 hours? (1) The solution in test tube I turned blue, only. (2) The solution in test tube II turned blue, only. (3) No change in color occurred in either test tube. (4) The solution in both test tubes turned blue.

C. DETAILS OF PHOTOSYNTHESIS

1. Structure of chloroplasts. Chloroplasts contain stacks of membranes called **grana**. The regions of the chloroplast surrounding the grana are called the **stroma**.

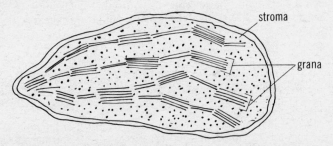

stroma

grana

Figure 2-1. Structure of a chloroplast. The grana consist of stacks of parallel membranes in which chlorophyll and enzyme molecules are embedded.

2. The photochemical (light) reactions. The membranes of the grana contain chlorophyll and the enzymes needed for the light reactions. Light energy is absorbed by the chlorophyll in the grana. Some of this energy is used to break water molecules into hydrogen atoms and free oxygen gas. This process is called *photolysis*. The process has been studied using water made with the isotope oxygen-18. (The number 18 refers to the mass of the atoms of the isotope. Ordinary oxygen is oxygen-16.) These studies have shown that all the oxygen released during photosynthesis comes from water molecules.

The hydrogen atoms released during the light reactions are transferred to *hydrogen carriers*. Some of the light energy absorbed by chlorophyll is used to produce molecules of **ATP**, the carrier of chemical energy in most living cells (see page 42 for discussion of ATP).

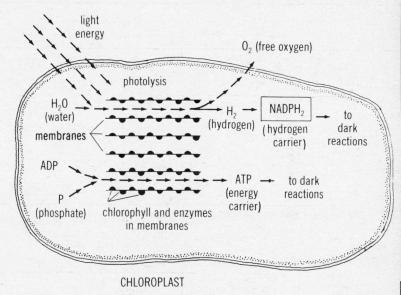

CHLOROPLAST

Figure 2-2. The light reactions. Two sets of reactions take place on the surface of the membranes of the grana. One set of reactions splits water into hydrogen and oxygen. The oxygen is released. The hydrogen is accepted by NADP. The other reactions form ATP from ADP and phosphate. Energy for both sets of reactions is absorbed from light by chlorophyll molecules.

3. Carbon fixation (dark) reactions. This set of reactions are called the dark reactions because they do not require light, although they occur during the day while the light reactions are proceeding. These reactions take place in the stroma of the chloroplasts. The necessary enzymes are present in the stroma. During the dark reactions, hydrogen atoms from the light reactions and carbon dioxide molecules from the air pass through a series of chemical changes that produces an important intermediate 3-carbon compound called *phosphoglyceraldehyde,* or **PGAL.** Glucose and other compounds are then synthesized from PGAL. The isotope carbon-14 has been used to trace the chemical pathways of carbon fixation. (Ordinary carbon is carbon-12.)

D. RESULTS OF PHOTOSYNTHESIS. The glucose formed during photosynthesis is used as an energy source by most organisms during the

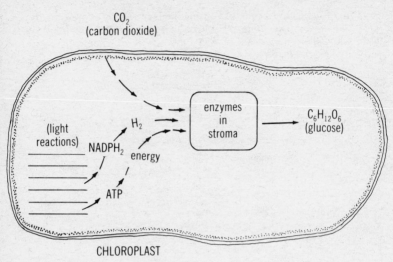

CO_2
(carbon dioxide)

(light reactions)

H_2

$NADPH_2$ energy

ATP

enzymes in stroma

$C_6H_{12}O_6$
(glucose)

CHLOROPLAST

Figure 2-3. The dark reactions. The dark reactions occur in the stroma. Under the action of enzymes, carbon dioxide from the environment combines with hydrogen to form glucose, a carbohydrate. Energy for this synthesis is obtained from the ATP and $NADPH_2$ produced by the light reactions.

process of cell respiration (see pages 42–46).   Glucose may also be used to synthesize other organic compounds, such as fats and proteins, that are needed for the metabolism of the organism. Excess glucose may be converted by dehydration synthesis to storage products for later use.

E. USE OF PRODUCTS OF PHOTOSYNTHESIS

1. Storage. Autotrophic organisms store the products of photosynthesis in the form of insoluble materials such as starches, lipids, and proteins.

2. Digestion. To use these stored materials, the plant cells first break them down (digest them) into soluble materials such as sugars. Digestion in plants occurs within the cells (intracellular digestion). Therefore, plants do not need a system of specialized digestive organs.

3. Transport. The end products of digestion in plants may be used within the same cells, or they may be transported to other tissues of the organism for use or for further storage.

QUESTIONS

1. During photosynthesis, the breakdown of water requires (1) starch (2) light (3) oxygen-18 (4) carbon-14

2. The first step in photosynthesis is the (1) formation of ATP (2) synthesis of water (3) absorption of light energy by chlorophyll (4) fixation of carbon dioxide

3. Which process is represented below? (1) aerobic respiration (2) dehydration synthesis (3) photolysis (4) carbon fixation

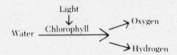

4. Through the use of the isotope oxygen-18, it has been shown that the oxygen released during photosynthesis is derived from (1) water (2) starch (3) carbon dioxide (4) chlorophyll

5. Carbon fixation is a series of chemical reactions which occurs during (1) ATP synthesis (2) photosynthesis (3) DNA synthesis (4) respiration

6. Carbon-14 was used in the study of photosynthesis to indicate (1) that free oxygen is produced from water (2) that green plants give off carbon dioxide in the dark (3) the path of carbon in the carbon fixation reactions (4) the role of root hairs in absorbing water

II-3. ADAPTATIONS FOR PHOTOSYNTHESIS

Algae and green plants carry on autotrophic nutrition by photosynthesis.

A. ALGAE. A large percentage of the world's photosynthesis is carried on by unicellular algae in the oceans. The raw materials for photosynthesis are absorbed directly into the individual cells.

B. VASCULAR PLANTS. Although some photosynthesis occurs in the stems of vascular plants, the organs most highly adapted for this process are the leaves. Leaves have several specific adaptations for photosynthesis (see Figure 2-4):

1. Large surface area permits maximum absorption of light energy.

2. Outer cell layers **(epidermis),** with waxy covering **(cuticle),** protect leaf against excessive water loss, mechanical injury, and attack by fungi.

3. Openings in cuticle and epidermis, called **stomates,** allow exchange of carbon dioxide and oxygen between internal air spaces of leaf and the external environment. Water vapor also escapes from the leaf through the stomates.

4. **Guard cells** surrounding the stomate regulate its size, opening to allow greater exchange of gases and water vapor and closing to reduce the exchange, depending on needs of the plant at any given time.

5. **Palisade layer** just below the upper epidermis consists of long cells with many chloroplasts. Most photosynthesis occurs in these cells.

6. **Spongy layer,** located below the palisade layer, contains many interconnected air spaces surrounded by moist cell surfaces. Exchange and circulation of gases and water vapor occur here. Some photosynthesis also occurs in the spongy layer.

7. Chloroplasts are usually present in the guard cells, the palisade cells, and the spongy layer.

8. Veins in the leaf contain conducting tissues, which bring water and dissolved materials to the sites of photosynthesis and carry synthesized nutrients away to other organs of the plant.

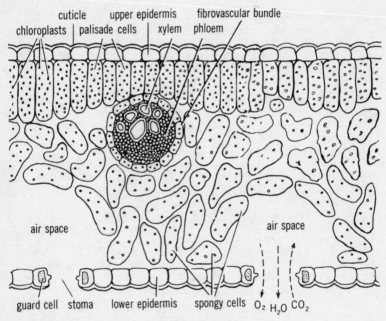

Figure 2-4. Structure of a leaf.

QUESTIONS

1. Most of the food for the animal life of the oceans is obtained from (1) material carried into the oceans by rivers (2) underwater plants (3) ocean currents (4) marine algae

2. Guard cells are located in (1) vascular tissue (2) leaves (3) roots (4) bark

3. The size of the stomates is regulated by the (1) lenticels (2) palisade cells (3) spongy tissue cells (4) guard cells

4. The moist intercellular spaces of a leaf aid chiefly in the (1) movement of starch (2) absorption of gases (3) transport of sap (4) diffusion of chlorophyll

5. The veins of leaves are actually (1) conducting tissues (2) nonliving structural supports (3) the main sites of photosynthesis (4) spaces for the exchange of gases

II-4. HETEROTROPHIC NUTRITION

A. PROCESSES OF HETEROTROPHIC NUTRITION. Heterotrophs obtain preformed organic molecules from other organisms or their parts or products. These materials are generally called the *food* of the organism.

1. Ingestion. The taking in of food by an organism from its environment is called **ingestion.**

2. Digestion. Food molecules that are insoluble or too large are unable to pass through the cell membranes of the organism. Breaking these molecules down into smaller, soluble molecules that can pass into the cells is called **digestion.** If this digestion occurs outside the cells of the organism, it is called **extracellular digestion.** If the food particles are first enclosed in vacuoles inside the cells, where they are digested, the process is called **intracellular digestion.** In either case, the end products of digestion then enter the cytoplasm of the cells by diffusion through membranes.

a. Physical changes. During ingestion, food is often broken down into smaller pieces by such physical processes as cutting, grinding, and tearing. This increases the surface area of the food so that it can be acted on more rapidly by chemical agents. However, it does not change the food molecules.

b. Chemical changes. The food molecules are broken down chemically by **digestive enzymes** secreted by the organism. Complete digestion of the main types of food compounds produces the soluble end products shown in Table 2-1.

TABLE 2-1. THE END PRODUCTS OF DIGESTION.

Large Molecules	End Products of Digestion
carbohydrates	simple sugars (monosaccharides)
lipids (fats, oils)	fatty acids and glycerol
proteins	amino acids

c. Enzymatic hydrolysis. The chemical process by which food molecules are digested is called **hydrolysis.** In this process, the molecules are split into smaller parts *(lysis)* by the addition of water *(hydro).* Because enzymes are necessary for the digestion of food in organisms, the process is described as **enzymatic hydrolysis.** Enzymatic hydrolysis is discussed in detail on page 67.

3. Egestion. A heterotrophic organism may be unable to digest all the food substances it ingests. The organism may lack specific enzymes for certain substances or the food may not be exposed to available enzymes for a long enough time. The removal, or elimination, of undigested or indigestible materials is called **egestion.** It should not be confused with excretion, which is the removal of wastes produced inside the tissues of an organism by its metabolic activities.

QUESTIONS

1. Which statement best identifies heterotrophs? (1) They synthesize chlorophyll. (2) They extract minerals from the soil. (3) They consume preformed organic compounds. (4) They make organic compounds from inorganic materials.

2. An end product of carbohydrate digestion is (1) glycerol (2) a fatty acid (3) glucose (4) an amino acid

3. Most end products of complete chemical digestion are described as (1) high-energy inorganic compounds (2) small, soluble organic molecules (3) large, insoluble organic molecules (4) complex inorganic compounds

4. Large insoluble food molecules are changed into small soluble food molecules by the process of (1) transport (2) hydrolysis (3) dehydration synthesis (4) excretion

5. Hydrolytic enzymes cause the breakdown of large molecules into smaller molecules by the (1) ingestion of substrates (2) synthesis of maltase (3) accumulation of food vacuoles (4) addition of water

6. Absence of hydrolyzing enzymes in the body of a human most directly affects the process of (1) respiration (2) digestion (3) absorption (4) secretion

7. Which process does not directly involve the synthesis of chemical compounds? (1) growth (2) cell division (3) reproduction (4) egestion

B. ADAPTATIONS FOR HETEROTROPHIC NUTRITION IN FUNGI.

Fungi live on or in their food supply, which may be a living organism or the decaying remains of an organism. They have adaptations for absorbing nutrients from their food source.

1. The main body of a fungus is a mass of tangled filaments. Some of these filaments, called **rhizoids,** penetrate the food source.

2. Digestive enzymes secreted by the rhizoids cause extracellular digestion of the food. The digested nutrients are then absorbed into the cells of the rhizoids.

C. PARAMECIUM

1. **Ingestion.** By the motion of **cilia,** the paramecium ingests food through a fixed opening at the base of its **oral groove.**

2. **Digestion.** A **food vacuole** forms at the base of the oral groove to receive ingested food particles. The food vacuole merges with a lysosome, which contains digestive enzymes. Food is digested in the vacuole and the end products of the digestion are absorbed into the cytoplasm. Digestion in a food vacuole is considered to be intracellular digestion.

3. **Egestion.** Undigested material in the food vacuole is carried to a fixed opening called the **anal pore,** where it is released (egested) to the environment.

D. AMEBA

1. **Ingestion.** The ameba ingests food particles by surrounding them with **pseudopods,** which merge and enclose the food in a food vacuole. This process is called **phagocytosis.**

2. Digestion. Digestion and absorption of end products occur in the food vacuole, after it merges with a lysosome, as in the paramecium.

3. Egestion. Undigested materials in food vacuoles are released when the vacuole touches the cell membrane and forms an opening to the outside.

E. HYDRA
1. Ingestion. The body of the hydra has a sac-type **digestive cavity** with a single opening. Food is ingested through this opening, often by manipulation with the **tentacles.**

2. Digestion.

　　a. Extracellular. Specialized cells in the lining of the digestive cavity secrete digestive enzymes into the cavity, thus bringing about extracellular digestion.

　　b. Intracellular. Some food particles are engulfed by phagocytosis in other specialized cells in the inner lining of the digestive cavity and digested intracellularly.

3. Egestion. Undigested material is egested through the same opening through which ingestion occurs.

F. EARTHWORM
1. Type of digestive system. The earthworm has a one-way tube-like digestive system with an opening at each end and a series of specialized organs through which the food passes, permitting efficient processing of the material.

2. Organs. Food is ingested through the **mouth** and the **esophagus** into the **crop** for temporary storage. It then enters the **gizzard,** where mechanical breakdown of the food into smaller pieces occurs. The food then enters the **intestine,** where chemical digestion occurs and end products are absorbed. Undigested material is egested through the **anus.**

G. GRASSHOPPER
1. Type of digestive system. The grasshopper has a tube-like digestive system similar to that of the earthworm.

2. Auxiliary organs. The grasshopper has specialized **mouth parts** for mechanical breakdown of ingested food. It also has **gastric caeca,** which secrete digestive enzymes into the digestive tract for chemical digestion.

H. HUMANS. The human digestive system is similar to those of the earthworm and grasshopper in that (a) it is a tube-like system with two openings and one-way travel of food from mouth to anus, and (b) it has specialized organs and glands for mechanical breakdown and chemical digestion of the food as it passes through the digestive tube. See pages 64-70 for further details.

QUESTIONS

1. Fungi obtain nutrients by (1) photosynthesis (2) extracellular digestion of food materials (3) ingestion of small organisms (4) absorption through cilia

FIGURE 2-5. REPRESENTATIVE DIGESTIVE SYSTEMS

AMEBA AND PARAMECIUM

Food vacuole forms around ingested food particle; digestive enzymes are secreted into vacuole and digestion products are absorbed through membrane between vacuole and cytoplasm. This is intracellular digestion.

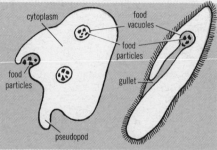

HYDRA

Food is ingested through mouth, which also serves as excretory orifice, and partially digested in body (gastrovascular) cavity. Specialized cells in inner layer of body wall receive partly-digested food substances and complete their digestion in cell vacuoles. Digestion, accomplished by enzymes secreted into cells and gastrovascular cavity, is both extracellular and intracellular.

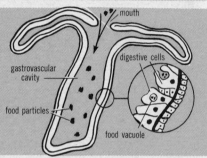

EARTHWORM

Food enters mouth and passes through digestive tract in one direction only, permitting functional differentiation of cells lining route. Digestion is extracellular, with intestinal absorption of digestion products.

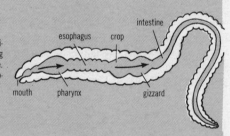

GRASSHOPPER

Basically the same one-way tube as the earthworm, but with more highly differentiated and elaborated organs. Salivary glands moisten dry food, as in higher animals; digestive enzymes are secreted by specialized tissues of salivary glands and gastric caeca. Absorption of digested food takes place in stomach.

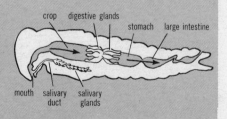

2. Amebas, earthworms, grasshoppers, and humans are similar in that each organism   (1) carries on autotrophic nutrition   (2) digests food extracellularly   (3) circulates food by peristalsis   (4) produces hydrolytic enzymes

3. In protozoans, digestion occurs in the   (1) food vacuole   (2) stomach   (3) contractile vacuole   (4) ribosome

4. Which organism lacks a digestive tract and accumulates ingested foods in vacuoles where digestion occurs?   (1) ameba   (2) earthworm   (3) grasshopper   (4) human

5. In which organism does digestion occur within a tube?   (1) ameba   (2) grasshopper   (3) protozoa   (4) hydra

Base your answers to questions 6 through 8 on the diagrams below of an earthworm and a hydra and on your knowledge of biology.

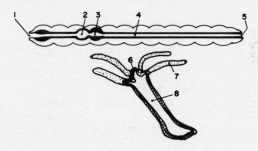

6. Most hydrolysis of ingested foods occurs in structures   (1) 1 and 6   (2) 2 and 3   (3) 4 and 6   (4) 4 and 8

7. Ingestion occurs through structures   (1) 1 and 6   (2) 2 and 8   (3) 3 and 4   (4) 5 and 7

8. Which structure functions in the mechanical digestion of food?   (1) 1   (2) 6   (3) 3   (4) 7

II-5. TRANSPORT

The term **transport** includes the passage of materials into the cells of an organism *(absorption)* and the distribution of materials within the cells and throughout the organism *(circulation)*.

A. ABSORPTION. Materials from the environment are not truly inside an organism until they have passed through a cell membrane into the cytoplasm. This process is called **absorption.**

B. THE CELL MEMBRANE

1. Structure of the cell membrane. The cell membrane consists mainly of lipids and proteins. Recent investigations indicate that the lipids form a layer two molecules thick with protein molecules in it. The **fluid-mosaic model** is a currently accepted model of the structure of the cell membrane (see Figure 2-6). A scientific **model** is a representation of a structure or process that cannot actually be observed. Models help to visualize objects and explain their properties and behavior.

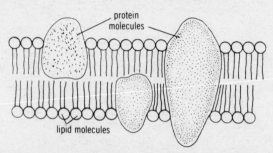

protein molecules

lipid molecules

Figure 2-6. The fluid-mosaic model of the structure of the cell membrane.

2. Properties of the cell membrane. Many small particles, such as molecules of water, gases, and dissolved solids, as well as ions (charged particles), can pass through the membrane by diffusion. Most large molecules, such as those of proteins and starch, cannot diffuse through the membrane; they must first be chemically digested. However, the size of a molecule is not necessarily a factor in determining whether it can pass through a cell membrane.

3. Functions of the cell membrane. The cell membrane *selectively* regulates the passage of materials into and out of the cell. It permits only certain substances to enter or leave. This regulation aids in maintaining homeostasis of the cell.

4. Passive transport. Some materials can pass through the cell membrane by **diffusion**, a process that does not require energy from the cell. It occurs because of the energy of motion (kinetic energy) of the particles. Diffusion of a material through a cell membrane always occurs in both directions. The net movement of material by diffusion is from a region of higher concentration of particles to a region of lower concentration. For example, if the concentration of a particular molecule or ion is higher outside the cell than inside, there will be a net diffusion of particles into the cell.

5. Osmosis. The diffusion of water through a membrane is called **osmosis.** It occurs from a region of higher concentration of water (fewer dissolved particles) to a region of lower concentration of water (more dissolved particles).

6. Active transport is the use of cellular energy to move particles through a cell membrane. The particles may be moved in the same direction as diffusion (from regions of higher to lower concentrations), or they may be moved against the normal direction of diffusion (from regions of lower to higher concentrations). Transport through the cell membrane is assisted by *carrier proteins* embedded in it.

7. In phagocytosis, a cell engulfs large, undissolved particles by flowing around them and enclosing them in a vacuole, where chemical digestion and absorption then occur.

8. Pinocytosis is a process by which large, dissolved molecules become enclosed in a vacuole. The cell membrane forms a pocket around the molecule by pinching inward (Figure 2-7). Both phagocytosis and pinocytosis require cellular energy.

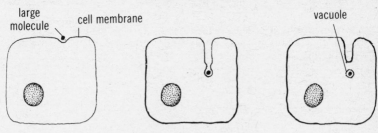

Figure 2-7. Pinocytosis.

QUESTIONS

1. The exchange of respiratory gases in a cell takes place through the (1) lungs (2) vacuoles (3) stoma (4) cell membrane

2. Cell membranes consist chiefly of (1) carbohydrates and lipids (2) carbohydrates and nucleic acids (3) protein and carbohydrates (4) protein and lipids

3. In cells, the selectivity of the cell membrane is most closely associated with the maintenance of (1) homeostasis (2) plasmolysis (3) phagocytosis (4) pinocytosis

4. During which process do molecules move from a region of higher concentration to a region of lower concentration? (1) diffusion (2) active transport (3) cyclosis (4) circulation

5. Osmosis is a physical process most closely associated with the life function of (1) absorption (2) irritability (3) locomotion (4) reproduction

6. Normally, in the process of osmosis, the net flow of water molecules into or out of the cell depends upon differences in the (1) concentration of water molecules inside and outside the cell (2) concentration of enzymes on either side of the cell membrane (3) rate of molecular motion on either side of the cell membrane (4) rate of movement of insoluble molecules inside the cell

7. If red blood cells are placed in distilled water, they will eventually be destroyed. Which process is most likely to be the chief cause of this destruction? (1) hydrolysis (2) dehydration synthesis (3) osmosis (4) plasmolysis

8. Freshwater protozoa may be distinguished from many marine protozoa by the fact that the freshwater species contain (1) plasma membranes (2) contractile vacuoles (3) chromosomes (4) cytoplasm

9. The destruction of all ATP molecules in a cell would interfere most immediately with the process of (1) diffusion (2) active transport (3) respiratory gas exchange (4) osmosis

10. Active transport of certain proteins from a cell's environment into the cell is most closely associated with the (1) cell membrane (2) cell wall (3) ribosome (4) nucleolus

11. Sodium ions are "pumped" from a region of lower concentration to a region of higher concentration in the nerve cells of humans. This process is an example of (1) diffusion (2) passive transport (3) osmosis (4) active transport

12. During which process is ATP not essential? (1) active transport (2) passive transport (3) phagocytosis (4) pinocytosis

13. The sequence of drawings (from left to right) is a simplified diagram representing a process which occurs in cells. What is the name associated with this process? (1) simple diffusion (2) passive transport (3) pinocytosis (4) osmosis

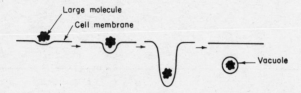

C. CIRCULATION

1. Intracellular circulation. Materials are moved within cells by diffusion, streaming of the cytoplasm **(cyclosis)**, and possibly by movement through the endoplasmic reticulum.

2. Circulation within the organism. Materials are moved from one part of an organism to another by active and passive transport between cells and by fluids flowing through tubes **(vessels)**. Tissues whose function is to transport fluids are called **vascular tissues.** They are present in most plants and animals.

D. ADAPTATIONS FOR CIRCULATION IN PLANTS AND ALGAE.
Within the cells, circulation is accomplished as described under ''intracellular circulation'' above. In the bryophytes, which are simple multicellular plants without vascular tissue, circulation occurs by diffusion and active transport. The tracheophytes, which are more complex plants, have specialized vascular tissues.

1. Transport in roots. Roots are specialized structures that anchor a plant, absorb water, nitrates, and other dissolved mineral salts from the soil, and conduct these materials to the stem. Growth of the root into the soil occurs by cell division at the root tip.

a. Root hairs. Just behind the growing root tip, epidermal cells produce extensions of their cell membranes called **root hairs,** which penetrate the soil and increase the surface area for absorption. Water and dissolved materials in the soil enter the root hairs by diffusion, osmosis, and active transport.

b. Xylem is specialized transport tissue extending from the roots through the stems to the edges of the leaves. The cells of the xylem are dead and hollow, forming continuous tubes. Water and minerals pass upward in the plant through the xylem.

c. Phloem tissue consists of living cells specialized for transport of organic materials synthesized by the plant. Materials are transported by the phloem both upward and downward to tissues of the plant for immediate use or for storage.

2. Transport in stems

a. Structure of stems. Stems are more complex in structure than roots, but they contain vascular tissues (xylem and phloem) that are continuations of those in the roots.

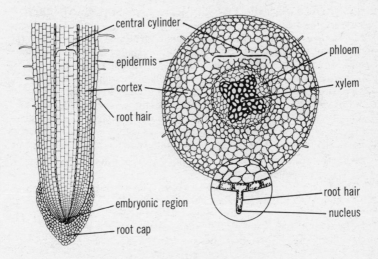

Figure 2-8. Structure of a growing root tip.

b. Function of stems. Stems support the leaves and expose them to light. They also provide transport of materials between the roots and the leaves and between the various tissues of the plant. Stems of large diameter also contain horizontal *rays*, which are specialized tissues that transport materials across the stem.

3. Transport in leaves. The veins of leaves contain extensions of the vascular tissues of the stem. The veins transport materials to and from the tissues of the leaf.

4. Mechanisms of transport in xylem. Three physical processes are involved in the upward movement of materials through the xylem:

a. Transpirational pull. Water continuously passes out of the leaves by evaporation into the air spaces. This loss of water by evaporation is called **transpiration.** Transpiration causes an upward pull (**transpirational pull)** on the columns of water in the xylem from the veins in the leaves through the stems and into the roots. The columns of water are held together by cohesive forces and drawn upward by this force.

b. Capillary action. Water tends to rise in tubes of narrow diameter. This effect is called **capillary action.** It accounts for a small part of the upward movement of water in the narrow tubes of the xylem in the roots and stems.

c. Root pressure. Osmosis and active transport into the root cells produces a pressure inside these cells. This pressure is transmitted upward into the xylem and also accounts for some of the upward movement of materials.

5. Mechanism of movement in phloem. No completely satisfactory explanation of movement of materials in phloem has been proposed up to this time.

E. ADAPTATIONS FOR TRANSPORT IN ANIMALS AND PROTO-ZOANS

1. Protozoans. The water in which protozoans, such as the paramecium and the ameba, live acts as a transport medium. Absorption occurs directly through the cell membrane. Circulation within the organism occurs by diffusion and cytoplasmic streaming (cyclosis).

2. Hydra. Most of the cells of the hydra are in direct contact with its water environment. Absorption occurs directly into each cell, as in protozoans, and from cell to cell through the cell membranes. No special transport system is needed. Cells lining the gastrovascular cavity have flagella, which aid in the circulation of materials within the cavity.

3. Earthworm. In the earthworm, many cells are not in direct contact with the environment. Nutrients, oxygen, and wastes are transported within the organism by a fluid called **blood.** The blood contains **hemoglobin,** which transports oxygen and carbon dioxide by combining with them. The blood is carried to all parts of the animal by tubes called **blood vessels,** and is pumped by organs called **aortic arches.** The blood remains inside the vessels or organs of the circulatory system at all times. Such a system is called a **closed circulatory system.**

Oxygen is absorbed into the blood through the moist skin, which is in contact with the environment. End products of digestion are absorbed from the digestive organs. The digestive tube has many folds, which increase the surface for absorption of nutrients into the blood.

4. Grasshopper. The circulatory system of the grasshopper is an open system. In an **open circulatory system,** the vessels that carry the blood empty into large body cavities called **sinuses.** The blood bathes the body tissues and is then reabsorbed into the circulatory system. Blood is pumped through the system by a pulsating blood vessel. Like the earthworm, the grasshopper has an infolded digestive tube to increase the area for passage of materials into the blood. The blood does not contain hemoglobin and is not significant in the transport of respiratory gases.

5. Humans. The human transport system is, like that of the earthworm, a closed system with hemoglobin aiding in the transport of respiratory gases. The pumping structure is called the **heart.** See pages 71–77 for further details.

QUESTIONS

1. One of the major processes involved in the transport of molecules within cells is (1) osmosis (2) hydrolysis (3) pinocytosis (4) cyclosis

2. Epidermal cells called root hairs are specialized in the function of (1) absorption (2) photosynthesis (3) reproduction (4) excretion

3. As a result of the function of root hairs, the fluid within the xylem tubes shows an increase in the amount of (1) chlorophyll (2) glucose (3) nitrates (4) proteins

4. Xylem is a plant tissue which (1) transports organic food materials (2) regulates the size of stomates (3) absorbs minerals from the soil (4) conducts water upwards

5. Which plant tissues are specialized for vertical transport? (1) xylem and phloem (2) xylem and cambium (3) phloem and cambium (4) phloem and cortex

FIGURE 2-9. REPRESENTATIVE CIRCULATORY SYSTEMS

AMEBA

Digested food diffuses from vacuole into cell cytoplasm, where cyclosis (circulating movement of cytoplasm within cell) distributes it.

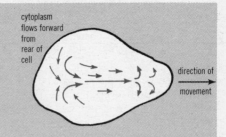

cytoplasm flows forward from rear of cell

direction of movement

HYDRA

Body wall movements and beating of flagella circulate digestion products in gastrovascular cavity. Nutrients diffuse into cells lining cavity, and cell wastes diffuse into cavity. Exterior cells absorb nutrients from adjoining cells bordering gastrovascular cavity.

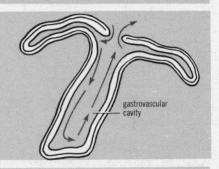

gastrovascular cavity

EARTHWORM

Closed circulatory system. Two major vessels, the dorsal and the ventral, run length of body and are connected by five paired hearts. Contractions of hearts force blood into ventral vessel, which leads to capillary networks throughout body. Blood returns through dorsal vessel, in which contractions aid flow back to hearts.

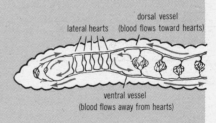

dorsal vessel
(blood flows toward hearts)

lateral hearts

ventral vessel
(blood flows away from hearts)

GRASSHOPPER

Open blood circulatory system. A single vessel, running almost entire length of grasshopper, pumps blood forward to head, where it empties out and flows freely through the tissues, exchanging nutrients and wastes with the cells. Blood diffuses back into the heart all along its length and is recirculated. There are no capillaries, blood bathing each cell directly.

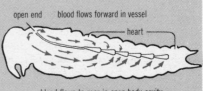

open end   blood flows forward in vessel

heart

blood flows to rear in open body cavity

6. In order to change the color of cut carnations from white to green, a florist would most likely (1) inject green dye into the petals (2) place them in an atmosphere of blue and yellow gases (3) set the cut stems in a container of green dye solution (4) place the cut stems in a magnesium solution to produce more chlorophyll

7. Sugars are transported from the leaves to the roots of a plant in the (1) xylem vessels (2) phloem tubes (3) guard cells (4) root hairs

8. The loss of water through plant leaves is known as (1) osmosis (2) capillary action (3) transpiration (4) root pressure

9. The physical factors believed to be most directly responsible for the rise of water in maple trees are (1) capillary action, transpiration pull, and osmotic root pressure (2) capillary action, transpiration pull, and photosynthesis (3) capillary action, chemosynthesis, and osmotic root pressure (4) phototropism, transpiration pull, and osmotic root pressure

10. In protozoa, which process serves a function similar to the circulation of blood in humans? (1) movement of the cilia (2) cyclosis (3) intracellular synthesis (4) hydrolysis

11. Which organisms contain an open transport system? (1) grasshoppers (2) fish (3) earthworms (4) humans

12. In the earthworm, (1) blood is pumped through a closed system of vessels (2) blood diffuses through the moist skin (3) blood flows out of open vessels into body cavities (4) blood does not transport much oxygen because it has no hemoglobin

II-6. RESPIRATION

A. BASIC PROCESS. Respiration includes all the processes by which the chemical bond energy in food molecules is converted to a form readily usable by the organism. The chemical energy is almost always stored in the bonds of the energy carrier called ATP (adenosine triphosphate). ATP is synthesized from ADP (adenosine diphosphate) and phosphate (P). The energy stored in ATP is released for use in the cell by the hydrolysis of the ATP to ADP and phosphate. These two processes, which are controlled by enzymes called ATP-ase, can be represented by the following reversible reaction:

$$H_2O + ATP \quad \overset{\longrightarrow}{\underset{\longleftarrow}{(ATP\text{-}ase)}} \quad ADP + P + Energy$$

If free (molecular) oxygen is used, the process is called **aerobic respiration.** If free oxygen is not involved, it is called **anaerobic respiration.**

B. GAS EXCHANGE. In aerobic respiration, oxygen must be absorbed from the environment and transported to where it is needed and carbon dioxide must be released. This exchange of gases with the environment occurs by diffusion through moist membranes. Complex organisms have specialized organs for this absorption and transport of gases. These organs make up the **respiratory system.**

C. CHEMICAL RESPIRATION. The chemical reactions that release the energy in food molecules and store it in ATP take place inside the cells of the organism. In aerobic respiration, most of these reactions occur in the mitochondria, where the necessary enzymes are present, except for monerans, which do not have mitochondria. Chemical respiration in plants is exactly the same as in animals. Respiration in plants goes on continuously, whether or not photosynthesis is also occurring.

D. ANAEROBIC RESPIRATION (FERMENTATION)

1. Occurrence. Some simple organisms, such as many bacteria, cannot carry on aerobic respiration. They rely on anaerobic respiration for their energy needs. Other organisms, such as yeasts, make use of aerobic respiration when sufficient free oxygen is present, but can live by anaerobic respiration when oxygen is lacking. Anaerobic respiration in these organisms is also called **fermentation.** Muscle cells in animals can function for a limited time on the anaerobic phase of cellular respiration.

2. End products. Most types of anaerobic respiration break glucose down to either **lactic acid** or **alcohol,** and release carbon dioxide. Lactic acid is produced in muscle cells when oxygen is lacking. The accumulation of lactic acid is associated with muscle fatigue. Lactic acid is also produced by anaerobic respiration in many bacteria. This process of fermentation is important to the dairy industry in the production of cheeses, buttermilk, and yogurt.

In yeasts, the products are usually alcohol and carbon dioxide. These end products are used in brewing alcoholic beverages and in baking, where the CO_2 causes the dough to "rise."

$$\text{glucose} \xrightarrow{\text{(enzymes)}} 2 \text{ lactic acid} + 2 \text{ ATP}$$
$$\text{(in bacteria and in muscle cells lacking oxygen)}$$

$$\text{glucose} \xrightarrow{\text{(enzymes)}} 2 \text{ alcohol} + 2 \text{ carbon dioxide} + 2 \text{ ATP}$$
$$\text{(in yeasts)}$$

3. Energy release. In anaerobic respiration only 2 ATP are produced for each molecule of glucose. The end products, lactic acid or alcohol, still contain most of the chemical bond energy of the original glucose.

4. Chemical reactions. The first series of reactions in anaerobic respiration converts each molecule of glucose to two molecules of a 3-carbon compound called **pyruvic acid.** Four molecules of ATP are produced during these reactions. However, two molecules of ATP are needed to activate the series of reactions. Therefore, there is a net output of only 2 ATP per molecule of glucose.

The pyruvic acid is then converted either to lactic acid alone, or to alcohol and carbon dioxide, with no further energy change.

$$\text{glucose} + 2 \text{ ATP} \xrightarrow{\text{(enzymes)}} 2 \text{ pyruvic acid} + 4 \text{ ATP}$$
$$2 \text{ lactic acid} \xleftarrow{\text{(enzymes)}} \xrightarrow{\text{(enzymes)}} 2 \text{ alcohol} + 2 \text{ carbon dioxide}$$

QUESTIONS

1. In which process do organisms transfer chemical bond energy from organic molecules to ATP molecules? (1) translocation (2) nutrition (3) excretion (4) respiration

2. Energy released from the cellular respiration of glucose is (1) first stored within ATP (2) stored in the liver as glycogen (3) turned into heat quickly (4) used directly for body activity

3. The process of fermentation is essential to an anaerobe because during this process (1) alcohol and carbon dioxide are produced (2) enzymes are necessary (3) lactic acid and carbon dioxide are produced (4) energy is made available

4. Fermentation is a less effective process than aerobic respiration because (1) more ATP molecules can be formed by anaerobic respiration (2) much potential energy for ATP production remains bound up in the resulting alcohol (3) two ATP molecules must be used to start the process (4) this process is not utilized to produce ATP

5. To release the same amount of energy as an aerobe, an anaerobic organism would have to (1) release more water (2) absorb more oxygen (3) oxidize more glucose (4) use fewer enzyme molecules

6. Which statement describes an organism that obtains its energy in the absence of free oxygen? (1) It must contain mitochondria. (2) It cannot metabolize carbohydrates. (3) It can ferment carbohydrate molecules. (4) It must contain hemoglobin.

7. Anaerobic respiration is similar in plants and animals because in both cases (1) most of the C—C and C—H bonds are broken (2) molecular oxygen is used (3) relatively small amounts of ATP are produced (4) alcoholic fermentation occurs

8. Lactic acid is produced in organisms as a result of (1) aerobic respiration (2) anaerobic respiration (3) dehydration synthesis (4) glycogen storage

9. Fermentation products of yeast plants include (1) water and minerals (2) water and alcohol (3) alcohol and carbon dioxide (4) carbon dioxide and minerals

10. When glucose is converted into alcohol by yeast, what is the net gain of ATP molecules per molecule of glucose? (1) ½ (2) 2 (3) 1/36 (4) 36

11. Muscular fatigue in an athlete is most probably due to a cellular increase of (1) pyruvic acid (2) carbon dioxide (3) adenosine triphosphate (4) lactic acid

E. AEROBIC RESPIRATION

1. General process. In aerobic respiration, molecules of food such as glucose are broken down completely to carbon dioxide and water in a series of steps by the action of enzymes. The bond energy of the glucose is gradually released, usually forming 36 molecules of ATP for each molecule of glucose.

2. Oxidation-reduction reactions. The steps of aerobic cellular respiration involve the removal of hydrogen atoms and the release of carbon dioxide. The removal of either hydrogen atoms or electrons from a substance is a type of chemical reaction called **oxidation**. The transfer of hydrogen atoms or electrons to a substance is called **reduction**. As glucose is oxidized in aerobic respiration, hydrogen atoms or their electrons are transferred from one compound to another in a series of **oxidation-reduction reactions.** During some of these transfers, energy is extracted and used to synthesize ATP.

3. Role of oxygen. Free oxygen is the final acceptor of the hydrogen atoms. The oxygen combines with the hydrogen, forming water.

4. Overall reaction. The overall process of aerobic respiration may be represented by the following equation:

$$C_6H_{12}O_6 + 6O_2 \xrightarrow{\text{enzymes}} 6H_2O + 6CO_2 + 36\,\text{ATP}$$
$$\text{(glucose)} \quad \text{(oxygen)} \qquad \text{(water)} \quad \text{(carbon dioxide)}$$

QUESTIONS

1. Most of the enzymes involved in aerobic cellular respiration are located primarily in the cell's (1) nucleus (2) mitochondria (3) ribosomes (4) endoplasmic reticulum

2. In cellular respiration, oxygen is used as the final acceptor of (1) carbon (2) hydrogen (3) nitrogen (4) iron

3. In the oxidation of glucose to water and carbon dioxide, enzymes are needed to catalyze the (1) combination of glucose molecules (2) release of energy by hydrogen removal (3) storage of energy in glycogen molecules (4) production of lactic acid

4. The release of energy from a molecule by the removal of hydrogen is known as (1) oxidation (2) active transport (3) dehydration synthesis (4) reduction

5. During aerobic respiration, the principal hydrogen acceptor is (1) pyruvic acid (2) lactic acid (3) carbon (4) oxygen

6. Which end products are formed when simple sugars are oxidized in body cells? (1) glucose, oxygen, and ATP (2) glucose, water, and ATP (3) carbon dioxide, ATP, and water (4) carbon dioxide, water, and oxygen

Base your answers to questions 7 and 8 on the following equation and your knowledge of biology.

$$C_6H_{12}O_6 + 6O_2 \xrightarrow{\text{enzymes}} 6H_2O + 6CO_2 + 36\,\text{ATP}$$
$$\text{(glucose)} \quad \text{(oxygen)} \qquad \text{(water)} \quad \text{(carbon dioxide)}$$

7. The equation represents the process of (1) fermentation (2) anaerobic respiration (3) photosynthesis (4) aerobic respiration

8. One of the products of this reaction is (1) oxygen (2) hydrogen (3) carbon dioxide (4) glucose

F. PHASES OF AEROBIC RESPIRATION

1. Anaerobic phase. Aerobic respiration begins with an anaerobic stage in which glucose is converted to pyruvic acid, and there is a net output of 2 ATP per glucose molecule. These reactions take place in the cytoplasm outside the mitochondria, where the necessary enzymes are present. This process is called **glycolysis.**

2. Aerobic phase. The pyruvic acid produced in the anaerobic phase then enters the mitochondrion. In the mitochondrion, the pyruvic acid is

BC

further oxidized in a series of reactions that release enough energy to form an additional 34 ATP molecules. Carbon dioxide is produced by some of the intermediate reactions. Free oxygen acts as the final acceptor of the hydrogen released by the oxidation reactions, forming water. The net gain from the complete oxidation of one glucose molecule by aerobic cellular respiration is 36 ATP.

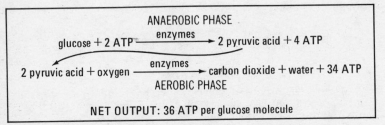

ANAEROBIC PHASE

glucose + 2 ATP $\xrightarrow{\text{enzymes}}$ 2 pyruvic acid + 4 ATP

2 pyruvic acid + oxygen $\xrightarrow{\text{enzymes}}$ carbon dioxide + water + 34 ATP

AEROBIC PHASE

NET OUTPUT: 36 ATP per glucose molecule

Figure 2-10. The two phases of aerobic respiration. Aerobic respiration begins with an anaerobic phase that is similar to the start of fermentation.

QUESTIONS

1. For each molecule of glucose, anaerobic respiration requires activation energy from (1) two molecules of ADP (2) two molecules of ATP (3) two molecules of pyruvic acid (4) four molecules of ATP

2. Chemical reactions which yield the greatest amount of ATP occur during the conversion of pyruvic acid to (1) ethyl alcohol (2) glucose and oxygen (3) carbon dioxide and water (4) lactic acid

3. The end products of aerobic respiration of one molecule of glucose are water, carbon dioxide, and (1) 1 molecule of enzyme (2) 6 molecules of oxygen (3) 36 molecules of ATP (4) 4 molecules of lactic acid

Base your answers to questions 4 through 6 on the diagram below and on your knowledge of biology.

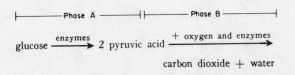

|———— Phase A ————||———— Phase B ————|

glucose $\xrightarrow{\text{enzymes}}$ 2 pyruvic acid $\xrightarrow{\text{+ oxygen and enzymes}}$

carbon dioxide + water

4. These reactions are of value to an organism because they result in the production of (1) lactic acid (2) water (3) ATP (4) CO_2

5. In human muscle cells, pyruvic acid is sometimes converted to lactic acid when (1) cell temperature exceeds 37°C (2) the amount of blood glucose decreases (3) different enzymes are supplied in the diet (4) the oxygen supply is low

6. Phase B includes those reactions which occur in the (1) chloroplasts of green plant cells (2) nucleus of both plant and animal cells (3) mitochondria of both plant and animal cells (4) endoplasmic reticulum of both plant and animal cells

II-7. ADAPTATIONS FOR PHYSICAL RESPIRATION

The chemical processes of respiration are similar in most organisms. In organisms that carry on aerobic respiration, there are various adaptations for the exchange of respiratory gases through moist membranes.

A. IN PLANTS AND ALGAE. Plants and algae carry on cellular respiration continuously, even though they also carry on photosynthesis during daylight. In algae, gas exchange occurs by diffusion through moist cell membranes. More complex plants have special structures for gas exchange.

1. Leaves. The outer surface of a leaf is dry and impermeable and is not a gas exchange surface. Gas exchange in a leaf takes place in interior air spaces, which connect to the environment through the stomates (see pages 29-30). Gases diffuse into and out of the cells lining the air spaces through their moist cell membranes.

2. Stems. Some gas exchange occurs through openings called **lenticels** in the stems of woody plants.

3. Roots. Gas exchange also occurs across the moist cell membranes of root hairs and other epidermal cells of roots.

B. IN ANIMALS AND PROTOZOANS. Animals and protozoans carry on cellular respiration continuously. They have adaptations of varying complexity for physical respiration.

1. Protozoans. In protozoans such as the paramecium and the ameba, respiratory gases diffuse through the moist cell membrane, which is in direct contact with the watery environment.

2. Hydra. As in the protozoans, each cell of the hydra is in contact with the watery environment and gas exchange occurs directly by diffusion through each cell membrane.

3. Earthworm. In the earthworm, oxygen for respiration is obtained by diffusion through the moist skin, and carbon dioxide is given off through the moist skin. The skin cells are kept moist by the secretion of mucus. Numerous small blood vessels in the skin take part in the exchange of the respiratory gases. Hemoglobin aids in the transport of the gases.

4. Grasshopper. The grasshopper has an open circulatory system, with blood that does not contain hemoglobin. This system is not used to transport the respiratory gases. Instead, the grasshopper has a branched system of air tubes called **tracheal tubules,** which connect with openings called **spiracles** in the body wall. Oxygen from the air enters the spiracles and passes to all regions of the body through the tracheal tubules. Carbon dioxide is carried away from all the tissues through the same system of tubules. Gas exchange occurs across the moist membranes of the cells lining the fine branches of the tubules. The external body surface is dry and impermeable.

5. Humans. In humans, as in the grasshopper, the external body surface is impermeable to respiratory gases. The lungs provide a thin, moist internal surface for the exchange of respiratory gases with the environment. As in the earthworm, the gases are transported by the blood of the circulatory system, which contains hemoglobin. See pages 78-80 for further details.

FIGURE 2-11. REPRESENTATIVE RESPIRATORY SYSTEMS

AMEBA

Oxygen is absorbed from surrounding water and carbon dioxide eliminated from cytoplasm by diffusion through cell membrane.

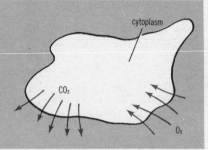

HYDRA

Cells of both body layers are in contact with oxygen-bearing water. Simple diffusion through cell membrane causes cells to lose carbon dioxide, gain oxygen.

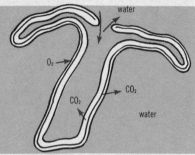

EARTHWORM

Gas transfer occurs by diffusion in capillaries beneath moist skin surface. Closed circulatory system carries oxygenated blood to cells, where diffusion again takes place, and cells receive oxygen, yield carbon dioxide.

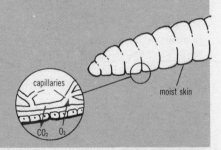

GRASSHOPPER

Air is drawn into porthole-like openings, called spiracles, that line either side of animal. It is transported through a complex system of tracheal tubes to every region of the body. Where needed, it dissolves into the moist tracheal lining and diffuses into the body fluid for transfer to cells.

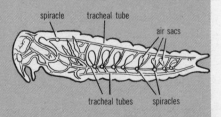

QUESTIONS

1. In a plant, the process of respiration is carried on in (1) all living cells, at all times (2) all living cells, during daylight, only (3) living cells which lack chlorophyll, only (4) living cells which contain chlorophyll, only

2. Green plants produce CO_2 as a result of the process of (1) aerobic respiration (2) transpiration (3) photosynthesis (4) carbon fixation

3. A common feature of aerobic respiration in plants and animals is that oxygen (1) is transported by a definite organ system (2) is transported combined with hemoglobin (3) passes through thick membranes (4) passes through moist membranes

4. Which are correctly paired according to their specialized functions? (1) lenticels and stomates (2) root hairs and meristem (3) xylem and cambium (4) phloem and cambium

5. In all animals, the exchange of oxygen and carbon dioxide is accomplished by (1) action of the alveoli of the lungs (2) activity of the trachea and bronchi (3) diffusion through moist cell membranes (4) contraction of the diaphragm and rib muscles

6. In living protists, when does respiration occur? (1) only during digestion (2) only in the daytime (3) only in total darkness (4) all the time

7. Protists obtain oxygen from the environment through (1) spiracles (2) cell membranes (3) contractile vacuoles (4) mitochondria

8. Which animal has the greatest percentage of its body cells in contact with the environmental source of its oxygen supply? (1) hydra (2) earthworm (3) grasshopper (4) human

9. Which structures are involved in the intake, distribution, and removal of respiratory gases in the grasshopper? (1) arterioles (2) alveoli (3) lungs (4) tracheal tubes

II-8. EXCRETION

A. PROCESS OF EXCRETION. Excretion is the removal of the waste products of metabolism.

1. Kinds of wastes. The chief wastes of metabolism are shown in Table 2-2.

TABLE 2-2. PRINCIPAL WASTES OF EXCRETION.

Metabolic Activity	Wastes Produced
respiration	carbon dioxide, water
dehydration synthesis	water
protein metabolism	nitrogenous wastes (ammonia, urea, uric acid)
some other metabolic activities	mineral salts

2. Disposal of wastes. Some wastes would be harmful, or *toxic*, if allowed to circulate through the organism. Animals usually release toxic wastes to the environment. Plants usually seal them off and store them.

Nontoxic wastes may be released, or they may be reused by the organism in other metabolic activities. For example, many desert animals use the water formed by cellular respiration.

B. ADAPTATIONS IN PLANTS AND ALGAE. Plants have no specialized organ systems for excretion, as the more complex animals do. Algae excrete wastes through their cell membranes directly to the environment.

1. Excretion of waste gases. Although carbon dioxide is a waste product of respiration in plants, it can also be reused for photosynthesis when light is present. Excess carbon dioxide is released through the stomates of leaves, the lenticels of stems, and the cells of roots.

2. Excretion of water. Although water is needed for photosynthesis, there is usually an excess of water taken in through the roots. Metabolic processes may also produce more water than is needed for photosynthesis. Excess water is released by transpiration in the leaves.

3. Reuse of nitrogenous wastes. Plants can use ammonia (NH_3) and other wastes of the breakdown of nitrogen compounds to synthesize amino acids and other organic compounds.

4. Toxic wastes. Some products of metabolism, such as organic acids, that may be toxic to the plant are sealed off in vacuoles.

C. ADAPTATIONS IN ANIMALS AND PROTOZOANS

1. Protozoans. Most wastes are excreted directly through the cell membrane. In the paramecium, excess water collects in a **contractile vacuole** and is removed by a pumping action.

2. Hydra. All of the cells excrete wastes, including water, directly through their cell membranes.

3. Earthworm. Carbon dioxide is excreted by diffusion through the moist skin. Most of the body segments contain a pair of excretory organs called **nephridia.** The nephridia absorb water, excess salts, and nitrogenous wastes in the form of **urea** from the blood and release them to the environment.

4. Grasshopper. Carbon dioxide diffuses from the blood into the tracheal tubes and passes out through the spiracles. Water, mineral salts, and nitrogenous wastes in the form of **uric acid** crystals collect in excretory organs called **Malpighian tubules.** These wastes are transported to the digestive tube. Most water is reabsorbed. Solid wastes are released through the anus. This process of excreting wastes in the form of nearly dry solids is an adaptation that conserves water in an organism that lives on land.

5. Humans. In humans, carbon dioxide is excreted through the respiratory system. The kidneys contain **nephrons,** which are excretory structures similar in function to the nephridia of earthworms. The main nitrogenous waste is **urea.** See pages 81-83 for further details.

QUESTIONS

1. Which activity produces nitrogenous wastes?   (1) fat metabolism   (2) dehydration synthesis   (3) protein metabolism   (4) carbohydrate metabolism

2. Water is excreted from paramecia by means of   (1) active transport   (2) passive transport   (3) diffusion   (4) osmosis

FIGURE 2-12. REPRESENTATIVE EXCRETORY SYSTEMS

AMEBA AND PARAMECIUM

Soluble wastes, such as carbon dioxide and ammonia, are excreted by simple diffusion through the cell membrane. Solid wastes are ejected from the food vacuole when it migrates to the cell membrane and breaks the surface. Water is similarly ejected by the contractile vacuole.

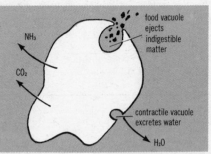

HYDRA

Carbon dioxide and nitrogenous wastes, mainly ammonia, are excreted by diffusion from cells through cell membrane into surrounding water or gastrovacular cavity. Excess water is removed through active transport.

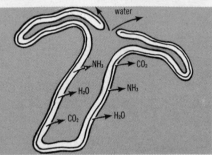

EARTHWORM

Paired excretory tubes (nephridia) in almost every segment. These collect wastes from body fluids, primarily ammonia and urea, and carry them to outside. Carbon dioxide diffuses through capillary walls and skin surface.

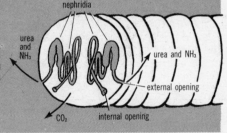

GRASSHOPPER

Malpighian tubules, opening into digestive tract, remove wastes from the freely-circulating blood. Nitrogenous wastes are converted to uric acid, which can be excreted as a semi-solid, thus conserving water. Uric acid and insoluble food wastes are passed out through anus. Carbon dioxide is diffused into the tracheal tubes and passes out through the spiracles.

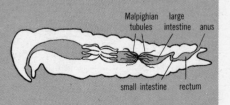

3. A student observing a protozoan under a microscope notices that the organism is swelling rapidly. This increase is most likely due to the improper functioning of the   (1) cilia   (2) contractile vacuole   (3) food vacuoles   (4) pseudopodia

4. Which microscopic structures in the earthworm remove urea from the body?   (1) contractile vacuoles   (2) Malpighian tubules   (3) nephrons   (4) nephridia

5. The Malpighian tubules are most closely associated with excretion in the   (1) paramecium   (2) hydra   (3) grasshopper   (4) earthworm

6. Uric acid is normally the principal nitrogenous waste excreted by (1) nephrons   (2) nephridia   (3) Malpighian tubules   (4) tracheae

7. Which organism conserves water by utilizing its digestive tract in the removal of dry nitrogenous wastes?   (1) grasshopper   (2) earthworm   (3) hydra   (4) human

II-9. SYNTHESIS

(This information is no longer required for the Regents Examination.)

A. THE PROCESS OF SYNTHESIS. Some of the end products of digestion are used by an organism to build complex compounds that it needs. The combination of smaller molecules to form larger ones is called **synthesis.** In most cases the joining of the molecules occurs by dehydration synthesis (see page 13).   Synthesis is usually a cellular process. Most organisms do not have special organs for synthesis.

B. PRODUCTS OF SYNTHESIS

  1. Secretions are useful substances synthesized in certain cells of an organism and then transported for use elsewhere in the organism. The following are the most important types of secretions:

  a. Enzymes. Cells synthesize thousands of different enzymes. Most enzymes are used to catalyze reactions within the cell that produces them. Some enzymes, however, may be secreted and used elsewhere in the organism.

  b. Hormones are secretions that regulate metabolic activities of an organism by either stimulating or retarding the functions of certain tissues or organs.

  c. Neurohumors are compounds, secreted by nerve cells, that are necessary for the transmission of nerve impulses (see pages 53-54). The chief neurohumors are *acetylcholine* and *noradrenalin.*

  d. Other types. Examples of other secretions are:

    (1) Mucus, a liquid mixture that coats the surfaces of many organs in animals.

    (2) Chitin, the hard material of the exoskeleton of insects.

    (3) Poisons secreted for defense or for capturing food.

    (4) Hydrochloric acid in the human stomach, used in digestion.

    (5) Tears to lubricate and wash the eyes.

    (6) Pheromones, which attract other individuals of the species and play a part in their mating behavior.

  e. Secretions used for human purposes. We make use of many compounds secreted by plants and animals, such as oils and waxes, drugs, flavorings, and fibers made of secreted materials..

2. Structural products. Many organelles and structures of cells are formed from materials synthesized by the cell. These include the proteins and lipids of the cell membrane; the ribosomes; and the cellulose of cell walls. Structural products of synthesis are used for growth of the organism and repair of structures.

3. Storage products. Food and nutrients not needed immediately by the organism may be converted by synthesis to products that can be stored for future use. **Fats** and **glycogen** are the most common storage products in animals. **Starches** and **oils** are the common storage products in plants.

QUESTIONS

1. The secretions of bees, ants, and tarantulas are formed by the process of (1) synthesis (2) regulation (3) excretion (4) digestion

2. Which organism normally produces chitin? (1) human (2) earthworm (3) hydra (4) grasshopper

3. The production of fat and glycogen reserves in animals is most directly the result of the process of (1) dehydration synthesis (2) biological oxidation (3) photosynthesis (4) fermentation

4. Which substances are not synthesized by any higher plants? (1) poisons (2) glycogens (3) waxes (4) drugs

5. The excess glucose manufactured in a plant is stored as (1) starch (2) glycogen (3) adenine (4) colchicine

II-10. NERVOUS REGULATION

The coordination and control of the life activities of an organism is called **regulation.** All organisms make use of *chemical control.* Animals also have *nerve control* mechanisms, which are discussed in this section.

A. STIMULI. A **stimulus** (plural, *stimuli*) is any change in the internal or external environment of an organism that causes a **response** (a change in behavior or function) by the organism.

B. RECEPTORS AND EFFECTORS. Structures specialized to detect stimuli are called **receptors.** For example, the eye contains receptors that detect light. Organs that produce responses to stimuli are called **effectors.** Muscles and glands are examples of effectors.

C. NEURONS. A **neuron** is a type of cell specialized for receiving and transmitting **impulses.** A nerve impulse consists of electrical and chemical changes in the cell membrane of a neuron. The neuron has the following structures:

1. Dendrites are cell branches that receive impulses from other neurons or from receptors.

2. The **cyton** is the cell body containing the nucleus.

3. The **axon** is a branch of the cell that transmits impulses away from the cyton.

4. Terminal branches are found at the end of the axon. They transmit impulses to the dendrites of other neurons or to effectors.

D. SYNAPSES. A **synapse** is a junction between a terminal branch of a neuron and the membrane of another cell. It includes a very small gap across which an impulse can pass. A synapse may connect a neuron to another neuron or to a receptor such as a muscle cell or gland cell.

E. NEUROTRANSMITTERS. Neurotransmitters are chemicals secreted into the synaptic gap by the end of a terminal branch. They transmit impulses across the synapse from one cell to another. *Acetylcholine* is a common neurotransmitter.

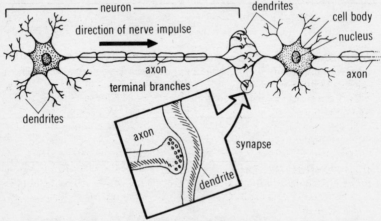

Figure 2-13. Structure of a neuron and the transmission of a nerve impulse from one neuron to another across a synapse.

F. NERVES. Nerves are bundles of neurons or parts of neurons that connect one region of an organism with another. The neurons in a nerve function independently, each carrying its own impulses.

QUESTIONS

1. Which structure is primarily involved in the transmission of impulses? (1) platelet (2) neuron (3) vacuole (4) nephron

2. Environmental factors which cause cells to move or to produce secretions are called (1) stimuli (2) synapses (3) ganglia (4) reflexes

3. An environmental stimulus first acts upon (1) effectors (2) connecting neurons (3) receptors (4) motor neurons

4. The junction spaces between two neurons are (1) axons (2) neurotransmitters (3) synapses (4) dendrites

5. Which secretions formed by the ends of neurons permit impulses to cross synapses? (1) lachrymal fluids (2) mucus (3) neurotransmitters (4) inorganic acids

6. The nerve impulse consists of a (1) series of sensations (2) series of electrochemical changes (3) flow of neutrons (4) flow of protons

7. Homeostasis in living things is regulated by the action of (1) the nervous system, only (2) the endocrine system, only (3) both the nervous and endocrine systems (4) neither the nervous nor the endocrine system

II-11. ADAPTATIONS FOR NERVOUS CONTROL

A. PROTOZOANS. In the paramecium there is a system of *fibrils* that transmit impulses to the cilia, thus regulating locomotion and ingestion of food. Some protozoans have specialized structures, such as eyespots, that receive stimuli and generate impulses to produce responses.

B. HYDRA. The hydra has specialized cells that are similar to neurons. These cells are connected to form a **nerve net,** which controls the activities of the animal. There is no central nervous system, and impulses may travel in any direction over the nerve net.

C. EARTHWORM. The earthworm has neurons organized into distinct structures and organs that form a true nervous system. The main parts of the nervous system are:

1. "Brain." This is a mass of **ganglia** (many neurons grouped together and interconnected), located on the upper *(dorsal)* side of the animal near the head *(anterior region)*.

2. Ventral nerve cord. A main nerve, connected to the "brain," runs along the length of the animal on the lower *(ventral)* side.

3. Nerve branches. Many smaller nerves branch from the ventral nerve cord to all parts of the body. Impulses generated by **receptors** (sense organs) travel through the nerves to **effectors** (muscles and glands).

D. GRASSHOPPER. The structure and function of the nervous system in the grasshopper is similar to that of the earthworm. The grasshopper also has **sensory organs,** including eyes, a tympanum that detects sound, and antennae.

E. HUMANS. The human nervous system includes a highly developed brain and a dorsal nerve cord, forming a central nervous system. See pages 83-86 for further details.

QUESTIONS

1. In which organism is a nerve impulse least likely to travel in a definite pathway? (1) hydra (2) earthworm (3) grasshopper (4) human

2. The regulatory system of a hydra can best be described as a (1) nerve net (2) fused ganglion (3) central nervous system (4) system similar to control in protozoa

3. Which organism's nervous system consists of a relatively simple dorsal brain, a ventral nerve cord, and connecting nerves? (1) mouse (2) human (3) frog (4) grasshopper

4. The nervous system of an earthworm differs from that of a hydra in that the earthworm (1) possesses a ventral nerve cord with connecting nerves (2) transmits impulses in either direction along a modified neuron (3) possesses fused ganglia and a nerve net (4) uses its nervous system to respond to external stimuli only

5. Which organism would be most likely to survive if exposed to a substance which prevents the production of neurotransmitters? (1) ameba (2) grasshopper (3) earthworm (4) human

6. Which organisms possess a central nervous system? (1) earthworms and grasshoppers (2) hydra and earthworm (3) hydra and grasshoppers (4) protozoa and humans

FIGURE 2-14. REPRESENTATIVE NERVOUS SYSTEMS

AMEBA AND PARAMECIUM

Amebas show coordinated movements in enveloping food particles, locomotion, and avoidance of harmful stimuli. They have no perceptible nervous system, and their reactions are probably chemical in nature. Paramecia possess a system of specialized fibrils arranged near the cell surface, which appear to control the coordinated beating of the cilia.

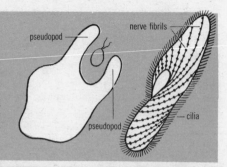

HYDRA

No central nervous system or organizing centers. A nerve net of neurons, randomly interconnected by synapses, receives sensory impulses from receptors in both inner and outer cell layers. Most stimuli affect only a small area, but complex coordinated activity occurs, as in feeding and locomotion.

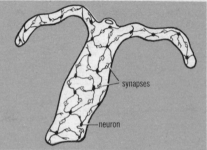

EARTHWORM

No head to hold sense organs or nerve center. Instead, fused ganglia located dorsally in third segment act as "brain," connect with ventral nerve cord, which has enlargements called ganglia in each segment, and nerve pairs branching from these. This makes up the worm's central nervous system. Specialized skin cells are sensitive to light and sound. Neurons transmit impulses in only one direction.

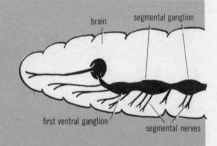

GRASSHOPPER

Head equipped with sense organs, fused dorsal ganglia functioning as "brain." Major nerve cord is ventral, has series of fused ganglia. Nervous system controls more complex movements than in earthworm, as well as such senses as sight, hearing, touch, and taste.

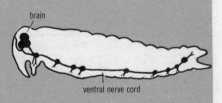

II-12. CHEMICAL REGULATION

As in the case of nervous regulation, chemical regulation controls and coordinates body processes by transmitting messages from one part of the organism to another. The message takes the form of a chemical substance, rather than an electrochemical impulse. While nervous regulation is found only in animals, chemical regulation occurs in both plants and animals.

A. HORMONES. In chemical regulation, a stimulus causes the secretion of a substance in one part of the organism. The substance is then transmitted to another part of the organism, where a response is produced. Chemical substances that perform a regulatory function in this way are called **hormones.** Hormones are often referred to as "chemical messengers."

B. CHEMICAL CONTROL IN PLANTS

1. Plant hormones. Plant hormones are produced chiefly in actively growing regions and structures, such as the growing tips of roots and stems, buds, and seeds. The hormones are produced by one group of cells, but affect the development of other cells. However, there are no plant tissues that are specialized for the secretion of hormones. **Auxins** are examples of plant hormones.

2. Effects of plant hormones. Plant hormones help to regulate growth, reproductive processes such as flower and fruit development, the dropping of fruit and leaves, and response to stimuli. The effects of plant hormones depend upon the hormone involved, its concentration, and the tissues that are affected. For example, high auxin concentrations stimulate stem growth, but reduce root growth. Low auxin concentrations have the opposite effect.

3. Tropisms. Auxins affect the rate of cell division and elongation in growth regions. Certain stimuli cause unequal distribution of auxins in a particular region, resulting in growth responses called **tropisms.** For example, when one side of a stem is more brightly lighted than the other, the concentration of auxins on the darker side increases. This increased concentration of auxins causes the dark side of the stem to grow more rapidly than the lighted side. The result is a bending of the stem toward the light. This effect is called **phototropism.** (See Figure 2-15.) **Geotropism** is a similar response to gravity, causing roots to grow downward. Tropisms are usually advantageous responses that increase the chances of survival of the plant.

C. CHEMICAL CONTROL IN ANIMALS. Most animals have cells and tissues that are specialized for the production of hormones. In this respect they differ from plants, in which there are no tissues specialized for hormone production. These specialized tissues in animals are found in organs called **endocrine glands,** and the endocrine glands make up the **endocrine system.** Endocrine glands do not have ducts to carry their secretions to other organs. Their hormones are secreted directly into the blood and are transported by the circulatory system. The endocrine glands are therefore also called **ductless glands.**

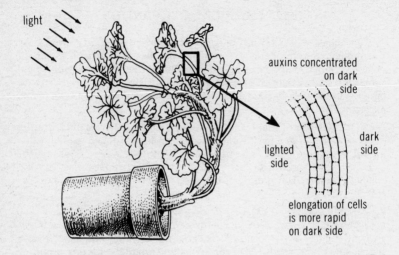

Figure 2-15. Phototropism in a growing stem. Unequal lighting causes an increased concentration of auxins on the darker side of the stem. This causes the darker side to grow more rapidly, resulting in a bending of the stem toward the light.

1. **Examples of animal hormones**
   a. **Juvenile hormone** in insects, which controls early development.
   b. **Thyroxin,** which regulates metabolism and development of the human body.
   c. **Insulin,** which regulates the sugar level in the blood by controlling the conversion of glucose to glycogen.

2. **Effects of animal hormones.** Some of the activities regulated by hormones in animals are growth patterns and rates, metamorphosis in insects, reproductive cycles, and blood sugar levels.

II-13. COMPARISON OF NERVOUS AND ENDOCRINE SYSTEMS

In many animals, regulation of life activities is accomplished by both a nervous system and an endocrine system. These systems have similarities and differences.

A. SIMILARITIES

1. Both systems have a major role in maintaining homeostasis.
2. Both systems function partly through the secretion of chemicals: neurohumors in the nervous system and hormones in the endocrine system.

B. DIFFERENCES

1. Nervous responses are much faster than responses caused by the endocrine system.

2. Endocrine responses last longer than nervous responses, continuing for a time after the stimulus ends.

3. Nervous impulses are transmitted by neurons, while hormones are carried by the transport system.

QUESTIONS

1. Substances secreted in one part of an organism that then have a regulatory effect on some other part are called (1) enzymes (2) neurotransmitters (3) hormones (4) pheromones

2. Which glands secrete their chemicals directly into the circulatory fluid? (1) endocrine glands (2) salivary glands (3) sweat glands (4) tear glands

3. Metamorphosis of an insect, such as a butterfly, is regulated so that it occurs at the proper stage of the animal's development. This regulation is effected by means of (1) daily changes in the amount of light (2) sudden changes in air temperature (3) stimulation of the central nervous system (4) activity of special hormones

4. Auxins are most closely associated with which process? (1) evaporation (2) root pressure (3) regulation (4) respiration

5. In plants, auxins increase the rate of (1) digestion (2) excretion (3) growth (4) ingestion

6. The stems of a plant bend toward light because (1) the plant needs light for photosynthesis (2) stomates open in those portions of leaves exposed to light (3) differences in the distribution of auxin cause differences in the growth of cells (4) the bending of a stem toward the light is an example of positive phototropism

7. Compared with the response to a nerve impulse, the response to a hormone is usually (1) longer in duration and more widespread in effect (2) longer in duration and less widespread in effect (3) shorter in duration and more widespread in effect (4) shorter in duration and less widespread in effect

8. Endocrine responses differ from nerve responses in that endocrine responses are (1) more rapid (2) electrical in nature (3) carried by neurons (4) of longer duration

9. The growth response that causes roots to grow downward is an example of (1) positive geotropism (2) negative geotropism (3) nervous regulation (4) negative phototropism

II-14. LOCOMOTION

A. DEFINITION. Locomotion is the ability of an organism to move from one place to another.

B. ADVANTAGES OF LOCOMOTION. Locomotion enables animals and protozoans to increase the chances of their survival by increasing their ability to:
1. Obtain food.
2. Find shelter.
3. Move away from their own toxic wastes or other harmful substances.
4. Escape from enemies *(predators)*.
5. Find and make contact with other individuals of the species in order to mate and reproduce.

C. ADAPTATIONS FOR LOCOMOTION IN PLANTS, ALGAE, AND BACTERIA. Locomotion is not characteristic of plants. However, some specialized plant cells, such as male gametes of mosses and ferns, are able to move from place to place. Some algae and bacteria have the ability to locomote by means of **flagella.**

D. ADAPTATIONS IN ANIMALS AND PROTOZOANS
1. Protozoans. The paramecium can move by means of **cilia.** The ameba moves by the streaming of its cytoplasm into temporary extensions called **pseudopods.** Several other types of protozoans move by means of **flagella.**
2. Hydra. The hydra is **sessile** (remains in one place) most of the time. **Contractile fibers** enable it to move its body and tentacles and to change its location by a somersaulting motion.
3. Earthworm. Sets of muscles in the body of the earthworm enable it to stretch and contract. **Setae** on its ventral surface enable it to grip the soil. Together, the muscles and setae enable the animal to perform locomotion.
4. Grasshopper. Locomotion in the grasshopper is made possible by **wings** and **jointed appendages (legs).** Muscles attached to the chitinous exoskeleton control movement of these structures. The grasshopper can walk, jump, and fly.
5. Humans. Locomotion in humans is accomplished by jointed appendages and muscles attached to the bones of an internal skeleton. See pages 91-92 for further details.

QUESTIONS

1. Organisms which lack the ability to move from place to place are referred to as (1) motile (2) sessile (3) autotrophic (4) saprophytic
2. Flagella, cilia, and pseudopodia are structures associated with the locomotion of (1) protozoa (2) hydras (3) earthworms (4) grasshoppers
3. Cyclosis is associated with the process of locomotion in the (1) ameba (2) paramecium (3) earthworm (4) hydra
4. Which organelles of a paramecium serve the same function as the pseudopodia of an ameba? (1) contractile vacuoles (2) mitochondria (3) nuclei (4) cilia

5. Locomotion in the earthworm is accomplished by the interaction of muscles and   (1) setae   (2) glands   (3) nephridia   (4) cartilaginous appendages

6. Movement in grasshoppers is accomplished by the interaction of muscles and   (1) setae   (2) bones   (3) chitinous appendages   (4) tentacles

UNIT III   HUMAN PHYSIOLOGY

III-1. HUMAN NUTRITION

(See pages 24-30 for introductory material on nutrition.)

A. HUMAN FOODS. Humans are heterotrophic and must therefore ingest food.

1. Nutrients are substances in foods that the human body can digest, absorb, and use for its metabolism. There are six kinds of nutrients: carbohydrates, proteins, lipids, vitamins, minerals, and water. All of these nutrients must be present in the human diet. Nutrients are needed to provide energy, materials for growth and repair of tissues, and substances needed for regulation of body functions.

2. Roughage (also called **fiber**) is indigestible material in foods. Roughage is not digested. It passes through the digestive tract chemically unchanged. However, it is needed for proper functioning of the muscles of the tract and regular elimination of undigested food wastes.

3. Digestion of nutrients. Vitamins, minerals, and water are present in foods as small molecules that can be absorbed without digestion. Carbohydrates, lipids, and proteins must be digested in order to be absorbed and used by the human body.

4. Nutritional needs of humans, including energy requirements, vary with an individual's age, sex, and physical activity.

B. ENERGY CONTENT OF FOOD. The chemical energy that can be obtained from a substance is measured in units called **calories.** The *food calorie* (also called a *kilocalorie*) is the amount of heat energy that will raise the temperature of 1 kilogram of water by 1°C.

C. CARBOHYDRATES

1. Chemical composition. See page 13.

2. Use by body. Carbohydrates are the main source of energy for humans. Carbohydrates in foods should furnish about 50% of the daily energy needs.

3. Source of roughage. Fresh fruits and vegetables, as well as whole grains, contain *cellulose,* a complex carbohydrate. The complex carbohydrates in these foods are the most common source of roughage in the human diet.

4. Storage of carbohydrates. Digested carbohydrates circulate in the blood mainly as the simple sugar glucose. Excess glucose is converted to the complex carbohydrate **glycogen** and is stored in that form. When supplies of glucose are needed, the glycogen is broken down to glucose for transport through the body.

HP

D. LIPIDS (FATS)

1. Chemical composition. See page 14.

2. Use by the body. Fats are used as a source of energy by the body. They provide more than twice as much energy per gram as either carbohydrates or proteins (9 cal/g for fats against 4 cal/g for carbohydrates or proteins). Excess carbohydrates and proteins are converted to fats and stored for later use when needed. Fats are also needed by the body for certain cell structures, such as cell membranes, for cushioning organs, and as insulation against cold. Excess consumption of fat should be avoided. Fats should provide no more than about 30% of the daily intake of calories.

3. Saturated and unsaturated fats. In *saturated fats*, all the carbon-carbon bonds are single and the fat contains as much hydrogen as is possible for its chemical structure. Saturated fats are solid at room temperature. There is evidence that excess intake of saturated fats is one of the factors that increases the chance of cardiovascular disease in humans. *Polyunsaturated fats* are fats with at least two double carbon-carbon bonds and less hydrogen than they could contain. They are liquids at room temperature (oils) and do not seem to be connected with cardiovascular disease.

E. PROTEINS

1. Chemical composition. See page 15.

2. Use by the body. Proteins in the diet provide the amino acids from which the body synthesizes all the proteins it needs. All enzymes and many hormones are proteins. Proteins also provide materials for building and repairing tissues, and can be used as a source of energy. Females of high school age need about 46 grams of protein per day, and males need about 56 grams. About 15-20% of the daily calorie intake should be in the form of proteins.

3. Essential amino acids. The body needs 20 different amino acids. The body can convert some of these to others, but there are eight amino acids the body cannot synthesize. The amino acids that the body cannot synthesize are called the **essential amino acids.**

4. Complete and incomplete protein. For the body to synthesize proteins, all the necessary amino acids must be present at the same time, because the body cannot store amino acids. If any essential amino acid is missing, protein synthesis stops. The excess of the other amino acids will be broken down **(deaminated)** and used for energy or stored as fat. **Complete protein foods** contain all eight of the essential amino acids in the proper proportions for protein synthesis. **Incomplete protein foods** lack one or more of the essential amino acids. In a diet containing mostly incomplete protein, such as a vegetarian diet, the proper balance of amino acids can be obtained by combining foods so that each one provides amino acids missing from the others. For example, wheat and beans together provide complete protein, although neither food does so by itself.

QUESTIONS

1. In addition to digestible nutrients, human food must contain indigestible material called   (1) calories   (2) additives   (3) roughage   (4) saturated fats

2. Among the nutrients that can be absorbed without digestion are the   (1) carbohydrates   (2) lipids   (3) proteins   (4) vitamins

3. If equal weights of the following nutrients are oxidized, the largest amount of energy will be released by the   (1) vitamins   (2) sugars   (3) proteins   (4) fats

4. The nutrient used by the body for growth and replacement of tissues is   (1) fat   (2) protein   (3) starch   (4) minerals

5. Excess glucose is stored in the body as   (1) glycogen   (2) cellulose   (3) amino acids   (4) lipids

6. Many medical authorities believe that the chief danger in a diet containing a large amount of saturated fat is an increased risk of   (1) heart attack   (2) vitamin deficiency diseases   (3) dehydration of body tissues   (4) tooth decay

III-2. HUMAN DIGESTION

A. HUMAN DIGESTIVE SYSTEM. The human digestive system consists of a one-way passage for ingested food together with certain accessory organs that assist the digestive functions of the system. The one-way passage is called the **gastrointestinal tract,** which is often abbreviated as the **GI tract.** The gastrointestinal tract is a hollow tube with an opening at each end. Food materials in the GI tract are actually outside the body tissues. Food is moved through the tract by slow, rhythmic muscular contractions called **peristalsis.**

B. THE MOUTH (ORAL CAVITY)
   1. Structures. The **mouth,** or **oral cavity,** includes the teeth, the tongue, and the openings of the salivary glands.
   2. Functions
      a. The **teeth** act to break pieces of food mechanically into smaller pieces, so as to expose a larger surface for enzyme action.
      b. The **salivary glands** secrete **saliva,** which flows through ducts into the mouth. Saliva contains the enzyme **salivary amylase,** which begins the digestion of starch, a carbohydrate. (*Amyl-* comes from a Greek word meaning *starch*.)
      c. The **tongue** acts to help mix the chewed food with saliva and to move it to the back of the mouth for swallowing.

C. THE ESOPHAGUS.
   1. Structure. The **esophagus** is a muscular tube that connects the mouth to the stomach.
   2. Function. The act of swallowing moves food into the esophagus. Persistalsis of the muscular walls of the esophagus moves food to the stomach.

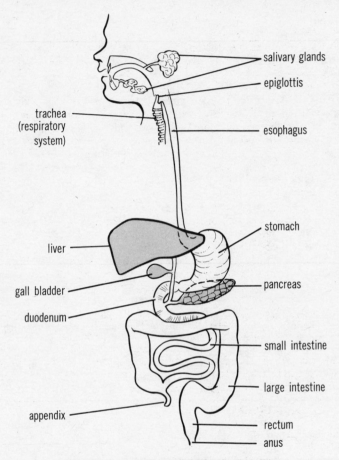

salivary glands

epiglottis

trachea
(respiratory
system)

esophagus

stomach

liver

pancreas

gall bladder

duodenum

small intestine

large intestine

appendix

rectum

anus

Figure 3-1. The human digestive system.

D. THE STOMACH

1. **Structure.** The **stomach** is a muscular sac. Its lining contains **gastric glands** that secrete enzymes and **hydrochloric acid.** (*Gastr*- comes from a Greek word meaning *belly* and refers to the stomach.)

2. **Functions.** Muscular contractions of the stomach wall mix the food with digestive juices. The enzyme **gastric protease** begins the digestion of proteins. The hydrochloric acid provides the proper pH for maximum effectiveness of the gastric protease.

E. THE SMALL INTESTINE

1. **Structure.** The **small intestine** is a long, coiled tube of small diameter. Its lining contains **intestinal glands** that secrete digestive enzymes into the intestine. Partially digested food enters the small intestine from the stomach.

2. Accessory organs

   a. The **liver** secretes **bile,** which is stored in the **gall bladder** and passes through a duct into the intestine.

   b. The **pancreas** secretes **pancreatic juice** through a duct into the intestine.

3. Digestive functions

   a. Bile does not contain enzymes. Its function is to mechanically break down **(emulsify)** fats into very small droplets, thus increasing the surface area of the fats for more rapid digestion by lipases.

   b. Pancreatic juice contains **proteases, lipases** (which digest lipids, or fats), and **amylases** (which continue the digestion of starch).

   c. Intestinal juice contains proteases, lipases, and **disaccharidases** such as **maltase** (which digests the disaccharide maltose).

4. Absorption

   a. Structures for absorption. The lining of the small intestine contains numerous fingerlike structures called **villi** (singular, *villus*), which greatly increase the surface area of the intestinal lining (see Figure 3-2). Most absorption of digested nutrients occurs through the walls of the villi. The interior of the villus contains a **lacteal,** which is a small vessel of the lymphatic system (see page 75), and numerous **capillaries** of the circulatory system (see page 72).

   b. Absorption of end products of digestion

   (1) Fatty acids and **gylcerol,** the end products of the digestion of fats, are absorbed through the villi into the lacteals. They are transported by the lymph to the circulatory system.

   (2) Monosaccharides, the end products of carbohydrate digestion, and **amino acids,** the end products of protein digestion, are absorbed through the villi into the capillaries. They are transported by the blood to the liver, where they are stored until needed.

F. THE LARGE INTESTINE

1. Structure. The **large intestine** is a tube of larger diameter and much shorter length than the small intestine. Undigested food passes from the small intestine into the large intestine.

2. Functions. Excess water in the undigested food mass is absorbed by the large intestine. The remaining wastes are moved by peristalsis into the **rectum** at the lower end of the large intestine. These semisolid wastes, called **feces,** are released *(egested)* through an opening called the **anus.**

QUESTIONS

1. Which is the correct order of structures through which food normally passes in the human alimentary canal? (1) oral cavity, esophagus, pharynx, stomach, large intestine, small intestine (2) oral cavity, pharynx, esophagus, stomach, small intestine, large intestine (3) oral cavity, pharynx, stomach, esophagus, large intestine, small intestine (4) oral cavity, esophagus, pharynx, small intestine, stomach, large intestine

2. The chemical digestion of which nutrient begins in the stomach? (1) fat (2) sugar (3) starch (4) protein

3. In humans, digestive glands are present in the (1) stomach, liver, and small intestine (2) stomach, small intestine, and large intestine (3) mouth, esophagus, and stomach (4) mouth, stomach, and small intestine

4. The function of bile is to (1) break down fats into small droplets (2) stimulate liver function (3) aid the digestion of proteins (4) initiate peristaltic action

5. The mechanical breakdown of food (1) occurs mainly in the large intestine (2) exposes a larger surface area for chemical digestion (3) produces the end products of digestion (4) is brought about by digestive enzymes

6. In humans, most protein digestion occurs in the (1) mouth and small intestine (2) mouth and stomach (3) stomach and large intestine (4) stomach and small intestine

7. Most absorption of the end products of digestion into the circulatory system in humans occurs (1) in the large intestine (2) in the stomach (3) in the liver (4) through the villi of the small intestine

8. Which activity occurs principally in the large intestine of humans? (1) Proteins and starches are completely digested. (2) End products of digestion diffuse into the bloodstream. (3) Water is absorbed into the bloodstream. (4) Bile digests fats and oils.

I. DETAILS OF CHEMICAL DIGESTION

1. Organs and their secretions. See Table 3-2.

2. Hydrolysis. Most digestion occurs by the chemical process of **hydrolysis.** In this process, large molecules are broken down into smaller molecules by the addition of water. It is the reverse of dehydration synthesis (page 13).

3. Digestion of polysaccharides (carbohydrates such as starches and complex sugars). Polysaccharides are made up of simple sugar units joined together by dehydration synthesis. Digestive enzymes break down starch and other polysaccharides into simple sugars, such as glucose, by hydrolysis (see Figure 3-2).

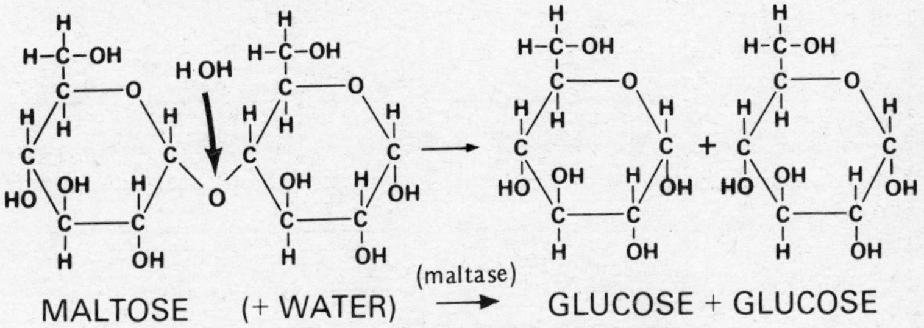

MALTOSE   (+ WATER) $\xrightarrow{\text{(maltase)}}$ GLUCOSE + GLUCOSE

Figure 3-2. Hydrolysis of maltose, a disaccharide.

4. Digestion of proteins. Digestive enzymes break down the polypeptide chains of proteins into amino acids by hydrolysis of the peptide bond (see Figure 3-3).

5. Digestion of lipids (fats). Digestive enzymes called lipases break down fats into fatty acids and glycerol by hydrolysis (see Figure 3-4).

BIOCHEMISTRY

TABLE 3-2. SECRETIONS OF THE HUMAN DIGESTIVE SYSTEM.

Organ	Secretions and Enzymes	Chemical Function
salivary glands in mouth (oral cavity)	saliva: amylase	enzyme that begins carbohydrate digestion; breaks down starch into maltose (a disaccharide)
esophagus	mucus (not an enzyme)	no chemical action; aids movement of food to stomach by peristalsis
stomach (gastric glands)	gastric juice: pepsin	enzyme that begins protein digestion; breaks down proteins into smaller molecules called peptones and proteoses
	hydrochloric acid	not an enzyme, but necessary for effective action of pepsin on proteins
liver	bile	not an enzyme; breaks down fat mechanically into small droplets (emulsification)
pancreas	pancreatic juice: amylase	enzyme that continues digestion of starch to disaccharides
	trypsin	enzyme that digests peptones and proteoses into small amino acid groups called peptides
	lipase	enzyme that digests fat droplets into fatty acids and glycerol
small intestine (intestinal glands)	intestinal juice: peptidases	enzymes that break down peptides into amino acids
	maltase	enzyme that breaks down maltose (a dissacharide) into glucose (a monosaccharide)
large intestine	———	no digestive function; absorbs water from undigested materials; forms feces

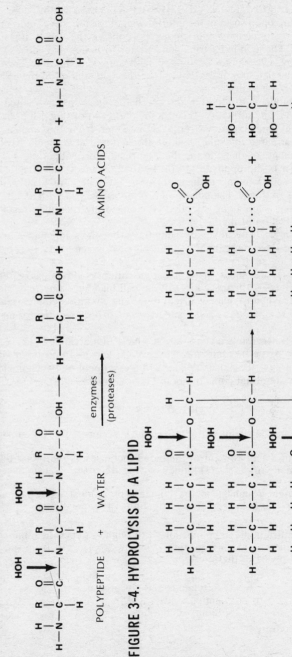

FIGURE 3-3. HYDROLYSIS OF A POLYPEPTIDE (PROTEIN)

POLYPEPTIDE + WATER

AMINO ACIDS

FIGURE 3-4. HYDROLYSIS OF A LIPID

LIPID (FAT) + WATER

3 FATTY ACIDS + GLYCEROL

EXTENDED AREA—BIOCHEMISTRY

J. SOME MALFUNCTIONS OF THE DIGESTIVE SYSTEM

1. Ulcers are open sores in the interior wall of the digestive tract, most often in the stomach or the upper portion of the small intestine *(duodenum)*. The acid in gastric juice irritates the sores and causes pain or discomfort. Ulcers can be treated with antacids, the avoidance of irritants in the diet, and drugs that reduce the acid content of the gastric juice. Their cause is unknown.

2. Constipation is a condition in which the feces are evacuated infrequently and with difficulty. It is usually the result of sluggish peristaltic movement and excessive removal of water from the undigested material in the large intestine, making the material abnormally hard or stiff. Insufficient roughage in the diet can result in constipation.

3. Diarrhea is the opposite of constipation. There is insufficient removal of water from the undigested food, the feces are watery, and evacuation is frequent. The condition is often associated with an intestinal disturbance such as an infection. Prolonged diarrhea may result in severe dehydration of the body tissues.

4. Appendicitis. The appendix sometimes becomes infected and inflamed. If the infection cannot be controlled, it is necessary to remove the appendix by surgery.

5. Gallstones are small, hard particles, often made of cholesterol, which sometimes form and collect in the gall bladder. They may block the bile duct and cause pain or discomfort. The condition can be treated by surgically removing the gall bladder, which is not essential for digestion.

6. Anorexia nervosa is a condition in which an individual is unable to take or retain food. It results in severe weight loss and nutritional deficiency symptoms. Its causes appear to be emotional or psychological, related to an abnormal concern about obesity (overweight).

QUESTIONS

1. Lipase aids in the digestion of (1) fats (2) proteins (3) enzymes (4) salts

2. The amino acid content of the blood increases as the blood flows through which organ? (1) kidney (2) gallbladder (3) pancreas (4) small intestine

3. Insufficient roughage in the human diet is most likely to cause (1) gallstones (2) diarrhea (3) constipation (4) appendicitis

For each nutrient given in questions 4 through 6, select the number of the end products, chosen from the list below, that result from the enzymatic hydrolysis of that nutrient.

End Products
(1) fatty acids and glycerol
(2) amino acids
(3) monosaccharides

4. Carbohydrates
5. Proteins
6. Fats

7. Which are the fundamental building blocks of proteins? (1) fatty acids (2) carboxyl groups (3) amino acids (4) glucose rings

8. The hydrolysis of a protein in the stomach requires the presence of (1) bile (2) fatty acids (3) a lipase (4) a protease

III-3. HUMAN CIRCULATION

The principal function of the human circulatory system is the transport of dissolved and suspended materials throughout the body. The system also plays a part in *immunity*—the defense of the body against disease organisms and other foreign materials.

A. FLUIDS OF THE CIRCULATORY SYSTEM

1. Blood. Although blood is a fluid that flows through the vessels of the circulatory system, it is considered to be a tissue because it contains cells. Blood serves as a transport medium and helps to maintain homeostasis for all the cells of the body. The parts of the blood are:

a. Plasma. The liquid portion of the blood is called **plasma.** The plasma is mostly water. Materials dissolved or in colloidal suspension in the plasma include inorganic ions, nutrients, wastes, nonprotein hormones, and proteins. The proteins include enzymes, antibodies, clotting factors, and certain hormones.

b. Red blood cells. The red blood cells do not have nuclei when mature. They contain **hemoglobin,** which combines with oxygen, thus enabling the red blood cells to transport and distribute oxygen to the body tissues.

c. White blood cells. All the white blood cells have nuclei. Some white blood cells, called **phagocytes,** are able to leave the capillaries and engulf and destroy bacteria by phagocytosis. This is one of the body's defenses against infection. Other white cells, called **lymphocytes,** produce substances called **antibodies,** which counteract foreign proteins, called **antigens.** This is another of the body's immunological defenses.

d. Platelets are cells that are smaller than both the red and white cells. They play a key part in the formation of blood clots.

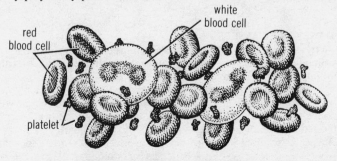

Figure 3-5. Cells in human blood.

2. Lymph. Blood plasma diffuses through the walls of the capillaries and forms a watery fluid surrounding the cells of all tissues. This fluid is called **intercellular fluid (ICF)**. The ICF diffuses into the lymph vessels, which return it to the blood. The fluid inside the lymph vessels is called **lymph.**

B. CLOTTING. When blood leaves a blood vessel as the result of an injury, a series of enzyme-controlled reactions causes a **blood clot** to form. The blood clot seals the opening in the blood vessel wall and stops the loss of blood.

1. Structure of a blood clot. The blood clot consists of a mass of fine threads of a protein called **fibrin,** which trap platelets and other blood cells to form the clot.

2. Mechanism of clotting. Proteins that take part in clot formation are always present in the blood. When an injury occurs, enzymes released by the damaged tissue cells and by the platelets start a series of reactions that eventually produce the threads of fibrin that form the clot.

QUESTIONS

1. The liquid portion of the blood is called   (1) plasma   (2) lymph   (3) water   (4) intercellular fluid

For each component of human blood in questions 2 through 5, select the *number* of the function, chosen from the list below, that is associated with that component.

Functions
(1) Transport of oxygen
(2) Blood clotting
(3) Defense against bacteria
(4) Transport of nutrients

2. Plasma
3. Red blood cells
4. White blood cells
5. Platelets

6. In the blood, the principal function of the phagocytes is to   (1) store neurotransmitters   (2) produce hemoglobin   (3) initiate clotting   (4) destroy bacteria

C. TRANSPORT VESSELS

1. Arteries are relatively thick-walled, muscular blood vessels that carry blood away from the heart. Contractions of the muscles in the artery walls aid in the flow of blood.

2. Capillaries. Arteries branch into successively thinner vessels and finally connect with **capillaries,** which are very narrow blood vessels with walls only one cell thick. Exchanges of materials between the body cells and the blood take place through the walls of the capillaries.

3. Veins. Capillaries join together and connect to **veins,** which are relatively thin-walled blood vessels. Veins carry blood to the heart. Most veins have **valves** that prevent backflow of blood.

4. Lymph vessels are tubes that branch through all the tissues. At the ends of the branches, the tubes are very narrow and have walls only one cell thick. Lymph vessels collect the fluid (ICF) that surrounds all the body cells and drain it back into the blood system as lymph.

D. THE HEART. The heart is a 4-chambered muscular organ that acts as a pump. It is divided into two halves (left and right) by a wall. Each half has two chambers—an **atrium** (plural, *atria*) and a **ventricle**—connected through a **valve.** The atria receive blood and the ventricles pump it out. The muscular walls of the ventricles are thicker and more powerful than those of the atria. The wall of the left ventricle is thicker than that of the right ventricle.

1. Circulation through the heart. Blood rich in oxygen (oxygenated blood) flows from the lungs through the pulmonary veins into the left atrium of the heart. It then passes through a valve from the left atrium to the left ventricle. The left ventricle pumps the oxygenated blood into arteries that carry the blood to all organs except the lungs. Blood poor in oxygen (deoxygenated blood) returns from the body organs through veins to the right atrium. It passes through a valve into the right ventricle. The right ventricle pumps the deoxygenated blood through the pulmonary arteries to the lungs.

2. Heartbeat cycle. The heart muscles alternately contract **(systole)** and relax **(diastole).** During systole, blood is pumped out of the ventricles under pressure into the arteries. During diastole, the atria fill with blood flowing in from the veins. A valve at the outlet of each ventricle opens during systole to allow blood to flow out. It closes during diastole to

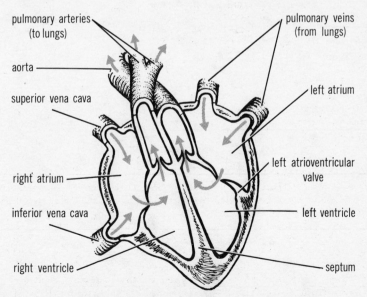

Figure 3-6. Structure and function of the human heart.

prevent backflow of blood into the ventricle. A valve between each atrium and its ventricle closes during systole to prevent backflow from the ventricle to the atrium.

E. BLOOD PRESSURE. Blood in the arteries is always under pressure. The term **blood pressure** refers to the pressure the blood exerts on the walls of the arteries. The blood pressure increases to a maximum during contraction of the heart (systole); this is called the **systolic pressure.** The blood pressure drops to a minimum during relaxation of the heart (diastole); this is called the **diastolic pressure.**

F. CIRCULATORY PATHWAYS

    1. Pulmonary circulation. The flow of blood from the right ventricle through the pulmonary arteries to the lungs and back through the pulmonary veins to the left atrium is called the **pulmonary circulation.**

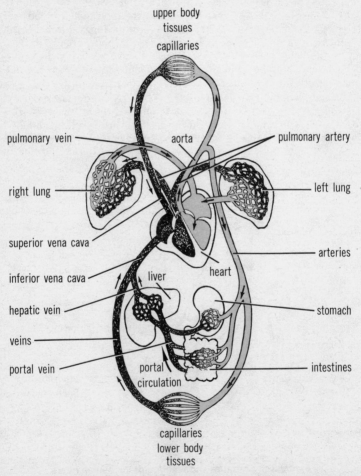

Figure 3-7. The human circulatory system.

2. Systemic circulation. The flow of blood from the left ventricle through arteries to all parts of the body except the lungs and back through veins to the right atrium is called the **systemic circulation.**

3. Coronary circulation. The muscle tissues of the heart are supplied with blood by its own system of arteries, veins, and capillaries, called the **coronary blood vessels.**

4. Lymphatic circulation. Intercellular fluid diffuses into lymph vessels, where it is called lymph. Small lymph vessels join to form larger vessels, which finally become two main vessels. These main lymph vessels join certain veins of the systemic system, and the lymph is returned to the blood.

QUESTIONS

1. If the flow of blood in a vessel is toward the heart, then the vessel is known as (1) a ventricle (2) an artery (3) an atrium (4) a vein

2. In humans, the backward flow of blood in veins is prevented by (1) muscles (2) heart action (3) valves (4) lymphatics

3. The number of chambers in the human heart is (1) 1 (2) 2 (3) 3 (4) 4

4. Blood flowing to the heart is received by a(n) (1) ventricle (2) valve (3) atrium (4) lymph duct

5. Blood pressure results from (1) contractions of the heart muscle (2) relaxation of the heart muscle (3) backflow of blood (4) the action of valves

6. Compared to the diastolic blood pressure (during relaxation of the heart), the systolic pressure (during contraction of the heart) is (1) always lower (2) always higher (3) usually the same (4) at first higher, then lower

For *each* function named in questions 7 through 10, select the number of the circulatory pathway, chosen from the list below, that is associated with that function.

Circulatory Pathway
(1) Pulmonary Circulation
(2) Systemic Circulation
(3) Coronary Circulation
(4) Lymphatic Circulation

7. Returns intercellular fluid to the blood
8. Carries blood to and from the lungs
9. Supplies blood to the heart muscle tissue
10. Carries blood to all organs except the lungs

EXTENDED AREA—HUMAN PHYSIOLOGY

G. IMMUNOLOGY

1. The immune response. An important function of the human transport system is associated with the body's defensive reactions to foreign organisms or substances. Substances that are not normally present in the body and that the body recognizes as "foreign" are called **antigens.** Most antigens are proteins. Specialized white blood cells produce specific **antibodies** that neutralize each antigen. This process is called the **immune response.**

2. Immunity. The presence of specific antibodies in the blood plasma that enable the individual to resist a specific disease is called **immunity.** Immunity can be acquired in several ways:

   a. Active immunity. In active immunity, the body produces the antibodies to a particular disease either (1) by contact with the disease organism or its products (called *toxins*), or (2) by receiving a vaccination of a weakened form of the disease organism or its products.

   b. Passive immunity. In passive immunity, antibodies from an outside source are introduced into the individual's blood. Passive immunity is usually temporary. The body gradually destroys and excretes the antibody.

   c. Inborn immunity. At birth, individuals possess many specific antibodies for particular antigens. This is called *inborn immunity,* and it is a form of active immunity.

3. Allergies. Certain substances that have little or no effect on most individuals act as antigens in the bodies of other individuals. The individuals who respond to these substances are said to be *allergic* to them, and the response is called an **allergy.** The substances that produce allergic responses include dust, pollen, certain foods, drugs, insect bites, and many others. The antibodies produced in an allergic individual may cause inflammations or other abnormal symptoms. They may also stimulate the production of histamine, a substance that dilates blood vessels and causes sneezing, itching, watering of the eyes, and breathing difficulty (asthma).

4. Blood types. A major classification of blood into types (the **ABO system**) is related to the presence or absence of certain antigens, called A and B, on the surface of the red blood cells. The plasma contains antibodies for the antigens *not* present on the red cells. For example, if the red cells have antigen A, but not B, the plasma will have the antibody anti-B. If both antigens are present, the plasma will have neither antibody. If neither antigen is present, the plasma will have both antibodies. These facts are summarized in Table 3-3.

TABLE 3-3. THE ABO SYSTEM OF HUMAN BLOOD TYPES.

Blood Type	Antigens	Antibodies
O	none	anti-A and anti-B
A	A	anti-B
B	B	anti-A
AB	A and B	none

5. Importance of blood type. In giving whole blood transfusions, it is important to consider the blood types of both the donor and the recipient. If the donor blood has red cells with an antigen not present in the recipient's red cells, the antibody in the recipient's plasma will cause the donor's red cells to clump together in the recipient's bloodstream. This can have painful or fatal effects on the recipient. For example, a person with Type A blood cannot safely receive Type B or Type AB blood because the recipient's anti-B antibody will cause clumping of the red cells in the transfused blood. Table 3-4 shows the kinds of transfusions that are safe in the ABO system.

TABLE 3-4. SAFE MATCHES OF BLOOD TYPES IN WHOLE-BLOOD TRANSFUSIONS.

Recipient	Donor
type O can safely receive	type O
type A can safely receive	type A or O
type B can safely receive	type B or O
type AB can safely receive	type A, B, AB, or O

6. Organ transplants. In organ and tissue transplants or grafts from one individual to another, the body's immunological system reacts to the foreign proteins of the transplanted tissue and destroys it. This effect is called **rejection** of the transplant or graft. It is a major problem in the replacement of damaged or diseased organs.

H. MALFUNCTIONS OF THE TRANSPORT SYSTEM

1. Cardiovascular diseases. Malfunctions and disorders of the heart and blood vessels are called **cardiovascular diseases.**

   a. High blood pressure, or **hypertension,** is a condition in which the arterial blood pressure remains above normal. It is the most common form of cardiovascular disease. Causes appear to be related to stress, excess consumption of sodium (salt) in the diet, hereditary factors, cigarette smoking, and the aging process.

   b. Atherosclerosis is a condition in which the arteries become narrower and inelastic because of deposits of cholesterol and other fatty materials on their inner walls. High blood pressure seems to be one of the factors contributing to the condition.

   c. Heart disease. Narrowing or blockage of the coronary arteries that supply the heart muscle can reduce the supply of oxygen to the muscle and cause various heart diseases.

   (1) Angina pectoris is characterized by pain radiating from the chest into the left shoulder and arm, especially during periods of physical exertion. It is caused by reduced blood supply to the heart muscle.

   (2) A "heart attack" occurs when the blood supply to a portion of the heart muscle is cut off completely. It is often caused by a clot of material that is caught in a coronary artery and blocks the flow of blood through it. The blockage is called a **coronary thrombosis.** It usually results in the death of the muscle cells in the affected region of the heart. If the damage to the heart muscle is sufficiently widespread, a heart attack may be fatal.

2. Blood conditions

   a. Anemia is a condition in which the blood fails to transport sufficient amounts of oxygen for normal body needs. It may result from insufficient amounts of hemoglobin or insufficient numbers of red blood cells. (Also see "sickle cell anemia," page 133).

   b. Leukemia is a disease of the bone marrow in which there is an uncontrolled production of nonfunctional white blood cells. It is considered to be a form of cancer.

QUESTIONS

1. Substances that the body recognizes as foreign are called   (1) antibodies   (2) antigens   (3) antibiotics   (4) allergies

2. An individual who has recovered from an attack of a disease often has developed   (1) inborn immunity to it   (2) passive immunity to it   (3) active immunity to it   (4) antigens for it

3. A person with type A blood is in need of a transfusion. Which blood type would definitely endanger his or her life?   (1) A   (2) B   (3) O   (4) Rh positive

4. Any type of blood in the ABO system may safely be given to a person with   (1) Type O blood   (2) Type A blood   (3) Type B blood   (4) Type AB blood

5. The reason for the correct answer to question 4 is that the blood of the recipient has   (1) no A or B antibodies   (2) both A and B antibodies   (3) no A or B antigens   (4) has Type O antigens

6. One major problem involved in organ transplants is   (1) antigen-antibody reaction   (2) phagocytosis   (3) race of recipient   (4) sex of donor

7. A frequent cause of cardiovascular disease is   (1) a heart attack   (2) an inadequate supply of red blood cells   (3) lack of sodium in the diet   (4) fatty deposits on the inner walls of the arterial vessels

III-4. HUMAN RESPIRATION

A. CELLULAR (CHEMICAL) RESPIRATION. Cellular respiration is the process by which the chemical bond energy in nutrient molecules is used to form ATP, which cells can readily use as a source of energy (see page 42).   In humans, cellular respiration is normally aerobic (uses free oxygen from the air). When supplies of oxygen are insufficient, cells of the liver and the muscles rely on anaerobic respiration. Much less energy is released, and lactic acid is formed as a waste product.

B. HUMAN RESPIRATORY SYSTEM

1. Function. The function of the respiratory system is to exchange gases between the blood and the external environment. Oxygen is taken in and transferred to the blood, which carries it to the body tissues. Carbon dioxide, the waste gas of cell metabolism, is removed from the blood and transferred to the environment. Some excess water is also removed by the respiratory system.

2. General description. The **lungs** are the principal respiratory organs of the human body. A system of passageways connects the lungs to the outside air and permits air to enter the lungs and waste gases to leave. The sequence of passageways is the *nose, pharynx, larynx, trachea, bronchi, bronchioles,* and *alveoli (air sacs)* of the lungs.

C. STRUCTURE AND FUNCTION OF THE RESPIRATORY ORGANS. See Table 3-5 (page 80).

D. DETAILS OF HUMAN RESPIRATION

1. Breathing. Movements of the diaphragm and the rib cage cause pressure changes in the chest cavity, resulting in the flow of air into or out of the lungs. This process is called **breathing.** The breathing rate is controlled by the medulla of the brain, which responds to the concentration of carbon dioxide in the blood. When the CO_2 concentration in-

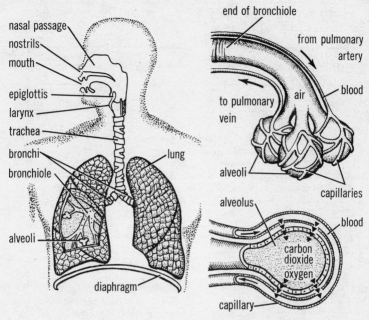

Figure 3-8. The human respiratory system.

creases, the medulla sends nerve impulses that increase the breathing rate. When the CO_2 concentration decreases, the medulla causes the breathing rate to slow down. This an example of a feedback mechanism that helps to maintain homeostasis.

2. Gas exchange in the lungs. Gas exchange in the lungs occurs between the alveoli and the blood capillaries. Oxygen that diffuses into the blood is picked up and carried mainly by the hemoglobin of the red blood cells. Carbon dioxide is carried mainly in the plasma in the form of the bicarbonate ion (HCO_3^-).

3. Gas exchange in the tissues. Gases transported by the blood are exchanged between the blood and the cells of the body tissues. The exchange occurs through the walls of the capillaries and through the intercellular fluid. Oxygen is released by the hemoglobin and diffuses out of the capillaries into the tissue cells. Carbon dioxide produced by cellular respiration diffuses out of the cells into the capillaries.

E. SOME MALFUNCTIONS OF THE RESPIRATORY SYSTEM

1. Bronchitis is an inflammation of the linings of the bronchial tubes. The air passages become swollen and clogged with mucus, causing coughing and difficulty in breathing.

2. Asthma is a severe allergic reaction in which contraction of the bronchioles makes breathing difficult.

3. Emphysema is a lung disorder in which the walls of the air sacs break down and there is less respiratory surface in the lungs. Shortness of breath and difficulty in exhaling are some results of emphysema.

HP

TABLE 3-5. FUNCTIONS OF THE STRUCTURES OF THE HUMAN RESPIRATORY SYSTEM.

Structure	Function
Nose	entering air is filtered, warmed, and moistened
Pharynx	passageway for air as it passes to the trachea
Larynx	contains the vocal cords, whose vibration makes speech possible
Trachea	connects the pharynx with the bronchi; the ciliated membrane lining the trachea sweeps inhaled foreign particles back up into the pharynx
Bronchi	connect the trachea with the bronchioles
Bronchioles	connect the bronchi with the alveoli
Alveoli	the functional units for respiration in the lungs; oxygen diffuses from the alveoli into the surrounding capillaries and carbon dioxide and some water diffuses from the capillaries into the alveoli

QUESTIONS

1. In humans, the small chambers of the lungs involved in the exchange of gases are the   (1) atria   (2) alveoli   (3) tracheal tubes   (4) pulmonary bronchi

Base your answers to questions 2 through 4 on the diagram below, which represents a microscopic portion of a human lung.

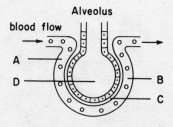

2. The process that occurs at location C is known as   (1) ultrafiltration   (2) breathing   (3) diffusion   (4) peristalsis

3. The type of blood vessel shown in the diagram is   (1) an artery   (2) a vein   (3) a lymph vessel   (4) a capillary

4. At which location would blood with a low oxygen content and a high carbon dioxide content be found?   (1) A   (2) B   (3) C   (4) D

5. When you hold your breath for half a minute, the carbon dioxide concentration in your blood (1) decreases (2) increases (3) remains the same

6. Among humans, an increase in the rate of respiration and heartbeat results when the blood contains (1) too little glucose (2) too little protein (3) too much nitrogenous waste (4) too much carbon dioxide

7. Rate of breathing in humans is controlled mainly by the (1) cerebellum (2) cerebrum (3) medulla (4) spinal cord

8. A disease involving breakdown of the air sacs in the lungs is (1) hardening of the arteries (2) coronary thrombosis (3) asthma (4) emphysema

III-5. HUMAN EXCRETORY ORGANS

A. THE LUNGS. Carbon dioxide diffuses from the capillaries surrounding the alveoli into the air spaces in the alveoli and is then removed during exhalation. Some water vapor is also excreted by diffusion into the alveoli.

B. THE LIVER. The liver is a large, glandular organ that performs many functions essential to human metabolism. Among its excretory activities are:

1. Disposal of hemoglobin. Old red blood corpuscles are destroyed in the liver and their hemoglobin is released. The liver converts this hemoglobin to waste products called **bile pigments.** The bile pigments are present in bile, which is stored in the gall bladder and discharged into the small intestine (see page 65).   The bile pigments are eliminated in fecal material.

2. Disposal of nitrogenous wastes. Nitrogenous compounds are broken down in the liver, forming **urea.** Urea is absorbed into the blood and removed from the blood in the kidneys (see below).

C. SWEAT GLANDS

1. Structure. Sweat glands are small, coiled, tubular glands found in the dermis of the skin. Their ducts lead to openings in the epidermis called **pores.** Blood capillaries surround the base of each sweat gland.

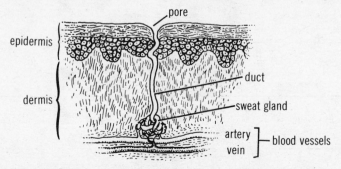

Figure 3-9. Sweat gland in human skin.

2. Function. Water, salts, and some nitrogenous wastes diffuse from the blood capillaries into the sweat glands and are eliminated through the pores as **sweat.** The formation of sweat is called **perspiration.**

3. Temperature regulation. The main function of perspiration is to help regulate the temperature of the body. When sweat evaporates from the surface of the skin, it absorbs heat from the skin tissues and carries it off into the air. The effect is to cool the body. The rate of perspiration varies with the cooling needs of the body and is an example of homeostasis.

D. THE KIDNEYS. The major functions of the two kidneys are to excrete nitrogenous wastes and to regulate the concentration of most of the substances in the blood. The functional unit of the kidney is the **nephron.** Each kidney contains about one million nephrons.

1. Structure of the nephron. The nephron contains a network of capillaries called a **glomerulus,** enclosed in a cuplike capsule called **Bowman's capsule.** The capsule is connected to a long, coiled **tubule. Capillaries** are closely entwined around the tubule.

2. Functions of the nephron

a. Filtration. As blood flows through the capillaries of the glomerulus, water, salts, urea, amino acids, and glucose diffuse out of the blood into Bowman's capsule. This stage of the process is called **filtration.**

b. Reabsorption. As the materials in Bowman's capsule flow through the tubule, some of the water, salts, amino acids, and glucose are reabsorbed by active transport into the capillaries surrounding the tubule.

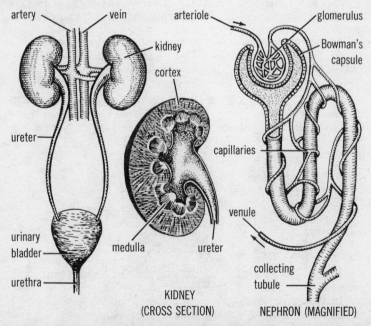

Figure 3-10. The human kidney.

c. Urine. The fluid that reaches the end of the tubule consists mostly of water, urea, and salts, and is called **urine.**

E. THE URINARY BLADDER. The tubules of each kidney empty into a tube called a **ureter,** which transports the urine to the **urinary bladder.** Urine is temporarily stored in the urinary bladder. The urine is periodically eliminated through a tube called the **urethra,** which leads to the outside of the body.

F. MALFUNCTIONS OF THE EXCRETORY SYSTEM

1. Kidney diseases include various conditions in which the kidneys or nephrons are unable to function effectively in excreting nitrogenous wastes. Very high protein diets can cause kidney disease by exceeding the capacity of the nephrons to dispose of the protein wastes.

2. Gout is a form of arthritis in which excess production of uric acid leads to deposits of crystals in the joints, causing pain and stiffness.

QUESTIONS

1. Which organ is most closely associated with the production of urea? (1) lung (2) kidney (3) stomach (4) liver

2. In humans, most of the wornout red blood cells are removed from the blood in the (1) liver (2) kidneys (3) lungs (4) bone marrow

3. In humans, nitrogenous wastes are removed from the blood in structures known as (1) nephridia (2) nephrons (3) Malpighian tubules (4) air sacs

4. The principal nitrogenous waste excreted by humans is (1) urea (2) mineral salt (3) ammonia (4) carbon dioxide

5. In which organ does the blood lose urea and reabsorb amino acids? (1) urinary bladder (2) gallbladder (3) liver (4) kidney

6. As air temperature decreases, the rate of perspiration usually (1) decreases (2) increases (3) remains the same

For each statement in questions 7 through 10, select the human excretory organ, chosen from the list below, that performs the operation described by that statement.

Excretory Organs
(1) Lungs
(2) Liver
(3) Skin
(4) Kidney

7. This organ excretes salts from its surface.
8. This organ produces urea and bile.
9. The functional units of this organ are known as alveoli.
10. The functional unit of this organ is the nephron.

III-6. HUMAN NERVOUS SYSTEM

A. NEURONS. Neurons are the units of the nervous system. There are three types, performing different functions: *sensory neurons, motor*

neurons, and *interneurons*. Impulses are transmitted by all three types in the same way, as described on pages 53-54.

1. Sensory neurons transmit impulses from **sense organs,** or **receptors,** to the brain and spinal cord (the **central nervous system).** Sensory neurons that respond to particular kinds of stimuli are concentrated in specialized **sense organs,** such as the eyes, ears, tongue, nose, and skin.

2. Motor neurons transmit impulses from the central nervous system to muscles and glands, or **effectors.**

3. Interneurons transmit and distribute impulses from sensory neurons to motor neurons.

B. NERVES. Nerves are bundles of neurons or the axons of neurons. **Motor nerves** contain only motor neurons. **Sensory nerves** contain only sensory neurons. **Mixed nerves** contain both.

C. SPINAL CORD

1. Structure and location. The **spinal cord** is a thick nerve that is enclosed in, and protected by, the vertebrae of the spinal column. It connects directly with the base of the brain.

2. Functions. The spinal cord carries nervous impulses between the brain and other structures of the body. The impulses that control many automatic responses, such as reflex actions, pass through interneurons in the spinal cord. The spinal cord coordinates many of the body activities and responses.

D. THE BRAIN

1. Structure and location. The brain is a large mass consisting mostly of interneurons enclosed by the cranium of the skull. The brain has three major divisions: the *cerebrum*, the *cerebellum*, and the *medulla*.

2. Functions of the brain

a. The cerebrum. In the cerebrum, sensory impulses are interpreted, all conscious motor activities are originated, and memory, thinking, and reasoning occur. Specific regions of the cerebrum are associated with sensations and motor control of specific parts of the body.

b. The cerebellum. The cerebellum coordinates motor activities and aids in maintaining balance.

c. The medulla. Impulses controlling many involuntary, or automatic, activities originate in the medulla. These activities include breathing, heartbeat, blood pressure, movements of the digestive organs, coughing, and sneezing.

E. PERIPHERAL NERVOUS SYSTEM. From the brain and the spinal cord, pairs of nerves extend to all parts of the body. These nerves make up the **peripheral nervous system.** It has two subdivisions—the *somatic nervous system* and the *autonomic nervous system.*

1. The somatic nervous system consists of nerves that control the voluntary muscles. Nerves that receive stimuli from the sense organs and transmit them to the central nervous system are also part of the somatic system.

2. The autonomic nervous system consists of the nerves that control the heart muscles, the glands, and the smooth muscles of the digestive organs and other organ systems not under conscious control. It is con-

HP

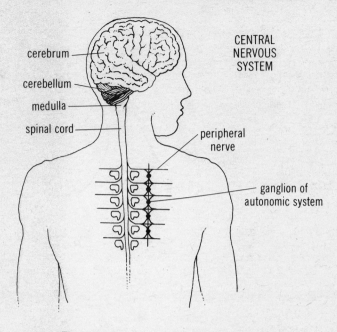

cerebrum

cerebellum

medulla

spinal cord

CENTRAL
NERVOUS
SYSTEM

peripheral
nerve

ganglion of
autonomic system

Figure 3-11. The central nervous system.

sidered to be an "involuntary" system, although there is some overlap with conscious control through the somatic system. For example, breathing is ordinarily unconscious, but we can consciously control breathing to some extent. Each organ that is controlled by the autonomic nervous system is actually controlled by a pair of nerves that have opposite effects. If one nerve causes an organ to speed up, the other causes it to slow down. Pairs of nerves with opposite effects are said to be antagonistic. They are another example of homeostatic regulation.

F. HUMAN BEHAVIOR

1. Involuntary behavior. Behavior that occurs automatically, without requiring conscious control, is called **involuntary behavior.** Some involuntary behavior is present at birth. This is called **inborn behavior.** Behavior that develops after birth as the result of experience is called **acquired behavior.**

    a. Simple reflexes. Simple reflex actions are inborn, automatic patterns of behavior. In a spinal reflex, impulses pass from (1) a receptor (sense organ) to (2) a sensory neuron to (3) an interneuron in the spinal cord to (4) a motor neuron to (5) a muscle or gland (see Figure 3-12).

    b. Conditioned behavior is automatic behavior that is acquired. **Habits** are examples of conditioned behavior. They form by repetition of an action that establishes pathways for nervous impulses. Once the pathways have been established, response to certain stimuli or performance of certain actions becomes rapid and automatic.

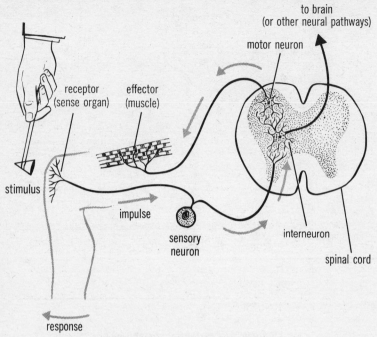

Figure 3-12. The reflex arc.

2. Voluntary behavior is conscious behavior and involves the cerebrum of the brain. It makes use of memory, association of ideas, imagination of possible results of actions, and judgment to choose a particular response or behavior.

G. SOME MALFUNCTIONS OF THE NERVOUS SYSTEM

1. Meningitis is an inflammation of the *meninges*, the membranes that surround the brain and spinal cord. It is usually caused by a bacterial or viral infection. Its symptoms are severe headache, fever, and chills. Stiffness of the neck and pains in the back follow.

2. Cerebral palsy is a group of disorders resulting from damage to the motor centers of the brain of the fetus or of the child during or after birth. The most common signs of the condition are poor coordination of the voluntary muscles and difficulties in speech. Intelligence is usually not affected and may be above normal.

3. A stroke is damage to the nerve cells of a region of the brain. Its causes include blockage of an artery or rupture of a blood vessel in the brain. The result may be paralysis of parts of the body or loss of some mental functions, such as word memory or speech.

4. Polio is a disease of the spinal cord caused by a virus. It destroys motor neurons in the spinal cord and causes paralysis of the muscles controlled by those neurons. It can be prevented by immunization with either the Salk or the Sabin vaccines.

QUESTIONS

1. The chief function of a motor neuron is to (1) transmit impulses to effectors (glands and muscles) (2) transmit impulses from sense organs to the central nervous system (3) relay impulses across synapses (4) receive stimuli from the environment

2. Which type of neuron is responsible for transmitting impulses to the central nervous system? (1) sensory (2) motor (3) interneurons (4) ganglionic

3. The central nervous system consists of (1) the spinal cord and the peripheral nerves (2) the cerebrum, cerebellum, and medulla (3) the brain and the spinal cord (4) the somatic system and the autonomic system

4. In which part of the human nervous system does the reasoning process take place? (1) cerebellum (2) cerebrum (3) spinal cord (4) medulla

5. Coordination of balance and motor patterns occurs principally in the (1) spinal cord (2) cerebrum (3) medulla (4) cerebellum

6. The nerve center that indirectly regulates the amount of oxygen in the blood is located in the (1) cerebellum (2) solar plexus (3) medulla (4) left atrium

7. The autonomic nervous system controls (1) digestion (2) thinking (3) walking (4) hearing

8. Which structure is not usually involved in a simple reflex reaction? (1) cerebrum (2) spinal cord (3) effector (4) receptor

III-7. HUMAN ENDOCRINE SYSTEM

(Review pages 57-58 on hormones and endocrine glands.)

A. PITUITARY GLAND

1. Location. The pituitary gland is located at the base of the brain.

2. Hormones and functions. The pituitary secretes many hormones. Some of these hormones are produced in the **hypothalamus,** a part of the brain closely associated with the pituitary gland. All the other endocrine glands are regulated by pituitary hormones.

a. TSH (thyroid stimulating hormone). An increase in secretion of TSH by the pituitary stimulates the thyroid to produce more of its hormone thyroxin.

b. FSH (follicle stimulating hormone). This hormone stimulates the development of egg cells (ova) in the ovary of the female and influences the secretion of other hormones involved in human reproduction.

c. Growth hormone. Normal development of the long bones of the body requires normal amounts of pituitary growth hormone during childhood.

B. THYROID GLAND

1. Structure and location. The thyroid gland has two connected lobes of tissue lying alongside the trachea in the neck.

2. Hormone and function. The thyroid produces the hormone **thyroxin,** which contains iodine. Small amounts of iodine are therefore essential in the diet. Thyroxin regulates the rate of metabolism and is necessary for normal physical and mental development.

C. PARATHYROID GLANDS

1. Location. The parathyroid glands are regions of tissue located within the thyroid gland.

2. Hormone and function. The parathyroid produces the hormone **parathormone.** It controls the metabolism of calcium, which is necessary for nerve function, blood clotting, and proper growth of teeth and bones.

D. ADRENAL GLANDS

1. Location. The adrenal glands are located at the top of the kidneys.

2. Hormones and functions. Two of the hormones of the adrenal glands are **adrenaline** (epinephrine) and **cortisol.** Adrenaline regulates the rate of the heartbeat, blood sugar levels, and blood clotting rate. In emergencies, extra amounts of adrenaline are secreted to help the body deal with the situation. Cortisol helps regulate sugar metabolism. *Cortisone,* a synthetic compound that is chemically similar to cortisol, is used as a drug to treat arthritis, an inflammation of the joints.

E. ISLETS OF LANGERHANS

1. Location. The islets of Langerhans are small groups of cells located in the pancreas.

2. Hormones and functions

a. Insulin is needed for the absorption of sugar into the body cells and for maintaining proper blood sugar levels. When blood sugar concentration increases, insulin assists the movement of sugar into the liver for storage as glycogen.

b. Glucagon stimulates the discharge of sugar from the liver into the blood when blood sugar levels are low.

F. GONADS. The sex glands are called **gonads.** Sex cells develop into gametes (sperm and eggs) in the gonads.

1. Male gonads. The male gonads are called **testes.** The testes secrete **testosterone,** a hormone that influences the development of the secondary male characteristics.

2. Female gonads. The female gonads are called **ovaries.** The ovaries secrete several hormones that influence sexual characteristics and the menstrual cycle. One of these is **estrogen,** which influences the secondary female characteristics.

G. FEEDBACK IN THE ENDOCRINE SYSTEM

1. Definition of feedback. *Feedback* is the term used to describe a system in which a change in one quantity causes a change in a second quantity, which then causes a change in the first quantity. If the change caused by the feedback is opposite to the initial change, the feedback is called **negative.** Negative feedback tends to keep the original quantity close to a constant level and is an important mechanism in homeostasis.

2. Example of feedback. The endocrine system has many feedback loops that tend to maintain desirable levels of hormones in the blood. For example, a decrease in the level of thyroxin causes the pituitary gland to secrete more TSH (thyroid stimulating hormone). The increase in TSH causes the thyroid to increase its output of thyroxin.

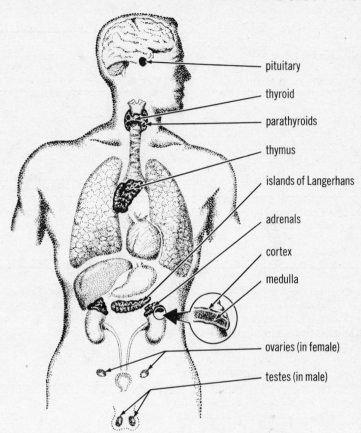

Figure 3-13. The human endocrine glands.

H. SOME MALFUNCTIONS OF THE ENDOCRINE GLANDS

1. Goiter is an enlargement of the thyroid glands that is usually associated with an inability of the thyroid to produce sufficient amounts of thyroxin. The enlargement is caused by excessive stimulation from the pituitary as the feedback mechanism attempts to increase thyroxin production. A deficiency of iodine in the diet is often a cause of goiter.

2. Diabetes is a disorder characterized by excessive levels of sugar in the blood. It is caused by a deficiency in insulin production by the islets of Langerhans in the pancreas. The disease can be controlled by periodic injections of insulin.

QUESTIONS

1. The hormone most closely associated with the control of calcium metabolism in man is produced by the (1) adrenal glands (2) ovaries (3) parathyroid glands (4) pancreas

2. Which hormone is not involved in the control of glucose metabolism? (1) adrenaline (2) parathormone (3) insulin (4) glucagon

3. Which gland produces cortisol? (1) adrenal (2) thyroid (3) parathyroid (4) pancreas

4. Immediately after a frightening experience, a person's blood is likely to show higher than normal concentrations of (1) antigens (2) hormones (3) enzymes (4) nucleic acids

5. If the amount of sugar in the blood is low, the islets of Langerhans will (1) secrete insulin (2) secrete glucagon (3) secrete pancreatic juice (4) become inactive

6. The homeostatic level of the blood sugar is primarily maintained through the combined action of (1) insulin and glucagon (2) insulin and parathormone (3) adrenalin and estrogen (4) glucagon and testosterone

7. An important function of gonads in addition to the production of gametes is the (1) development of the embryo (2) differentiation of germ layers (3) elimination of cellular wastes (4) secretion of hormones

8. Some men develop a heavy beard growth. The hormone that is most probably responsible for this beard growth is (1) testosterone (2) estrogen (3) parathormone (4) cortin

For each glandular function in questions 9 through 12, select the number of the gland tissue, chosen from the list below, which is most closely associated with that function.

Gland Tissue
(1) Adrenal
(2) Islets of Langerhans
(3) Parathyroid
(4) Pituitary
(5) Thyroid

9. Secretes a hormone which causes the heart to beat more rapidly in an emergency

10. Secretes a hormone which most directly regulates the rate of oxidation in body cells

11. Secretes the hormone glucagon, which stimulates the discharge of glucose from the liver into the blood

12. Stimulates the secretion of those hormones which regulate gamete maturation

13. Homeostasis in the human body is illustrated by the effect of insulin upon the (1) absorption of proteins by villi (2) concentration of glucose in the blood (3) constant temperature of the body (4) synthesis of vitamin A from carotenes

14. The nervous and endocrine systems in humans are similar in that both (1) secrete chemical compounds (2) operate at the voluntary as well as the involuntary level (3) use highly specialized pathways (4) respond very rapidly to stimuli

III-8. HUMAN LOCOMOTION

Locomotion in the human body is brought about by certain structures and tissues specialized for that function.

A. BONES. The human body has an **endoskeleton** (internal skeleton) made mostly of bones of various shapes and sizes. Bone is relatively hard and inflexible. Bones serve the following functions:
1. Support and protection of body structures.
2. Points of attachment for muscles.
3. As levers to produce body movements.
4. Production of blood cells in their marrow.

B. CARTILAGE. Cartilage is a flexible, fibrous, and elastic tissue. Most of the skeleton of the embryo is at first made of cartilage. Most of this cartilage is replaced by bone during development. Some cartilage remains in the adult. It is found at the ends of ribs, between the vertebrae and in other movable joints, and in the nose, ears, and trachea. Cartilage has the following functions:
1. Provide support of structures while permitting some bending or motion.
2. Provide flexibility of joints between bones.
3. Provide cushioning against impact or pressure.

C. MUSCLES. Muscle tissue consists of cells that have the ability to contract and exert a pulling force. There are three types of muscle tissue in the human body:
1. **Skeletal muscle tissue** has a **striated** (striped) appearance under the microscope. It is under conscious control and is used to make voluntary movements of parts of the body.
2. **Smooth muscle tissue** is not striated. It is involuntary, that is, not under conscious control. Smooth muscles control automatic, involuntary movements such as those of breathing and of the digestive organs.
3. **Cardiac muscle tissue** (muscles of the heart) is involuntary, but has a striated appearance.

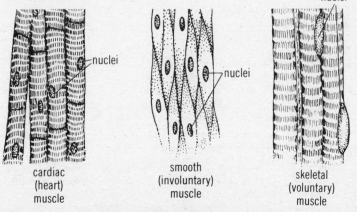

cardiac (heart) muscle

smooth (involuntary) muscle

skeletal (voluntary) muscle

Figure 3-14. Types of human muscle tissue.

D. FUNCTIONS OF MUSCLES

1. Skeletal muscles are attached to bones in coordinated pairs controlled by the nervous system. To produce movement of a bone, one muscle of a pair contracts while the other relaxes. To produce the opposite movement, the first muscle relaxes while the second contracts. A muscle that causes a limb to be extended outward is called an **extensor.** The muscle that bends the limb back is called a **flexor.**

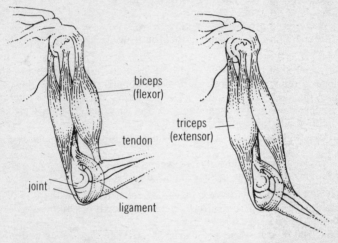

biceps
(flexor)

triceps
(extensor)

tendon

joint

ligament

Figure 3-15. A pair of skeletal muscles controlling motion at a joint.

2. Fatigue of skeletal muscles. When skeletal muscles are used vigorously for a time, their cells may use oxygen faster than it can be replaced by the circulatory system. The cells then function by anaerobic respiration, which produces an accumulation of lactic acid. The sensation of **fatigue** is associated with this buildup of lactic acid in the muscle tissues.

3. Smooth muscles. Layers of smooth, involuntary muscles are found in the walls of the digestive organs, other internal organs, and the blood vessels. Contraction of these muscles is controlled by the nervous system automatically and unconsciously.

4. Cardiac muscle tissue is found only in the heart. It contracts and relaxes continuously throughout life, mainly under its own internal controls, producing the regular beating action of the heart.

E. TENDONS. Tendons are tough, inelastic, fibrous cords of connective tissue. They attach muscles to bones.

F. LIGAMENTS. Ligaments are connective tissue similar to tendons, but with fibers not so regularly arranged. Ligaments also contain elastic fibers. They connect the ends of bones together at movable joints, such as those of the elbows, fingers, knees, and vertebral column.

G. SOME MALFUNCTIONS ASSOCIATED WITH LOCOMOTION

1. Arthritis is a general term that refers to a number of conditions that cause pain, stiffness, inflammation, and deformity of the joints.

2. Tendonitis is an inflammation of a tendon, usually near its attachment to the bone. It is a condition that often affects athletes.

QUESTIONS

1. In humans, which serves as a lever for muscles? (1) bone (2) spinal cord (3) skin (4) ligament

2. Which type of muscle tissue found in the walls of the human stomach is most closely associated with the process of peristalsis? (1) striated (2) cardiac (3) voluntary (4) smooth

3. The muscle used in straightening the human arm is known as (1) a flexor (2) a smooth muscle (3) an involuntary muscle (4) an extensor

Base your answers to questions 4 through 7 on the diagram of the human arm shown below.

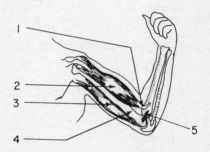

4. Which structure is a ligament? (1) 1 (2) 3 (3) 5 (4) 4

5. Which structure is a tendon? (1) 1 (2) 2 (3) 3 (4) 4

6. Which structure functions as a flexor? (1) 5 (2) 2 (3) 3 (4) 4

7. Which two structures are controlled by motor impulses from the brain? (1) 1 and 2 (2) 2 and 3 (3) 3 and 4 (4) 4 and 5

8. Various conditions that cause stiffness and pain in joints are called (1) allergies (2) arthritis (3) anemia (4) thrombosis

UNIT IV   REPRODUCTION AND DEVELOPMENT

IV-1. MITOTIC CELL DIVISION

All cells arise from other cells by cell division. In a cell containing a nucleus, the nucleus and the cytoplasm divide by separate processes. Most cells divide by the process called *mitotic cell division,* in which the nucleus divides by a series of events called *mitosis.* In sexual reproduction, certain cells divide by *meiotic cell division,* which is described in Section IV-3, pages 99-100.

A. MITOSIS. In **mitosis,** there is an exact duplication of all the chromosomes in the nucleus, which are then separated into two identical sets. This is accomplished by a single, continuous process. However, for convenience in studying it, scientists have divided the process into the following stages.

1. Interphase. During the interval between cell divisions, each chromosome is **replicated,** or duplicated. The two identical strands produced by this replication remain attached at a region called the **centromere.** The separate strands are called **chromatids.**

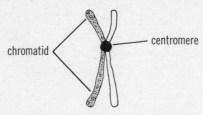

Figure 4-1. A replicated chromosome.

2. Prophase. During the first stage of mitosis, the nuclear membrane disintegrates. Fibers radiating from opposite poles in the cell form a structure called a **spindle.** The double-stranded chromosomes coil and contract, and become visible under the microscope.

3. Metaphase. The double-stranded chromosomes become attached to the spindle fibers at their centromeres and move to the central plane of the cell.

4. Anaphase. The centromeres replicate and then separate. The spindle fibers shorten, pulling the chromatids apart and collecting them near the poles. The separated chromatids become the chromosomes of the daughter cells that are about to form.

5. Telophase. A nuclear membrane forms around each new set of chromosomes, forming two new nuclei. The new nuclei have the same number and types of chromosomes as the original nucleus had before mitosis began.

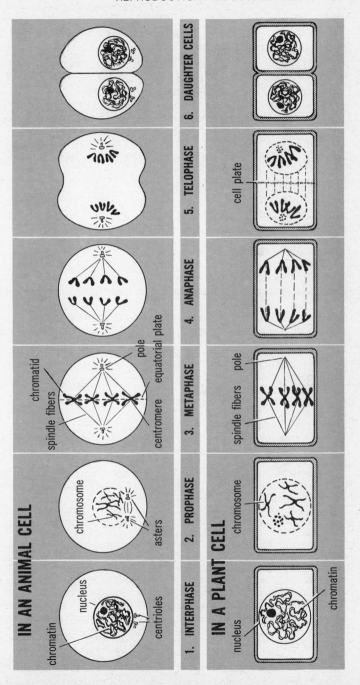

FIGURE 4-2. MITOSIS

B. CYTOPLASMIC DIVISION. At the end of mitosis, the cytoplasm usually divides, forming two new **daughter cells** identical to each other and to the original parent cell.

C. DIFFERENCES BETWEEN MITOTIC CELL DIVISION IN PLANT AND ANIMAL CELLS. Certain differences are usually observed between plant and animal cells during mitotic division.

1. Animal cells usually contain two small structures called **centrioles,** which move to the poles and take part in the formation of the spindle apparatus. In most seed plants, there are no centrioles.

2. In animal cells, division of the cytoplasm is brought about by a pinching in of the cell membrane. In plant cells, a **cell plate** forms and becomes a new cell wall dividing the cytoplasm into two parts.

D. UNCONTROLLED CELL DIVISION. In multicellular animals, cell division normally occurs only as needed for growth or tissue repair. Sometimes, a group of cells begins to divide in an uncontrolled fashion, invading surrounding tissue and interfering with normal organ functions. Such harmful, uncontrolled cell division is called **cancer.**

QUESTIONS

1. The nucleus of an ameba is removed with the use of microdissection instruments. The organism will then no longer be able to carry on the process of (1) passive transport (2) osmosis (3) diffusion (4) reproduction

2. During normal mitosis, which occurs first? (1) cytoplasmic division of the cell (2) spindle formation (3) growth and development of daughter cells (4) chromosome duplication

3. The structure pictured at the right is chromatids most closely associated with which process? (1) mitosis (2) cyclosis (3) hydrolysis (4) phagocytosis

4. During mitosis, a double-stranded chromosome is attached to a spindle fiber at the (1) centriole (2) centromere (3) centrosome (4) cell plate

5. By which process are two daughter nuclei formed that are identical to each other and to the original nucleus? (1) meiosis (2) synapsis (3) fertilization (4) mitosis

6. After mitotic cell division, the number of chromosomes in each daughter cell as compared to the parent cell is (1) the same (2) one-fourth as great (3) one-half as great (4) twice as great

7. As a result of mitosis, the chromosome number within each cell of a developing embryo will (1) be halved (2) be doubled (3) remain the same (4) vary at random

8. When mitosis has been completed, the quantity of DNA in each daughter cell nucleus will be (1) half as much as in the parent nucleus (2) the same as in the parent nucleus (3) twice as much as in the parent nucleus (4) variable, depending on the activity within the cytoplasm during interphase

9. Which would result if cytoplasmic division did not accompany mitosis? (1) two cells, each with one nucleus (2) one cell with no nucleus (3) two cells, each lacking a nucleus (4) one cell with two nuclei

10. A cell that is undergoing cellular division is examined with a microscope. The cell is most likely an animal cell if the (1) chromosomes twist about each other (2) nucleoli disappear (3) centrioles migrate (4) chromosome pairs separate from each other

11. A structure found during plant cell mitosis that is not found during animal cell mitosis is a (1) centriole (2) cell plate (3) cell membrane (4) mitochondrion

IV-2. ASEXUAL REPRODUCTION

A. DEFINITION. Asexual reproduction is reproduction that does not involve the fusion of nuclear material from two different cells. In asexual reproduction there is only one parent organism. The new organisms are produced usually by mitotic cell division of the parent cell.

B. METHODS OF ASEXUAL REPRODUCTION

1. Binary fission is cell division in which the nuclear material and the cytoplasm of the parent cell divide equally and form two daughter cells of the same size. When a nucleus is present, it divides by mitosis.

2. Budding

a. In unicellular organisms, budding is similar to binary fission, but the cytoplasm divides unequally, with the new cell, or bud, receiving the smaller portion. The new cells may separate from the parent or may remain attached, forming a **colony.** *Example:* Budding in yeast cells.

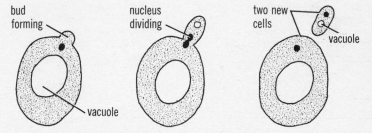

Figure 4-3. Budding in yeast.

b. In multicellular organisms, budding occurs by production of a multicellular outgrowth from the body of the parent, which develops into a complete organism. Buds may detach from the parent *(example:* hydra) or may remain attached, forming a colony (*examples:* sponge, coral).

3. Sporulation. In many multicellular organisms, single specialized cells called **spores** are released by the parent. Spores are usually enclosed in a protective capsule and develop into a new individual when environmental conditions are favorable. (*Example:* Spore formation in bread mold.)

4. Regeneration is the development of lost parts or the growth of an entire new organism from a part of the original organism. When a new individual develops by regeneration, the process is considered to be a type of asexual reproduction. (*Example:* Regeneration of a starfish from one ray and a portion of the central body.) Invertebrates show a greater ability to regenerate than vertebrates.

5. Vegetative propagation is a type of regeneration that occurs in plants. Complete new plants develop from a part of the parent plant, such as a root, stem, or leaf.

    a. Natural vegetative propagation

        (1) Bulbs: Enlarged, underground stems surrounded by leaves and containing stored food. New plant develops from the bulb.

        (2) Tubers: Enlarged, underground stem with buds and stored food. New plants develop from the buds.

        (3) Runners: Stems that grow along the ground. At intervals, new roots form and penetrate the soil, and new plants develop at these points.

    b. Artificial vegetative propagation

        (1) Cuttings: A stem or leaf of a plant is placed in soil and a complete plant develops from it.

        (2) Grafting: The stem of one plant to be propagated is attached to the cut end of another growing plant.

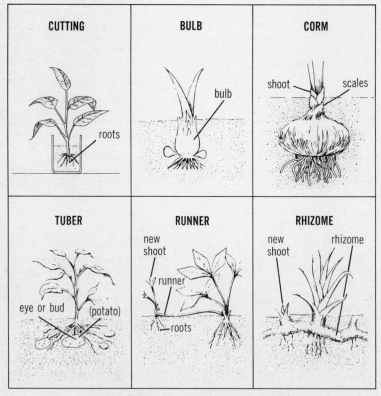

Figure 4-4. Types of vegetative propagation.

REPRODUCTION AND DEVELOPMENT 99

C. RESULTS OF ASEXUAL REPRODUCTION. New individuals produced by asexual reproduction are genetically identical to the parent; that is, they contain the same hereditary material and have the same characteristics.

QUESTIONS

1. Many unicellular organisms reproduce by the process of (1) binary fission (2) regeneration (3) ovulation (4) nondisjunction

2. Which method of reproduction is carried on by both yeast and hydra? (1) budding (2) binary fission (3) sporulation (4) multiple fission

3. Which is a characteristic of budding in yeast? (1) the formation of polar bodies (2) the production of sperm (3) equal division of hereditary material (4) equal division of cytoplasm

4. Regeneration is more often a characteristic of (1) one-celled than multicellular organisms (2) animals than plants (3) invertebrates than vertebrates (4) vertebrates than invertebrates

5. Which process in a multicellular organism is similar to the process of asexual reproduction in bacteria? (1) meiotic cell division (2) metamorphosis (3) maturation (4) mitotic cell division

6. By which process do multicellular plants reproduce asexually? (1) binary fission (2) meiosis (3) fertilization (4) vegetative propagation

7. Plant breeders have an advantage over animal breeders in reproducing a desired type of offspring because the plant breeder can utilize (1) gene mutations (2) hybridization (3) vegetative propagation (4) selection

8. Which is a form of vegetative propagation? (1) grafting (2) pollination (3) conjugation (4) sporulation

9. Fruit growers often propagate their plants by asexual means because the resulting offspring (1) is an improved variety over the parent (2) bears larger fruit than the parent (3) shows no environmental variation (4) shows little or no genetic variation from the parent

10. If a branch of a yellow rosebush is grafted on the stem of a red rosebush, the grafted branch will produce roses which are (1) orange (2) red, only (3) yellow, only (4) both yellow and red

IV-3. SEXUAL REPRODUCTION

A. DEFINITION. Sexual reproduction involves the fusion of nuclear material from two cells. The two cells are called **gametes.** The cell resulting from the fusion is called a **zygote.**

B. MEIOTIC CELL DIVISION. Meiosis is a type of nuclear division that occurs only in special reproductive cells of an organism. It is a variation of mitosis in which the daughter cells receive half the usual number of chromosomes of the species. This is accomplished by distributing only one chromosome of each homologous pair to the daughter cells. The normal chromosome number is called the **diploid number,** represented as **2n.** The number after reduction by meiosis is called the **monoploid number,** represented as **n.** Gametes produced by meiotic cell division have the monoploid number of chromosomes (n).

1. First meiotic division. Meiotic division involves two successive cell divisions, which produce four monoploid cells. Each division has stages similar to those of mitotic division, but with certain important differences.

a. Synapsis. During the early stage of the first meiotic division, the homologous chromosomes come together and join at their centromeres. This process is called **synapsis.** Since each chromosome had replicated before synapsis, the combination at synapsis has four chromatid strands. This group of chromatids is called a **tetrad.**

b. Crossing-over. During synapsis, the chromatids twist around each other and sometimes exchange segments. This exchange is called **crossing-over.**

c. Metaphase. The tetrads of homologous chromosomes become attached to the spindle fibers and move to the central plane of the spindle apparatus, as in mitosis.

d. Disjunction of the homologous chromosomes. The homologous pairs separate at their centromeres, and the separate chromosomes move to opposite poles. The separation of the homologous pairs is called **disjunction.** The cluster of chromosomes around each pole is now monoploid—half the number of an ordinary cell. The chromosomes are still double-stranded, with the two strands attached at their centromere.

e. Cytoplasmic division. New nuclei form and the cell divides into two new cells, as in mitotic division.

2. Second meiotic division. The second meiotic division follows the same course as mitotic division. The double-stranded chromosomes become aligned in the center of the cell, the centromere replicates, and the chromatids separate and move to opposite poles. The chromatids become the single-stranded chromosomes of the new cells. The cytoplasm divides in the usual manner.

C. MITOTIC AND MEIOTIC DIVISION COMPARED

1. Chromosome number. Mitosis produces cells with the normal diploid number of chromosomes (2n). Meiosis produces cells with the monoploid number (n).

2. Distribution of chromosomes. Mitotic division gives each daughter cell the same number and types of chromosomes as the original cell. Meiotic division gives the daughter cells only one chromosome from each homologous pair. The selection of the particular chromosome from each pair that goes to each daughter cell is random.

3. Functions of cells produced. Mitotic division produces additional body cells for growth or replacement of tissue. It is also involved in asexual reproduction. Meiotic division produces **gametes,** which are cells specialized for sexual reproduction.

QUESTIONS

1. The process of meiosis is most closely associated with (1) sexual reproduction (2) vegetative propagation (3) budding (4) fission

2. The pairing of homologous chromosomes during meiotic cell division is known as (1) synthesis (2) synapsis (3) linkage (4) fertilization

FIRST MEIOTIC DIVISION

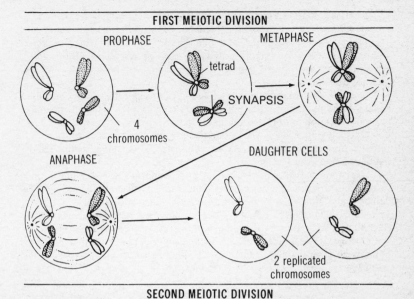

SECOND MEIOTIC DIVISION

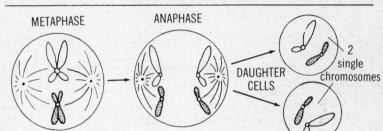

Figure 4-5. The two meiotic divisions.

3. Two cells which have a chromosome number different from that of their single parent cell are normally produced during the process of (1) meiosis (2) mitosis (3) fertilization (4) cleavage

4. At metaphase of the first meiotic division, the chromosomes are attached to the spindle fibers as (1) single chromatid strands (2) double chromatids (3) a tetrad of four chromatids (4) nonhomologous pairs

5. As a result of disjunction during meiotic cell division, (1) duplicate chromosomes are produced (2) tetrads are formed (3) crossing-over occurs (4) homologous chromosomes are separated

6. In the second meiotic division, the chromosome number (1) is doubled (2) is halved (3) is equalized (4) does not change

7. An organism which can successfully reproduce without utilizing the process of meiosis is (1) an ameba (2) a dog (3) a grasshopper (4) an earthworm

8. Chromosomes do not normally occur in pairs in (1) somatic cells (2) fertilized eggs (3) gametes (4) zygotes

D. GAMETE FORMATION

1. Gonads. Male and female gametes develop in organs called **gonads.** The male gonads are called **testes.** The female gonads are called **ovaries.**

2. Male gametes are usually called **sperm** or **sperm cells.** Four functioning monoploid sperm cells usually develop from each primary sex cell by meiotic division.

3. Female gametes are usually called **eggs** or **egg cells.** Only one functioning monoploid egg cell is usually produced by meiosis of the primary sex cell. A supply of food accumulates in the egg cell, thus accounting for its relatively large size. The other three monoploid cells produced by meiotic division of the primary sex cell are called **polar bodies.** They usually disintegrate.

4. Hermaphrodites. Most animals have separate sexes. Males have testes that produce sperm cells. Females have ovaries that produce egg cells. Some animals have both sexes in the same individual. Each individual has testes and ovaries. These organisms are called **hermaphrodites.** The hydra and the earthworm are examples. Hermaphrodites do not usually fertilize themselves. Instead, two organisms mate by exchanging sperm cells with each other. The sperm cells from each individual fertilize the egg cells of the other.

E. ZYGOTE FORMATION.

A **zygote** is formed by the fusion of a monoploid sperm nucleus (n) with a monoploid egg nucleus (n). This process is called **fertilization.** It produces a diploid zygote (2n).

1. External fertilization. In external fertilization, the gametes fuse outside the body of the female. This occurs in many aquatic animals, such as fish and amphibians.

2. Internal fertilization. In internal fertilization, the gametes fuse inside the moist reproductive tract of the female. This occurs in most animals that live on land.

3. External and internal fertilization compared. Animals that carry on external fertilization produce many more eggs than those that carry on internal fertilization. This results in large numbers of zygotes and increases the chances of survival of offspring. In animals that carry on internal fertilization, the male deposits sperm in the female reproductive tract. Both individuals secrete fluids that provide a moist environment for transport of the motile sperm to the eggs. Few eggs are produced because the internal environment provides sufficient protection to insure survival of the developing zygotes.

QUESTIONS

1. The immediate result of the process of meiosis is the formation of (1) embryos (2) gametes (3) gonads (4) cytoplasm

2. Sperm cells have a monoploid number of chromosomes (n) rather than a diploid number of chromosomes (2n) as a result of the process of (1) fertilization (2) meiosis (3) cleavage (4) mitosis

3. The diploid number of chromosomes results from (1) fertilization (2) maturation (3) reduction division (4) ovulation

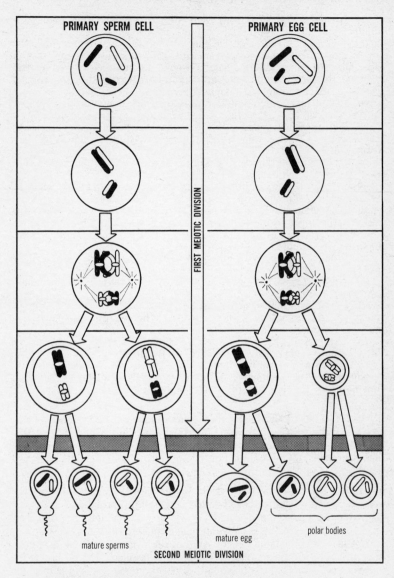

Figure 4-6. Gametogenesis. The primary sex cells have the diploid chromosome number, which in this example is 4 (2 pairs). By meiotic division, each primary sex cell gives rise to four monoploid cells containing one chromosome from each original pair. In the male, all four of the monoploid cells develop into functional gametes, or sperm cells. In the female, only one functional gamete — the egg cell or ovum — develops, and the other three cells become nonfunctional polar bodies.

4. In the ovary of a frog, each primary egg cell that undergoes meiosis will probably produce (1) one active gamete (2) one gamete and one zygote (3) three active gametes (4) four active gametes

5. Human eggs and sperms are similar in that both (1) develop in specialized organs called gonads (2) have adaptations for locomotion (3) have the same relative amount of cytoplasm surrounding their nuclei (4) are produced in approximately the same numbers

6. In humans, homologous chromosome pairs do not ordinarily occur in the (1) skin cells (2) zygotes (3) gametes (4) fertilized eggs

7. During which process in humans are polar bodies formed? (1) cleavage (2) male gamete formation (3) fission (4) female gamete formation

8. In the human female, the number of gametes normally produced from a primary sex cell is (1) 1 (2) 2 (3) 3 (4) 4

9. In sexual reproduction, a zygote is formed as a direct result of (1) cleavage (2) pollination (3) mitosis (4) fertilization

10. If all gametes in a pea plant were formed only as a result of mitosis, the chromosome number of any zygote produced as a result of the self-fertilization of this plant would be (1) reduced by half (2) unchanged (3) doubled (4) tripled

11. Which reproductive method most likely produces organisms that possess adaptations for survival in a changing environment? (1) sexual reproduction (2) parthenogenesis (3) budding (4) vegetative propagation

12. When both male and female functional gonads are present in an organism, the organism is known as a (1) heterotroph (2) heterozygote (3) hermaphrodite (4) homozygote

13. External fertilization is most common among organisms that live in (1) deserts (2) oceans (3) fields (4) forests

14. Which evolutionary adaptation was necessary for successful reproduction by land animals? (1) external fertilization (2) internal fertilization (3) motile eggs (4) motile sperms

F. PARTHENOGENESIS. Parthenogenesis is the development of an egg cell into a mature organism without fertilization by a sperm cell. It occurs naturally in certain species, as in the production of male bees. It has been induced artificially by stimulation of egg cells of such animals as frogs, sea urchins, rabbits, and turkeys.

G. EMBRYO FORMATION. After fertilization the zygote divides repeatedly by mitotic division. The early stages of this process, in which no growth occurs, is called **cleavage.** Growth and differentiation, producing a fully-formed embryo, is called **development.**

1. Cleavage. Repeated cell division of the zygote produces a hollow ball with a single layer of cells, called the **blastula.** Cells do not grow between divisions, so the blastula is about the same size as the original zygote.

2. Gastrulation. One side of the blastula becomes indented, forming the **gastrula.** The outer layer is called the **ectoderm;** the inner layer is the **endoderm.** A third layer of cells, called the **mesoderm,** forms between the ectoderm and the endoderm.

3. Differentiation. The cells of the three layers *differentiate* into the various tissues and organs of the animal.

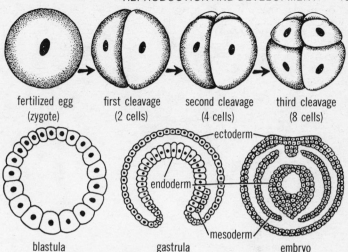

fertilized egg | first cleavage | second cleavage | third cleavage
(zygote) | (2 cells) | (4 cells) | (8 cells)

blastula | gastrula | embryo

Figure 4-7. Development of the vertebrate embryo.

TABLE 4-1. SOME OF THE TISSUES AND ORGANS THAT DEVELOP FROM THE THREE LAYERS OF THE GASTRULA.

Ectoderm	Mesoderm	Endoderm
nervous system epidermis of skin	muscles and skeleton circulatory system excretory system reproductive system	lining of digestive and respiratory tracts liver and pancreas

    4. Growth results from an increase in the number of cells as well as an increase in cell size.

H. EXTERNAL DEVELOPMENT. Development that occurs outside the female's body is called **external development.**

I. INTERNAL DEVELOPMENT. Animals may have internal fertilization, but external development. Most mammals have both internal fertilization and **internal development.** In these mammals, the embryo develops inside a female organ called the **uterus.**

    1. Umbilical cord. In most mammals, the developing embryo obtains nutrients and oxygen, and releases wastes, through a structure called the **umbilical cord.** The umbilical cord is attached to the wall of the uterus.

    2. Placenta. The region of attachment of the umbilical cord is a specialized organ called the **placenta.** The placenta is rich in blood vessels of both the mother and the embryo. However, there is no direct connection between the two circulatory systems. Materials are exchanged between the embryo and the mother in the placenta by diffusion and active transport. Mammals with this system of exchange are called **placental mammals.** Humans are placental mammals. Eggs of placental

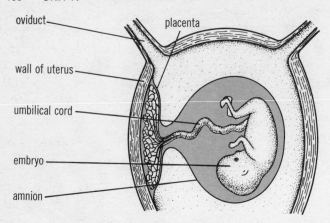

Figure 4-8. The mammalian embryo.

mammals need relatively little **yolk** (food supply) and are therefore much smaller than eggs of non-placental mammals.

J. TYPES OF EXTERNAL DEVELOPMENT

1. In water. The eggs of most fish and amphibians are fertilized externally and develop externally in an aquatic (water) environment. Yolk stored in the egg is the source of food for the developing embryo.

2. On land. The eggs of birds, many reptiles, and some mammals develop externally in a land environment, after internal fertilization. These eggs have special adaptations to insure survival under the conditions of a land environment.

    a. Yolk. These eggs have relatively large amounts of yolk and are therefore large in size. This permits the embryo to develop to an advanced stage before emerging into the environment.

    b. Shell. A hard shell provides protection for the embryo.

    c. Special membranes

        (1) Chorion—lines the shell.

        (2) Allantois—functions in the exchange of respiratory gases and excretion of wastes.

        (3) Amnion—contains amniotic fluid, which provides a watery environment for the embryo and protects it against shock.

        (4) Yolk sac—surrounds the yolk and is penetrated by blood vessels, which transport food to the developing embryo.

K. POUCHED MAMMALS.

In some mammals, some internal development occurs in the uterus of the female without a placenta and attachment of the embryo to the uterus. In these **non-placental mammals,** the embryo obtains its food from yolk stored in the egg. It is born before development is complete and completes its development in a pouch on the outside of the mother's body. The embryo then obtains its nutrients from **mammary glands** located in the pouch.

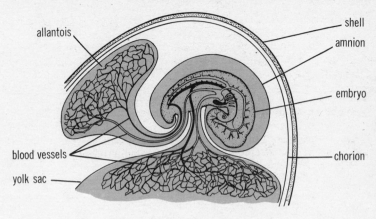

allantois

shell

amnion

embryo

blood vessels

chorion

yolk sac

Figure 4-9. Embryo of a bird.

QUESTIONS

1. In a beehive, the development of an unfertilized egg results in a male bee called a drone. This is an example of (1) parthenogenesis (2) synapsis (3) hermaphroditism (4) polyploidy

2. A frog zygote begins to develop by a process known as (1) meiotic division (2) cleavage (3) reduction division (4) parthenogenesis

3. The fertilized eggs of most mammals normally develop in the (1) ovary (2) placenta (3) uterus (4) umbilical cord

4. In animals that have external development, fertilization (1) does not occur (2) is always internal (3) is sometimes internal (4) is never internal

5. The mammalian embryo normally completes its development within the mother's (1) uterus (2) placenta (3) ovary (4) stomach

6. During development, the mammalian embryo is nourished through the (1) placenta (2) oviduct (3) mesoderm (4) allantois

7. Cleavage leads to the formation of the (1) blastula (2) egg (3) gamete (4) fertilized egg

8. The cells of an animal blastula are characterized by (1) frequent mitotic divisions (2) frequent meiotic divisions (3) monoploid chromosome numbers (4) many hormonal secretions

9. The variety of tissues, organs, and systems in multicellular animal organisms originally develops from (1) a fused yolk sac (2) the placenta (3) three embryonic layers (4) the umbilical cord

10. In humans, which system will develop from the ectoderm? (1) digestive (2) reproductive (3) skeletal (4) nervous

11. The nitrogenous waste products of a developing chick embryo collect in the (1) allantois (2) chorion (3) amnion (4) yolk sac

12. One difference between placental mammals and nonplacental mammals is that for nonplacental mammals (1) greater parental care of the young is provided (2) fertilization and embryonic development are external (3) the period of embryonic development is so brief that no source of nourishment is necessary during this stage (4) the embryo's principal source of nourishment is the yolk of the fertilized egg

IV-4. REPRODUCTION AND DEVELOPMENT IN HUMANS

A. MALE REPRODUCTIVE SYSTEM

1. Testes. The male gonads are called **testes.** The testes produce the male gametes, or sperm. The testes are located in an outpocketing of the body wall called the **scrotum.** The temperature inside the scrotum is 1 or 2 degrees Celsius lower than normal body temperature, providing optimum temperature for production and storage of sperm.

2. Ducts. A series of ducts furnish a passageway for sperm from the testes to the **urethra** in the **penis.** The penis is adapted for depositing sperm in the female reproductive tract (internal fertilization).

3. Secretions. Glands secrete various fluids into the ducts. The fluids provide a transport medium for the sperm and are an adaptation for life on land.

4. Semen. The mixture of fluids and sperm is called **semen.**

5. Hormones. The testes produce male sex hormones, which regulate the development of **secondary sex characteristics,** such as beard development and lowering of voice pitch.

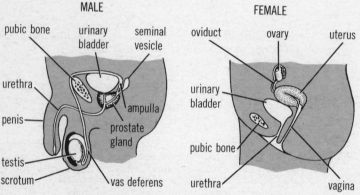

Figure 4-10. The human reproductive systems.

B. FEMALE REPRODUCTIVE SYSTEM

1. Ovaries. The pair of female gonads are called **ovaries.** They produce the female gametes or eggs. The ovaries are located within the lower portion of the abdominal cavity. Eggs are produced by meiotic division of sex cells in small cavities in the ovaries called **follicles.** Approximately once a month an egg cell is released from a follicle in one of the ovaries. This is called **ovulation.** All of the eggs that a female will produce are present in immature form when the female is born.

2. Fallopian tubes. Very close to each ovary there is the funnel-shaped opening of a **Fallopian tube,** or **oviduct.** The egg, released from the follicle, enters the Fallopian tube and is transported through the tube to the uterus. Fertilization of the egg normally occurs in the Fallopian tube if sperm are present.

3. Uterus. The **uterus** is a hollow, oval organ in which development of the fertilized egg occurs.

4. Vagina. The lower end of the uterus connects to the **vagina,** or **birth canal,** a muscular tube leading to the outside of the body.

5. Hormones. The ovaries produce female sex hormones, which regulate development of the secondary sex characteristics, such as development of the mammary glands and broadening of the pelvis. The ovarian hormones also have a role in the menstrual cycle, along with hormones produced by the pituitary gland.

6. Menstrual cycle. The **menstrual cycle** is a series of changes in the ovary and uterus that occur at approximately one-month intervals. The menstrual cycle begins at puberty. It is temporarily stopped during *pregnancy*, and it stops permanently at *menopause*. The menstrual cycle averages about 28 days, but may vary considerably from one individual to another.

    a. Follicle stage. The ovaries secrete the hormone **estrogen,** and an egg matures in an ovarian follicle.

    b. Ovulation. The egg is released from the follicle.

    c. Corpus luteum stage. The follicle becomes a mass of cells called the **corpus luteum.** The corpus luteum secretes the hormone **proges-**

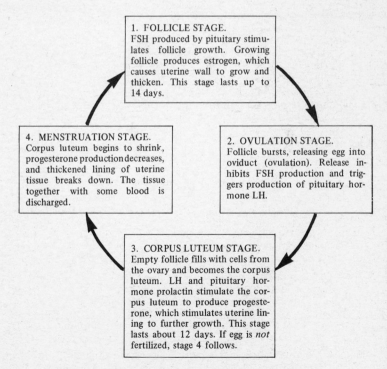

1. FOLLICLE STAGE.
FSH produced by pituitary stimulates follicle growth. Growing follicle produces estrogen, which causes uterine wall to grow and thicken. This stage lasts up to 14 days.

2. OVULATION STAGE.
Follicle bursts, releasing egg into oviduct (ovulation). Release inhibits FSH production and triggers production of pituitary hormone LH.

3. CORPUS LUTEUM STAGE.
Empty follicle fills with cells from the ovary and becomes the corpus luteum. LH and pituitary hormone prolactin stimulate the corpus luteum to produce progesterone, which stimulates uterine lining to further growth. This stage lasts about 12 days. If egg is *not* fertilized, stage 4 follows.

4. MENSTRUATION STAGE.
Corpus luteum begins to shrink, progesterone production decreases, and thickened lining of uterine tissue breaks down. The tissue together with some blood is discharged.

Figure 4-11. The menstrual cycle in the human female.

terone. Progesterone causes the lining of the uterus to thicken, accompanied by a great increase in blood vessels in the lining **(vascularization).**

d. Menstruation. If the egg has not been fertilized, the thickened uterine lining breaks down and passes out through the vagina, accompanied by a small flow of blood lasting about 4 days. This stage is called **menstruation.** The unfertilized egg leaves the body during this time.

e. Hormone feedback cycle. Maturation of an egg is stimulated by **follicle stimulating hormone (FSH)** secreted by the pituitary. As the follicle matures, it secretes estrogen, which reduces the production of FSH by the pituitary. After menstruation, the level of estrogen in the blood drops and the pituitary secretes FSH again, starting a new menstrual cycle.

7. Menopause. The menstrual cycle stops permanently usually at some time between the ages of 45 and 50, although it may occur much earlier. This permanent cessation of the cycle is called **menopause.**

QUESTIONS

1. In the human male, gametes are produced in the   (1) urethra (2) testes   (3) prostate gland   (4) bladder

2. In the human male, sperm leave the body through the   (1) urethra (2) testes   (3) bladder   (4) vas deferens

3. The fluid mixture in which human sperm pass out of the body is called   (1) blood   (2) urine   (3) testosterone   (4) semen

4. In mammals such as humans, the fusion of gamete nuclei usually occurs in the   (1) oviduct   (2) ovary   (3) uterus   (4) vagina

For each phrase in questions 5 through 7, select the number of the reproductive structure, chosen from the list below, that is described by that phrase. (A number may be used more than once or not at all.)

Female Reproductive Structures
(1) Ovary
(2) Oviduct
(3) Uterus
(4) Vagina

5. The process of fertilization usually occurs in this structure.

6. A developing embryo is implanted in the lining of this structure.

7. This structure, in association with embryonic tissue, forms an organ that nourishes the embryo during development.

8. Which represents the typical sequence in the human menstrual cycle? (1) follicle formation—corpus luteum—menstruation—ovulation (2) ovulation—menstruation—follicle formation—corpus luteum (3) menstruation—follicle formation—corpus luteum—ovulation   (4) follicle formation—ovulation—corpus luteum—menstruation

9. The follicle stimulating hormone (FSH) is   (1) an ovarian hormone which is responsible for building up the uterine lining   (2) a pituitary hormone which stimulates the growth of a follicle   (3) a hormone which is stimulated by the follicle and is responsible for building up the uterine lining   (4) an ovarian hormone which stimulates a follicle to produce an egg

10. During the menstrual cycle, ovulation occurs when (1) the embryo is implanted in the uterine wall (2) an egg is fertilized (3) the uterine wall begins to break down (4) an egg is released from the follicle

Base your answers to questions 11 through 14 on the following diagram of the human female reproductive system.

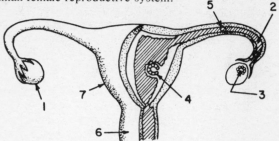

11. Which number indicates the usual site of the union of gametes? (1) 1 (2) 2 (3) 3 (4) 4

12. Which number indicates the site where a placenta is being formed? (1) 1 (2) 2 (3) 3 (4) 4

13. Where is the female gamete produced? (1) 5 (2) 6 (3) 3 (4) 7

14. Which number indicates a site of cleavage? (1) 1 (2) 6 (3) 3 (4) 5

C. ZYGOTE FORMATION IN HUMANS

1. Fertilization. The fusion of a male gamete (sperm) with a female gamete (egg) usually occurs in the upper portion of an oviduct. If fertilization does not occur within about 24 hours after ovulation, the egg degenerates.

2. Implantation. Cleavage of the fertilized egg begins at once in the oviduct. About 6 to 10 days later, the embryo (in the blastula stage) becomes **implanted** in the uterine lining.

3. Multiple embryos. More than one embryo may form and develop in the uterus at the same time. This may be the result of the release and fertilization of two different eggs, leading to the development of **fraternal** (unlike) **twins.** Multiple embryos may also result from the dividing of the embryo during an early stage of cleavage, leading to the development of **identical twins.**

4. *In vitro* fertilization. Techniques have been developed for fertilization of a human egg by sperm outside the female body. The embryo is then implanted in a female uterus, where normal development and birth occur.

D. DEVELOPMENT IN HUMANS

1. Prenatal development. Gastrulation of the embryo usually occurs after implantation in the uterine wall. Differentiation and growth then occur as described on pages 104-105. The placenta and umbilical cord develop, and an amnion filled with fluid surrounds the embryo.

2. Birth. Birth normally occurs through the vagina about 9 months after fertilization. This is called the period of **gestation.**

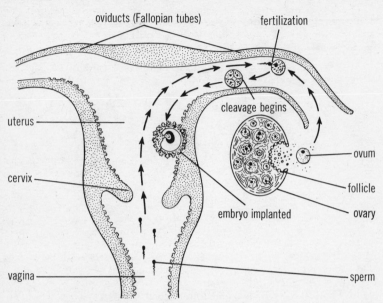

Figure 4-12. Ovulation and fertilization in the human female.

3. Postnatal development. After birth, cell multiplication, differentiation, and growth of the body continue. Various parts of the body develop at different rates until the **adult** stage is reached, at which time growth ceases.

4. Puberty. The reproductive tissues develop slowly. This development is controlled by hormones. The time at which the individual is capable of reproduction is called **puberty.** Puberty usually occurs between the ages of 9 and 14 in females, and between 12 and 18 in males.

5. Aging. After maturity is reached, the structures and functions of the body systems slowly weaken. This process is called **aging,** and it is a normal part of the continuing development of the individual. The causes of aging are not understood. The rate of aging varies among individuals and appears to be the result of an interaction of both hereditary and environmental factors.

6. Death. The aging processes eventually end in death of the organism. No precise definition of the moment of death has been agreed upon. One definition is the irreversible cessation of all brain functions.

QUESTIONS

1. Twins that develop from a single zygote are   (1) heterozygotes (2) nonplacental (3) identical (4) fraternal

2. Twins which are not identical result from the fertilization of (1) one egg by one sperm   (2) one egg by two sperms   (3) two eggs by one sperm   (4) two eggs by two sperms

For each human process in questions 3 through 7, write the number of the organ, chosen from the list below, in which that process usually occurs. (A number may be used more than once.)

Organs
(1) Ovary
(2) Oviduct
(3) Uterus

3. Egg fertilization
4. Embryo implantation
5. Ovum formation
6. Transfer of nutrients through the placenta
7. Cleavage in the first stages

8. Development becomes a process of cellular differentiation and specialization after the formation of the (1) lining of the uterus (2) gastrula (3) neural tube (4) notochord

9. Before birth the human embryo obtains its food and oxygen through the (1) mammary glands (2) ovaries (3) placenta (4) yolk

10. Allantois and the yolk sac are almost vestigial in humans because (1) gestation is external (2) fertilization is internal (3) an amnion is present (4) placenta development occurs

11. In humans, the major portion of prenatal development occurs in the (1) oviduct (2) uterus (3) follicle (4) corpus luteum

12. The period of time between fertilization and birth in mammals is referred to as (1) maturation (2) gestation (3) differentiation (4) cleavage

IV-5. SEXUAL REPRODUCTION AND DEVELOPMENT

IN PLANTS

A. THE FLOWER. The **flower** is a structure specialized for sexual reproduction in the higher plants called **angiosperms.**

1. The **stamen** is the male reproductive organ. It consists of two parts: a structure called the **anther** and a stalk called the **filament. Pollen grains** containing the monoploid male gametes are produced by meiosis in the anther.

2. The **pistil** is the female reproductive organ. It consists of the **stigma,** where pollen grains are deposited; a stalk called the **style;** and the **ovary,** containing **ovules** in which the female monoploid gametes are produced by meiosis and where fertilization occurs.

3. Other structures. Modified leaves called **petals** and **sepals** may be present in the flower.

4. Variations of flower structure. In some species of plants, some of the flowers contain only stamens **(staminate flowers),** while others contain only pistils **(pistillate flowers).**

B. ZYGOTE FORMATION

1. Pollination is the transfer of pollen grains from the anther of a stamen to the stigma of a pistil.

a. Self-pollination is the transfer of pollen from an anther to the stigma of the same flower or to the stigma of another flower on the same individual plant.

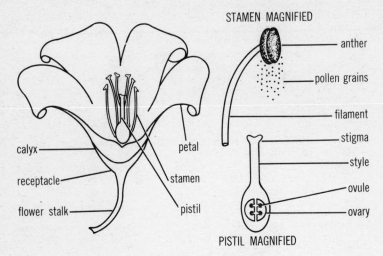

Figure 4-13. Parts of a flower.

b. Cross-pollination is the transfer of pollen from an anther of one flower to the stigma of a flower on another plant.

c. Agents of pollination. Pollination may result from the action of gravity (in some cases of self-pollination), wind, water, insects, and birds. Colored petals or sepals may act to attract insects and birds and thus increase the likelihood of pollination. The thick wall of the pollen grain protects the sex cells and reduces loss of water in a dry environment during transfer to the stigma of a flower.

2. Germination of the pollen grain. If the pollen grain is "recognized" by the stigma as belonging to the same species, the pollen grain **germinates** on the stigma. A **pollen tube** then grows down through the style to the ovary. Two monoploid **sperm nuclei** develop from the monoploid pollen grain nucleus and travel down the style with the pollen tube.

3. Fertilization. The pollen tube penetrates the ovary and enters one of the ovules. One of the monoploid (n) sperm nuclei fuses with the monoploid (n) egg nucleus in the ovule, forming a diploid (2n) zygote. The second sperm nucleus fuses with the endosperm nuclei and develops into the **endosperm,** a food-storage tissue.

4. Development of the embryo. The zygote in the ovule multiplies by mitotic division and develops into the plant embryo. The ovule develops into a **seed.** The ovary develops into a **fruit** containing the seeds.

QUESTIONS

1. Pollen formation in a flowering plant takes place in the (1) stamen (2) pistil (3) ovary (4) ovule

2. Gamete production in plants involves the process of (1) vegetative propagation (2) germination (3) gestation (4) reduction division

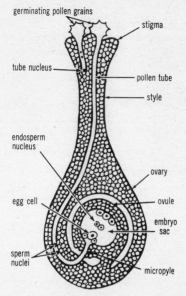

germinating pollen grains

stigma

tube nucleus

pollen tube

style

endosperm
nucleus

ovary

egg cell

ovule

embryo
sac

sperm
nuclei

micropyle

Figure 4-14. Fertilization in the flower.

3. The thick wall of a pollen grain prevents (1) pollination (2) fertilization (3) germination (4) dehydration

4. In tulip blossoms, the function of the stigma is to (1) form sperm nuclei (2) pollinate the ovule (3) produce the pollen (4) receive the pollen

5. Self-pollination can be prevented by removing the flower's (1) anthers (2) petals (3) sepals (4) epicotyls

6. Germinating pollen grains of a plant contain (1) male gametes (2) female gametes (3) zygotes (4) ovules

7. Following pollination, a sperm nucleus will reach the egg nucleus in the ovule of a flowering plant by way of (1) a pollen tube (2) a flagellum (3) the wind (4) insects

8. Fertilization in a flowering plant takes place in the (1) stigma (2) pollen tube (3) ovule (4) stamen

9. In flowering plants, which represents the order of events for sexual reproduction? (1) fertilization, pollination, growth of pollen tube, formation of pollen (2) formation of pollen, pollination, growth of pollen tube, fertilization (3) growth of pollen tube, formation of pollen, pollination, fertilization (4) growth of pollen tube, formation of pollen, fertilization, pollination

10. In flowering plants, after the processes of pollination and fertilization have been completed, the ovary develops into a (1) seed (2) flower (3) sperm cell (4) fruit

11. Ovules in the ovaries of plants develop into (1) fruits (2) micropyles (3) seeds (4) pollen grains

C. SEED FORMATION

1. Structure of the seed. The outer layers of the ovule develop into a **seed coat,** which surrounds and protects the embryo. The seed may also contain the food-storage tissue called the **endosperm.**

2. Structure of the embryo

a. The **epicotyl** is the portion of the embryo that develops into the leaves and upper portion of the stem.

b. The **cotyledon** stores food for the early growth of the embryo when the seed germinates. The flowering plants (angiosperms) are divided into two groups: the **monocots,** in which only one cotyledon is present (for example, corn) and the **dicots,** in which two cotyledons are present (for example, beans).

c. The **hypocotyl** develops into the root and in some species the lower portion of the stem.

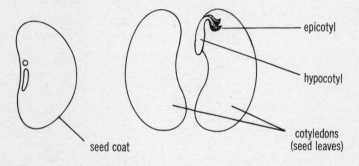

epicotyl

hypocotyl

cotyledons
(seed leaves)

seed coat

Figure 4-15. Structure of a dicot seed.

D. FRUITS. In flowering plants the ovary develops into a **fruit** containing the seeds. Fruits are specialized for aiding the **dispersal** of the seeds. They may disperse the seeds by being carried by wind or water, on the bodies of animals, or in the bodies of animals that eat the fruits and later eliminate the seeds.

E. SEED GERMINATION. Seeds may germinate in the proper environmental conditions, which include sufficient moisture, proper temperature, and sufficient oxygen. When a seed germinates, the embryo develops into a mature plant by cell division, differentiation, and growth.

F. GROWTH. Growth in the higher plants occurs by mitotic division of unspecialized cells in specific regions of the plant called **meristems.**

1. Apical meristem is found near the tips of roots and stems. Cell division of apical meristem causes growth in length of roots and stems.

2. Cambium is meristem tissue located between the xylem and phloem of roots and stems. Cell division of cambium results in increase in diameter of roots and stems.

3. Differentiation. As meristem tissue grows by cell division, the new cells differentiate into the various tissues of the plant, such as xylem, phloem, leaves, and floral structures.

QUESTIONS

1. A structure which is important in scattering seeds is the (1) embryo (2) cotyledon (3) hypocotyl (4) fruit

2. In cherry blossoms, the zygote undergoes mitotic division in the (1) ovule (2) seed (3) bud (4) stigma

Base your answers to questions 3 through 6 on the diagram below of the internal structure of a bean seed.

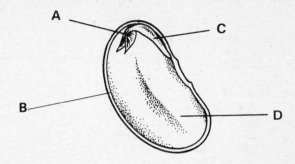

3. In which region of the seed are most polysaccharides stored? (1) A (2) B (3) C (4) D

4. Which part of the seed is known as the epicotyl? (1) A (2) B (3) C (4) D

5. Which part of the seed develops into the lower part of the stem and roots? (1) A (2) B (3) C (4) D

6. Bean seeds of this type do not ordinarily germinate in seed packets because they lack (1) water (2) light (3) chlorophyll (4) food

7. The upper portion of the stem of a bean seedling was produced from the (1) epicotyl (2) hypocotyl (3) seed coat (4) cotyledon

8. Which statement describes a function of the cotyledon in a seed? (1) It develops into the upper portion of the plant. (2) It develops into the lower portion of the plant. (3) It protects the ovary from drying out. (4) It provides nutrients for the developing embryo.

9. Energy for the early growth of a developing bean plant embryo is obtained most directly from (1) food in the soil (2) food in the seed (3) light from the sun (4) water in the soil

10. The process in which dormant seeds develop into new plants when conditions are favorable is known as (1) pollination (2) germination (3) spontaneous generation (4) differentiation

11. Which condition is not necessary in order for seeds to begin to germinate? (1) moisture (2) favorable temperature (3) fertile soil (4) oxygen

12. In a bean seed, which event does not normally occur during the first day of germination? (1) aerobic respiration (2) hydrolysis (3) DNA replication (4) photosynthesis

13. Which plant tissue contributes most directly to increasing the diameter of a dicotyledonous stem? (1) cambium (2) phloem (3) cortex (4) pith

UNIT V   THE TRANSMISSION OF TRAITS FROM GENERATION TO GENERATION

V-1. FOUNDATIONS OF GENETICS

A. MENDEL'S WORK. Gregor Mendel studied the inheritance of specific traits in pea plants. The traits, or characteristics, he observed occurred as **contrasting characters**. For example, a plant was either tall or short; its seeds were either smooth or wrinkled; its flowers were either purple or white; etc. Mendel crossed plants with contrasting characters and made a mathematical analysis of the results in successive generations. From his observations, he concluded that the characteristics of offspring were the result of inheriting certain **factors** from the parents. The results of any particular cross could be predicted by the laws that Mendel derived: the laws of *dominance, segregation, recombination,* and *independent assortment*. When large numbers of offspring are produced, these laws predict the ratios among the characteristics of each generation.

B. GENE-CHROMOSOME THEORY. Mendel's work was ignored when he reported it and forgotten. When it was rediscovered in 1900, it was recognized that the distribution of chromosomes during meiotic division can be related to the factors of heredity that Mendel proposed. Breeding experiments with the fruit fly, *Drosophila,* showed that each chromosome carries many hereditary factors, which were given the name of **genes.** It was found that genes are arranged along the chromosomes at specific positions, or **loci** (singular, **locus**). Different forms of the gene associated with a particular character are called **alleles.** For example, the genes for tallness and shortness in pea plants are alleles. Alleles are located at the same position, or locus, on homologous chromosomes. The separation of alleles during meiosis and their recombination during fertilization account for the laws of heredity that Mendel observed.

V-2. MAJOR GENETIC CONCEPTS

A. DOMINANCE
   1. Definition. If a zygote receives two different alleles for a particular trait, and only one of the alleles is expressed, that allele and its trait are said to be **dominant.** The gene that is present, but not expressed, is called **recessive.** For example, if a pea plant zygote has one allele for tallness and one allele for shortness, the plant that develops is always tall. The tallness allele is expressed and is dominant over the shortness allele, which is recessive.
   2. Symbols for alleles. By general agreement, a capital letter (usually the initial of the dominant trait) is used to represent a dominant allele.

The lower case (small) form of the same letter represents the recessive allele. For example, T stands for the dominant allele for tallness; t stands for the recessive allele for shortness.

3. Genotype. The genetic makeup of an individual is called its **genotype,** and is represented by two letters for each trait.

4. Homozygous genotypes. If both alleles for a trait are the same, the genotype is said to be **homozygous,** or **pure.** A pure tall plant has the genotype TT. A pure short plant has the genotype tt.

5. Heterozygous genotypes. If the two alleles for a trait are different, the genotype is said to be **heterozygous,** or **hybrid.** A plant that is hybrid for stem length has the genotype Tt.

6. Phenotype. The traits that appear in an individual are called its **phenotype.** Individuals with different genotypes (genetic makeup) may have the same phenotype (appearance). For example, a hybrid for stem length (Tt) has the same appearance as a plant that is pure for tallness (TT). For a recessive phenotype to develop, the genotype must be pure recessive. Only tt plants are short.

7. Phenotype of hybrids. If an individual homozygous for a dominant trait is crossed with an individual homozygous for the corresponding recessive trait, all the offspring are heterozygous for that trait. Because of the principle of dominance, the phenotype of the offspring is like that of the pure dominant parent. For example, if a pure tall pea plant (TT) is crossed with a pure short plant (tt), the genotype of all offspring is heterozygous (Tt), and the phenotype is tall. The parents in such a cross are called the P_1 generation, and the offspring are called the F_1 generation.

QUESTIONS

1. Because of a short life cycle and few chromosomes, ideal organisms for experimental studies in genetics are   (1) garden peas   (2) humans   (3) fruit flies   (4) maple trees

2. The genes located at corresponding positions on homologous chromosomes are known as   (1) autosomes   (2) homozygotes   (3) alleles   (4) heterozygotes

3. An individual possesses two identical genes for a certain trait. For this trait, the individual is said to be   (1) dominant   (2) hybrid   (3) homozygous   (4) heterozygous

4. In the homologous chromosomes shown, which pair of genes is an allelic pair? (1) AB   (2) Dc   (3) ef   (4) fF

a B c d e F

A B c D e f

5. The outward appearance (gene expression) of a particular trait in an organism is referred to as   (1) a genotype   (2) a phenotype   (3) an allele   (4) a chromosome

6. The phenotype of a pea plant can be most easily determined by (1) looking at it   (2) crossing it with a recessive plant   (3) crossing it with a similar plant   (4) looking at the parents

7. Which pair of terms is most alike in meaning?   (1) segregation, dominance   (2) heterozygous, hybrid   (3) phenotype, genotype   (4) recessiveness, blending

B. SEGREGATION AND RECOMBINATION

1. Gametes of a heterozygous parent. When a heterozygous individual produces gametes, homologous chromosomes are separated and distributed at random to the gametes. Half the gametes receive the chromosome carrying the dominant allele, and half receive the recessive allele. For example, a heterozygous tall pea plant *(Tt)* produces equal numbers of gametes with the dominant allele *(T)* and gametes with the recessive allele *(t)*. This process is called **segregation.**

2. Hybrid cross. When two heterozygous individuals are crossed, each parent produces equal numbers of the two types of gamete (dominant or recessive). When gametes fuse during fertilization, each type of gamete from one parent has an equal chance of combining with either type of gamete from the other parent, as shown by the diagram in Figure 5-1.

There are four possible combinations. If the parents are F_1 pea plants with the genotype *Tt,* of the four combinations in the F_2 generation, 1 is *TT,* 2 are *Tt,* and 1 is *tt.* The genotype ratio in the F_2 generation is 1:2:1. Since *T* is dominant, the phenotype ratio is 3:1 (3 tall to 1 short).

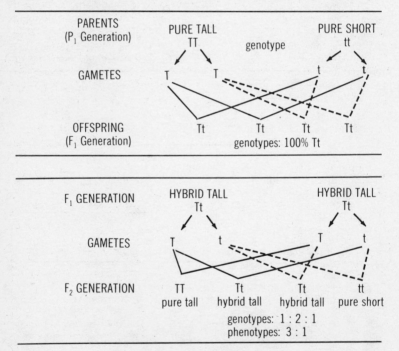

Figure 5-1. Results of a hybrid cross.

The reappearance in the F_2 generation of genetic types not present in the F_1 generation is called **recombination.** Segregation and recombination account for the reappearance of the recessive trait in the F_2 generation.

3. Punnett squares. The results of any particular cross can be predicted by a diagram called a **Punnett square.** The genotypes of the gametes of one parent are placed over the columns of the diagram, and the genotypes of the gametes of the other parent are placed next to the rows. Where the rows and columns cross, each possible combination is entered. The ratios of genotypes and phenotypes of the offspring can be determined by counting squares of the same type. Each square represents a 25% chance of occurrence. See Figure 5-2.

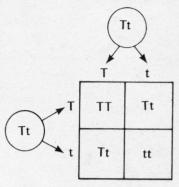

Figure 5-2. Punnett square for a hybrid cross.

4. Test cross. To find out whether an individual showing a dominant trait is homozygous or heterozygous, the individual can be crossed with another showing the recessive trait, and therefore known to be homozygous recessive. If any recessives develop in the offspring, the unknown parent must be heterozygous. If the parent had been homozygous dominant, all offspring would have been heterozygous dominant. This procedure is called a **test cross.** The Punnett squares for a test cross are shown in Figure 5-3.

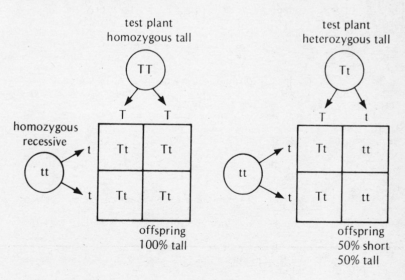

Figure 5-3. The test cross. An individual showing a dominant trait is crossed with a recessive. If any offspring show the recessive trait, the test individual must be hybrid.

QUESTIONS

1. What is the probability that a hybrid tall pea plant will produce a gamete carrying a gene for tallness? (1) 0% (2) 25% (3) 50% (4) 75%

2. With respect only to the alleles G and g, a heterozygous female could normally produce how many different kinds of egg cells? (1) 1 (2) 2 (3) 3 (4) 4

3. Mendel was able to formulate the law of segregation from his experiments with pea plants when he had (1) produced hybrids (2) produced mutations (3) recorded F_1 results (4) counted F_2 types

4. Which of the crosses below best illustrates Mendel's principle of segregation? (1) BB x bb (2) Bb x Bb (3) bb x bb (4) BB x BB

5. In a biology laboratory, a student flipped a coin ten times, obtaining 10 heads. The probability that the 11th flip will produce tails is (1) 1 in 10 (2) 1 in 2 (3) 2 in 5 (4) 10 in 11

6. In guinea pigs, rough hair is dominant over straight hair. If heterozygotes are crossed, the largest number of any one genotype of offspring would probably be (1) homozygous straight hair (2) homozygous rough hair (3) heterozygous rough hair (4) intermediate between rough hair and straight hair

7. A pair of black (B) mice produce some offspring which are black and some which are white (b). The genotypes of the parents are most probably (1) BB and bb (2) BB and Bb (3) Bb and Bb (4) bb and bb

8. Two individuals heterozygous for a given trait are mated. In the resulting offspring, the ratio of the dominant phenotype to the recessive phenotype for this trait is expected to be (1) 1:1 (2) 2:1 (3) 3:1 (4) 4:1

9. A cross is made between two organisms, both of which have a genetic makeup of Bb for a particular trait, and two offspring are produced. The first offspring exhibits the dominant trait. What is the probability that the second offspring will exhibit the recessive trait? (1) ¼ (2) ½ (3) ¾ (4) 0

10. It is possible for parents both of whom have brown eyes to have a blue-eyed child. The most probable explanation is that (1) a back cross has occurred (2) both parents were pure for the trait (3) blue eyes is a recessive trait (4) nondisjunction has occurred

11. From a single ear of corn, a farmer planted 200 kernels which produced 140 tall plants and 40 short plants. The genotypes of these offspring are most likely (1) TT and tt, only (2) TT and Tt, only (3) Tt and tt, only (4) TT, Tt, and tt

12. To discover whether an animal showing the dominant trait is homozygous or heterozygous, it must be crossed with (1) homozygous dominant (2) homozygous recessive (3) heterozygous (4) hybrid

13. If dimpled cheeks are dominant over nondimpled cheeks, what percentage of offspring with dimpled cheeks may be expected if a hybrid dimpled individual is crossed with a pure dimpled individual? (1) 25% (2) 50% (3) 75% (4) 100%

14. In Dalmatian dogs, the desired type is white with small black spots. Assume that the mating of two dogs, each with small black spots, results in some offspring with solid white coats, some offspring with large black spots, and some with small black spots. What is the probable genotype of the Dalmatians with small black spots? (1) homozygous dominant (2) homozygous recessive (3) heterozygous (4) sex-linked recessive

C. INCOMPLETE DOMINANCE

1. Definition. In some cases of contrasting alleles, one of them is only partly dominant over the other. In a heterozygous individual, the dominant allele is only partially expressed, and the phenotype (appearance) of the individual is intermediate between that of the contrasting homozygous forms. This type of dominance, in which the dominant allele is only partially expressed when the recessive allele is present, is called **incomplete dominance.**

2. Examples. A cross between red and white four-o'clock flowers produces pink flowers in the F_1 hybrid offspring. A cross between long and round squash produces oval squash. When the hybrids are crossed, recombination produces homozygous and heterozygous individuals with a phenotype ratio that is the same as the genotype ratio—1:2:1. In a cross of pink four-o'clocks, ¼ of the offspring are red, 2/4 are pink, and ¼ are white.

3. Genotype symbols. The following symbols may be used to represent the genotypes of four-o'clocks: RR is homozygous red; $R'R'$ is homozygous white; and RR' is heterozygous pink. The prime mark (') indicates that the allele is incompletely recessive to the dominant allele.

4. Punnett square for incomplete dominance. Figure 5-4 shows the genotype and phenotype ratios for crosses involving red and white four-o'clocks.

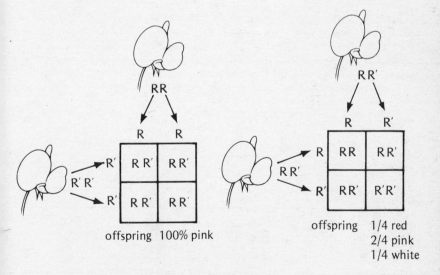

Figure 5-4. Incomplete dominance. The hybrids of the F_1 generation show a trait intermediate between the pure dominant and the pure recessive. When these hybrids are crossed, one-fourth of the F_2 generation are pure dominant, one-fourth pure recessive, and the remaining two-fourths show the intermediate hybrid trait.

D. CODOMINANCE

1. Definition. In some cases of contrasting alleles, neither one is dominant over the other. In a heterozygous individual, both alleles are expressed. This type of dominance, in which two alleles are considered equally dominant, is called **codominance.**

2. Examples. The alleles for red coat and white coat are codominant in certain cattle. In the heterozygous animal, the coat is **roan.** It consists of a mixture of red and white hairs, because both alleles are expressed equally. The following symbols may be used to represent the genotypes of roan cattle: $C^R C^R$ is homozygous red coat; $C^W C^W$ is homozygous white coat; and $C^R C^W$ is heterozygous roan coat. Sickle-cell trait and blood groups are examples of codominance in humans.

E. INDEPENDENT ASSORTMENT.
Mendel studied seven traits in pea plants. The genes for those traits are all on different chromosomes. Therefore, the segregation of the alleles for one trait is independent of the segregation of any of the others. These traits are inherited independently of one another. Mendel was therefore led to propose the **law of independent assortment** of traits, which states that traits are inherited independently. This law applies, however, only to traits controlled by genes on nonhomologous chromosomes.

F. GENE LINKAGE.
If the genes for two different traits are on the same chromosome, the genes are said to be **linked.** Alleles that are linked tend to be inherited together. Since a chromosome usually carries thousands of genes, every gene is linked to large numbers of other genes.

G. CROSSING-OVER.
Early investigations of gene linkage in *Drosophila* showed that linkage is never perfect. Alleles on the same chromosome are usually distributed together, but in a certain percentage of cases, the alleles become separated. One allele on the chromosome is replaced by its contrasting allele from the homologous chromosome. This result is due to the process of crossing-over that may occur during synapsis in meiosis (see page 100). It produces new combinations of alleles and increases the variations in offspring. See Figure 5-5.

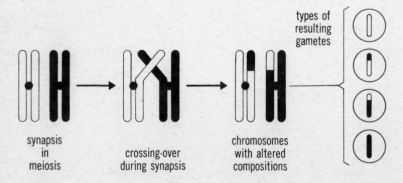

Figure 5-5. The result of crossing-over during synapsis in meiosis.

QUESTIONS

1. A cross between a red rose and a white rose results in 100% pink offspring. When two of these pink roses are crossed, assuming large numbers of offspring, the ratio of offspring produced most probably will be (1) 100% pink (2) 75% pink; 25% red (3) 25% red; 50% pink; 25% white (4) 50% red; 50% white

2. When long radish plants were pollinated with pollen from round radish plants, the plants obtained produced oval radishes. This illustrates the principle of (1) dominance (2) segregation (3) independent assortment (4) incomplete dominance

3. When homozygous red cattle are bred with homozygous white cattle, the offspring are roan. The F_1 generation of a roan mated with a white will be (1) 50% red, 50% white (2) 50% roan, 50% white (3) 75% roan, 25% white (4) 100% roan

4. The coat of roan cattle is found to be a mixture of red hairs and white hairs. This is an example of (1) recombination (2) codominance (3) independent assortment (4) segregation

5. When a pure brown-eyed sheep is crossed with a pure green-eyed sheep, blue-eyed offspring are produced. After several matings of these blue-eyed sheep, what percentage of their offspring will most probably have blue eyes? (1) 25% (2) 50% (3) 75% (4) 100%

6. When one of two traits can be inherited without the other, the genes for these two traits are said to be (1) dominant (2) recessive (3) blended (4) independent

7. Mendel developed the principle of independent assortment while studying the inheritance of seven different traits in pea plants. Modern geneticists explain this principle by inferring that each of these traits (1) is located on different chromosomes (2) is linked to the others on homologous chromosomes (3) fails to segregate during gametogenesis (4) modifies the other during inheritance

8. A black guinea pig which has a smooth coat is mated with a white guinea pig which has a rough coat. Some of the offspring have smooth, white fur. This is an example of (1) autosomal linkage (2) sex linkage (3) nondisjunction (4) independent assortment

9. If the genes for two different traits are located on the same autosome, the two traits would be expected to be (1) inherited together (2) visible in the offspring (3) recessive in the offspring (4) sex-linked

10. Crossing-over occurs between (1) gametes (2) amebas (3) stigma and stamen (4) chromosomes

H. SEX DETERMINATION

1. The sex chromosomes. In the diploid cells of many organisms, there is one pair of homologous chromosomes that are not alike in the genes they carry and that often have different shapes and sizes. This chromosome pair controls the sex of the individual, and they are called the **sex chromosomes.** The other chromosomes are called **autosomes.**

2. Human sex chromosomes. Human diploid cells contain 22 pairs of autosomes and one pair of sex chromosomes, called X and Y. The diploid cells of females contain two X chromosomes; their genetic makeup is XX. The genetic makeup of males is XY.

3. Human gametes. Since all female cells are XX, all female gametes contain one X chromosome. Since male cells are XY, half the male gametes carry an X chromosome and the other half carry a Y.

4. Sex of the zygote in human fertilization. During fertilization, an egg nucleus containing an X chromosome fuses with a sperm nucleus, which may carry either an X or a Y. If the sperm nucleus is X, the zygote is XX, and it develops into a female. If the sperm nucleus is Y, the zygote is XY, and it develops into a male.

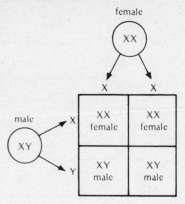

Figure 5-6. Sex determination in humans.

I. SEX LINKAGE

1. Definition. The X chromosome carries many genes that do not have alleles on the Y chromosome. The expression of these genes is therefore affected by the sex of the individual. The traits controlled by these genes are said to be **sex-linked.**

2. Expression of sex-linked genes. Since females are XX, they have two alleles for each sex-linked trait—one on each X chromosome. If the two alleles for a trait are different, and one is recessive, the recessive trait will not be expressed. Males, however, are XY. They can have only one allele for each sex-linked trait, since the Y chromosome does not have an allele for that trait. Therefore, recessive alleles on the X chromosome of a male will always be expressed. Thus, certain recessive sex-linked traits appear more often in males than in females.

3. Examples. Hemophilia (poor clotting ability of the blood) is a recessive sex-linked trait in humans. **Color blindness** is another. Females may carry the genes for these defects without showing the condition, because the dominant normal allele on the other X chromosome is expressed. The trait may, however, be transmitted by a mother to her sons with a 50% probability. Females show the trait only when their two X chromosomes are homozygous for the recessive allele.

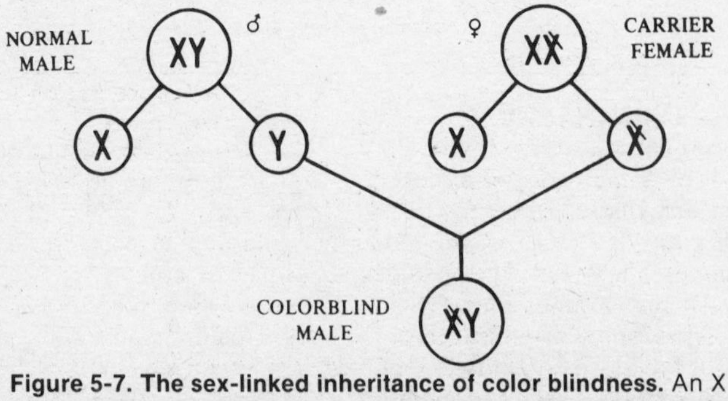

NORMAL MALE   ♂ XY   ♀ XX   CARRIER FEMALE

X   Y   X   X̶

COLORBLIND MALE   X̶Y

Figure 5-7. The sex-linked inheritance of color blindness. An X with a crossed arm represents an X chromosome carrying the gene for color blindness.

QUESTIONS

1. The number of autosomes and type of sex chromosome normally present in a human egg cell is (1) 44 + XY (2) 44 + XX (3) 22 + Y (4) 22 + X

2. The sex of a human individual is determined at the time of (1) gametogenesis (2) mitosis (3) meiosis (4) fertilization

3. If a family has 4 children, 3 boys and 1 girl, what are the chances that the next baby will be a girl? (1) 0 (2) ⅓ (3) ¼ (4) ½

4. The fact that in humans color blindness occurs more frequently among men than among women is an example of (1) sex linkage (2) independent assortment (3) incomplete dominance (4) pure-line inheritance

5. Because the gene for hemophilia is located on the X-chromosome, it is normally impossible for a (1) carrier mother to pass the gene to her son (2) hemophiliac father to pass the gene to his son (3) hemophiliac father to pass the gene to his daughter (4) carrier mother to pass the gene to her daughter

6. If a color-blind man marries a normal (homozygous) woman, it is most probable that, in the F_1 generation, all of the (1) sons will be carriers (2) sons will be color-blind (3) daughters will be color-blind (4) daughters will be carriers

7. A man who is color-blind marries a woman who is not color-blind and is not carrying a gene for it. What is the chance that their sons will be color-blind? (1) 0% (2) 25% (3) 50% (4) 100%

8. Which parents are most likely to produce a daughter who is color-blind? (1) a mother who is a carrier and a father who is normal (2) a mother who is color-blind and a father who is normal (3) a mother who is neither a carrier nor color-blind and a father who is color-blind (4) a mother who is a carrier and a father who is color-blind

J. MULTIPLE ALLELES

1. Pattern of heredity. In some cases there are more than two contrasting alleles for a particular trait. However, the cells of an individual cannot contain more than two different alleles for a trait, one on each chromosome of a homologous pair. The phenotype will then depend on which possible genotype pair the individual has inherited.

2. ABO blood groups. The inheritance of blood types in humans can be explained by a model in which there are three alleles for blood type, represented as I^A, I^B, and i. I^A produces Type A blood. I^B produces Type B blood. The allele i produces Type O blood. I^A and I^B are codominant, and each is expressed independently of the presence of the other. I^A and I^B are dominant over i. For i to be expressed, the individual must be homozygous for it (*ii*).

There are six possible allele pairs of these three alleles; $I^A I^A$, $I^A I^B$, $I^A i$, $I^B I^B$, $I^B i$, and *ii*. These six combinations produce four different blood types, as shown in Table 5-1.

TABLE 5-1. THE GENETIC BASIS OF ABO BLOOD TYPES.

GENOTYPE	BLOOD TYPE
$I^A I^A$ or $I^A i$	A
$I^B I^B$ or $I^B i$	B
$I^A I^B$	AB
ii	O

QUESTIONS

1. There are a great number of shades of skin coloring in humans. From this fact, it may be assumed that the trait for skin coloring in humans is determined by (1) a single pair of alleles (2) cytoplasmic alleles (3) more than one pair of alleles (4) linked alleles

2. The inheritance of the ABO blood groups in humans may be explained by a model using (1) linkage (2) multiple alleles (3) crossing-over (4) independent assortment

3. There are three alleles for ABO blood type. Why are only two alleles normally present in any individual? (1) There is not sufficient RNA in the cell to produce a third allele. (2) Each parent contributes only one allele to the offspring. (3) Every gene must be dominant or recessive. (4) Each trait can be determined by only one gene.

4. A man with a blood genotype $I^A i$ marries a woman with a blood genotype $I^A i$. What blood types could be expected in their children? (1) type A, only (2) type O, only (3) both type A and type O (4) neither type A nor type O

5. Marriages between persons of blood type AB and type A are not likely to produce offspring with blood type (1) A (2) B (3) AB (4) O

V-3. MUTATIONS

A. NATURE OF MUTATIONS

1. Definition. A **mutation** is any change in the genetic or hereditary material of a cell.

2. Inheritable mutations. A mutation that occurs in the primary sex cells, or germ cells, of an organism can be inherited by its offspring and passed on to future generations.

3. Nonheritable mutations. A mutation that occurs in a body cell, or somatic cell, of an organism may spread in that organism if the cell multiplies; however, the mutation cannot be transmitted to the sex cells and therefore cannot be inherited.

B. TYPES OF MUTATIONS

1. Chromosomal alterations. Any change in the structure of a chromosome or in the number of chromosomes in a cell is called a **chromosomal alteration** (also called a **chromosomal mutation**). The effects of a chromosomal alteration can often be seen in the phenotype because many genes on the chromosome are involved.

   a. Changes in chromosome number

   (1) Nondisjunction. In meiosis, homologous chromosomes normally separate from each other and are distributed to different gametes. This normal process is called **disjunction.** The failure of this to occur is called **nondisjunction.** It results in gametes with either one more or one fewer chromosome than the normal number (n). If these gametes take part in fertilization, the resulting zygote will have one more or one fewer than the normal number of chromosomes (2n).

   (2) Effects of nondisjunction. In humans, **Down's syndrome** occurs when one of the gametes in fertilization has two chromosomes No. 21, instead of only one. The zygote, and the individual, develops with three of these chromosomes instead of two. All cells of the individual have an extra chromosome.

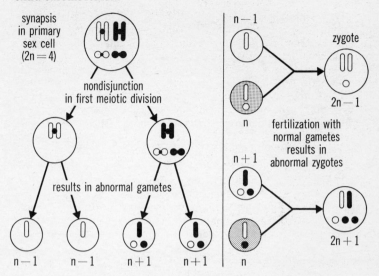

Figure 5-8. Results of nondisjunction during meiosis.

(3) Polyploidy. During gamete formation, nondisjunction of an entire set of chromosomes may occur. The result is a gamete with 2n chromosomes. If this gamete fuses with a gamete with the normal (n) number of chromosomes, the zygote will be 3n. Sometimes, both gametes are 2n, producing a 4n zygote. The presence of one or more extra sets of chromosomes is called **polyploidy.** In plants, polyploid individuals are usually larger or more vigorous than the ordinary diploid types. Certain varieties of cotton, wheat, potatoes, apples, tobacco, and zinnias are polyploid. Some polyploid plants are sterile and produce fruits without seeds.

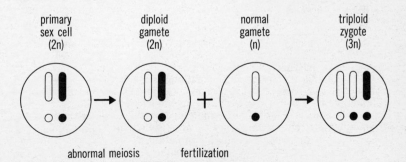

Figure 5-9. Polyploidy.

MG

b. Changes in chromosome structure. During meiosis, parts of chromosomes may break off and then join other chromosomes. The results are changes in the genes carried by the chromosomes.

(1) **Translocation** is a chromosomal alteration in which a section of one chromosome is transferred to a nonhomologous chromosome.

(2) **Addition** and **deletion** are chromosomal alterations in which a portion of a chromosome is added on or lost.

2. Gene mutations. A gene mutation is a change in the chemical structure of the genetic material, DNA. Some gene mutations produce noticeable effects, for example, albinism (absence of skin pigments). The effects of other gene mutations may not be readily observable.

3. Most gene mutations are recessive, and they are not observed in the phenotype unless they occur homozygously. Mutations are usually disadvantageous to the individuals in their normal environment, and sometimes *lethal* (the individual does not survive).

C. MUTAGENIC AGENTS. Certain environmental factors can cause mutations to occur at a greater than normal rate. Such factors are called **mutagenic agents.** Examples are (1) **radiation,** such as x rays, ultraviolet rays, cosmic rays, and radiations from radioactive substances, and (2) certain **chemicals,** such as formaldehyde, benzene, and asbestos.

QUESTIONS

1. A new trait, not previously present in the species, which continues to appear in succeeding generations is called a   (1) mutation (2) heterozygote (3) polyploid (4) disjunction

2. Most mutations in organisms are (1) recessive and advantageous (2) recessive and of no advantage   (3) dominant and advantageous (4) dominant and of no advantage

3. A child is born with an extra chromosome in each of its cells. This condition is usually the result of (1) nondisjunction (2) crossing-over (3) segregation (4) hybridization

4. If a sperm cell in which nondisjunction of the sex chromosomes has occurred fertilizes a normal human female egg, how many chromosomes will the resulting zygote contain? (1) 47 (2) 46 (3) 24 (4) 23

5. The nondisjunction of chromosome pair number 21 occurs during the formation of a human egg cell. Which would be the chromosome number of a zygote resulting from the fertilization of this egg cell by a normal sperm? (1) 23 (2) 24 (3) 46 (4) 47

6. The cells of an individual contain 47 chromosomes. This number of chromosomes could cause the condition known as (1) Down's syndrome (2) hemophilia (3) color blindness (4) phenylketonuria

7. A plant has 18 chromosomes, although the species normally has 12 chromosomes. This mutation is an example of (1) recombination (2) polyploidy (3) crossing-over (4) incomplete dominance

8. Albinism is a hereditary condition initially resulting from (1) a gene mutation (2) crossing-over (3) nondisjunction (4) polyploidy

9. To the organism, a genetic mutation is usually (1) harmful (2) sex-linked (3) beneficial (4) dominant

10. Mutations resulting from X-radiation probably are due to changes in (1) ATP (2) DNA (3) ADP (4) Rh

V-4. INTERACTION OF HEREDITY AND ENVIRONMENT

Heredity, through genes, gives each individual organism the potential for the development and expression of certain traits. The extent of this expression is affected by the environment of the individual. Examples include:

1. Effect of light on the production of chlorophyll. If normally green parts of plants, such as leaves, are screened from light, the cells of those parts stop making chlorophyll.

2. Effect of temperature on hair color in the Himalayan rabbit. If some of the white fur is shaved from the rabbit's back and the area is kept cold with an ice pack, the fur grows back black. The gene for black fur is active only at low temperatures.

3. Studies of the development of identical twins. The relative strength of heredity and environment in controlling certain traits can be studied by comparing identical twins raised in different environments with identical twins raised in the same environment.

QUESTIONS

1. A Himalayan rabbit which lives in a cold environment normally has black fur on its ears and feet. If this black fur is plucked out and the rabbit is kept in a much warmer environment while new hair grows in, the new hair will not be black. This provides evidence that (1) there are similarities and differences from one generation to another (2) many characteristics are not inherited (3) inherited characteristics vary from generation to generation (4) there is interaction between heredity and environment

2. Two paramecia formed by fission from the same parent cell differ in phenotype when cultured in separate containers. These differences are most likely due to their (1) genes (2) environments (3) nitrogen bases (4) autosomes

3. The relationship between heredity and environment can best be studied by using organisms (1) with identical genotypes (2) with a high mutation rate (3) which are unrelated (4) which exhibit polyploidy

4. Identical twin studies have contributed much to the study of heredity, chiefly in the area of understanding the (1) mechanism of meiosis (2) mechanism of sex determination (3) influence of hormones on sexual reproduction (4) influence of environment on heredity

V-5. HUMAN HEREDITY

A. DIFFICULTIES IN STUDYING HUMAN HEREDITY. Since scientists cannot interfere with the free choice of mates by human beings, controlled experiments in human heredity are not possible. Studies of the transmission of traits in human families are also limited by the small number of offspring per generation and the long time between generations.

B. PEDIGREE CHARTS. Some knowledge of the inheritance of human genetic traits has been obtained by studying the characteristics of many members of related families through several generations. This leads to the construction of **pedigree charts,** which show the presence or absence of certain traits in the members of each generation. From pedigree charts it is often possible to detect the presence of recessive genes in "carriers."

QUESTIONS

Base your answers to questions 1 and 2 on the information below.

In humans, red-green color blindness is due to a sex-linked recessive gene.

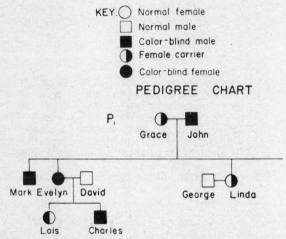

KEY: ○ Normal female
☐ Normal male
■ Color-blind male
◐ Female carrier
● Color-blind female

PEDIGREE CHART

1. Which assumption about the P_1 generation is true? (1) John had one gene for color blindness. (2) John had two genes for color blindness. (3) Grace carried two genes for color blindness. (4) Grace was color-blind.

2. If Linda and George have a son, what is the probability that he will be color-blind? (1) 0% (2) 25% (3) 50% (4) 75%

C. GENETICALLY RELATED DISEASES.
Many human diseases and defects have been shown to be related to the presence of certain recessive genes. These include *phenylketonuria (PKU), sickle-cell anemia,* and *Tay-Sachs disease*. In some cases, the presence of the disease can be detected in the fetus before birth, or in the infant shortly after birth, and corrective measures may be taken. Carriers of these defective genes can also be identified in some cases. Genetic counseling can be given to individuals who may be carriers of genetic diseases to influence marriage and child-bearing decisions.

1. Phenylketonuria (PKU)

a. Symptoms. Mental retardation is one of the conditions associated with this genetic disease.

b. Cause. PKU develops when the individual is homozygous for a certain recessive mutant gene. The mutant gene fails to direct the production of an enzyme needed for the normal metabolism of phenylalanine, an amino acid.

c. Treatment. When the condition is detected early enough, the mental retardation associated with the disease can be prevented by limiting the amount of phenylalanine in the diet.

2. Sickle-cell anemia

a. Symptoms. Pain, weakness, and anemia (lack of oxygen in the blood) are among the symptoms of this disease, which is most likely to occur in individuals of African descent. The red blood cells have an abnormal sickle shape that causes them to clump together and block the small blood vessels. The cells also have a shorter life span and less ability to carry oxygen than normal red cells.

b. Cause. The sickle-shaped cells form because a mutation of a gene that controls the synthesis of hemoglobin substitutes one amino acid for another at a single point in the hemoglobin molecule. As a result, the molecules, which occupy a large part of the red blood cell, have an abnormal shape. The mutant gene is recessive. Only an individual homozygous for the trait develops the disease in its severe form.

c. Relationship to malaria resistance. Individuals who are heterozygous for the sickle-cell gene (having one normal gene) have only mild symptoms of the disease. They also have above-average resistance to malaria. This effect has tended to maintain the gene for sickle-cell anemia in African populations.

3. Tay-Sachs disease

a. Symptoms. In this disease there is deterioration of nerve tissue and malfunctioning of the nervous system, leading to death at an early age. It is more likely to occur among Jewish people from Central Europe.

b. Cause. The disease is caused by the accumulation of fatty tissue in the nervous system because the cells do not have the gene for the synthesis of a particular enzyme.

4. Techniques for detecting genetic defects

a. Amniocentesis. Amniotic fluid is withdrawn during pregnancy and examined for the presence of certain substances or cell types.

b. Karyotyping. A **karyotype** is an enlarged photograph of the pairs of homologous chromosomes in a cell undergoing mitosis. The karyotype shows abnormal chromosomes or abnormal chromosome number.

c. Screening. Body fluids, such as blood and urine, can be analyzed chemically to detect the presence or absence of certain enzymes or cellular products.

QUESTIONS

1. Genetically related diseases are usually the result of (1) a recessive gene in the heterozygous state (2) a recessive gene in the homozygous state (3) two codominant genes (4) a mutant gene

EXTENDED AREA—MODERN GENETICS

2. One purpose of genetic counseling is to (1) correct genetic defects (2) improve the human species (3) try to avoid genetic disease in offspring (4) eliminate genetic diseases

3. Genetic diseases are often related to the failure of the body cells to synthesize an essential (1) enzyme (2) antigen (3) amino acid (4) nucleotide

4. A disease that results from a change in an amino acid in the hemoglobin molecule is (1) PKU (2) hemophilia (3) Tay-Sachs disease (4) sickle-cell anemia

5. PKU is a hereditary disease resulting from a gene-induced inability to produce a necessary (1) hormone (2) enzyme (3) nucleotide (4) vitamin

V-6. GENETIC APPLICATIONS TO ANIMAL AND PLANT BREEDING

Breeders improve the qualities of animals and plants used for human purposes and produce and maintain new varieties by the following methods:

1. Artificial selection. Individuals with desirable traits are mated to produce offspring with those traits.

2. Inbreeding. The offspring with desirable traits are then mated with one another to maintain and reinforce those traits.

3. Hybridization. Sometimes, two varieties of a species have different desirable traits. A variety combining the two traits in each individual can be obtained by crossing the varieties to produce hybrid offspring.

4. Preservation of desirable mutations. A mutant variety of a plant may have a recessive desirable trait. To be sure of perpetuating the trait, the plant may be propagated by vegetative means, such as grafting, bulbs, and runners.

QUESTIONS

1. Which best explains why inbreeding could lead to the expression of undesirable traits? (1) New gene combinations are produced. (2) The probability of the recombining of recessive genes is increased. (3) The probability of the occurrence of crossing-over is decreased. (4) The possibility of genetic variation is increased.

2. Plant and animal breeders often cross two organisms with different desirable traits with the hope that the desirable traits of both parents will be combined in the offspring. This technique is called (1) hybridization (2) grafting (3) inbreeding (4) vegetative propagation

V-7. MODERN GENETICS

A. THE HEREDITARY MATERIAL

By the turn of this century it was known that the chromosomes carry the genetic or hereditary information. Chromosomes consist of proteins and **DNA** (deoxyribonucleic acid). It is now known that the genetic material in the chromosome is the DNA. A gene is a portion of the DNA in a chromosome. In some viruses, **RNA** (ribonucleic acid) is the genetic material.

B. CHEMICAL STRUCTURE OF DNA

1. Nucleotides. DNA is a polymer with a very large molecule consisting of thousands of repeating units called **nucleotides.** Each nucleotide has three parts (see Figure 5-10):

a. A **phosphate** group.

b. A **deoxyribose** molecule, which is a sugar molecule with 5 carbon atoms.

c. A **nitrogenous base,** which may be one of four kinds: **adenine, thymine, guanine,** or **cytosine.**

2. Watson-Crick model of the DNA molecule. James Watson and Francis Crick developed a model of the DNA molecule. According to this model, the DNA molecule consists of two chains of nucleotides in a ladderlike structure (see Figure 5-10):

a. The "uprights" or sides of the ladder are made of alternating molecules of phosphate and deoxyribose (5-carbon sugar).

b. A nitrogenous base is attached to each sugar molecule. Bases attached to opposite sides of the ladder are joined together by weak chemical bonds called **hydrogen bonds.** These pairs of bases form the "rungs" of the ladder.

c. Base-pairing rule: Only two base pair combinations can form in the DNA molecule: Adenine *(A)* can join with thymine *(T)*, and guanine *(G)* can join with cytosine *(C)*. *A-T* (or *T-A*) and *G-C* (or *C-G*) are the only possible base pair rungs of the DNA ladder.

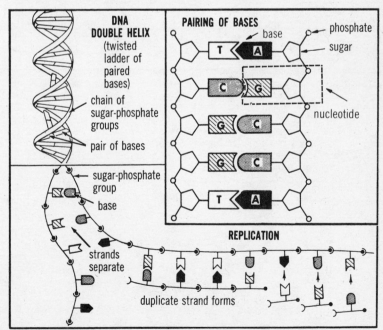

Figure 5-10. Structure and replication of DNA.

d. Double helix. The DNA ladder as a whole is twisted so as to form a structure called a **double helix.**

e. Usefulness of the Watson-Crick model. This model explains:

(a) How replication of the DNA molecule during mitosis produces exact copies of the molecule for each daughter cell, thus passing on the genetic information from generation to generation.

(b) How the DNA can act as a code that specifies the enzymes and other proteins to be made by the cell, thus controlling cellular activities.

C. DNA REPLICATION

During the processes of mitosis and meiosis, the DNA molecule replicates (forms duplicates of itself) as follows:

1. The double-stranded DNA molecule separates, or "unzips," along the weak hydrogen bonds between the base pairs.

2. Free nucleotides that are present in the nucleus attach themselves by new hydrogen bonds to the exposed bases. The only base that can be bonded to an exposed base is the same as the base that was originally joined to it. Therefore, the new double-stranded molecules that form are identical to the original molecule.

QUESTIONS

1. Which type of compound is found in every DNA nucleotide? (1) starch (2) nitrogenous base (3) lipid (4) amino acid

2. The "ribo" part in the name deoxyribonucleic acid refers to the (1) rungs of the spiral ladder (2) bonds that hold two strands together (3) sugar component of DNA (4) type of helical arrangement

3. A molecular group consisting of a sugar molecule, a phosphate group, and a nitrogen base is a (1) nucleoprotein (2) nucleic acid (3) nucleotide (4) nucleolus

4. A nucleotide of DNA could contain (1) adenine, ribose, and phosphate (2) nitrogenous base, phosphate, and glucose (3) phosphate, deoxyribose, and thymine (4) uracil, deoxyribose, and phosphate

5. A nucleotide would least likely contain the element (1) sulfur (2) carbon (3) nitrogen (4) phosphorus

6. In a DNA molecule, a base pair normally could be composed of (1) adenine and guanine (2) adenine and cytosine (3) thymine and guanine (4) guanine and cytosine

Base your answers to questions 7 through 11 on the diagram below which represents part of a double-stranded DNA molecule.

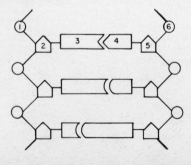

MG

7. How many nucleotides are represented in the diagram?   (1) 6
(2) 12   (3) 3   (4) 18
8. Which parts of the molecule could produce nitrogenous waste
products?   (1) 1 and 2   (2) 3 and 4   (3) 2 and 6   (4) 1 and 6
9. The element phosphorus is found in the parts of the molecule
labeled   (1) 1 and 2   (2) 3 and 4   (3) 2 and 5   (4) 1 and 6
10. When this molecule of DNA replicates, it separates between the
parts represented by   (1) 1 and 2   (2) 2 and 3   (3) 3 and 4   (4) 1 and 3
11. If number 3 represents a molecule of adenine, then number 4
represents a molecule of   (1) cytosine   (2) guanine   (3) uracil
(4) thymine

D. GENE CONTROL OF CELLULAR ACTIVITIES

A gene is a particular section of a DNA molecule. It is believed that the
base-pair sequence of the gene controls cellular activity by specifying a
protein to be made in the cytoplasm. The message of the gene and the
synthesis of the protein involve RNA as well as the DNA of the gene.

1. Structure of RNA. RNA, like DNA, is a polymer formed by a sequence of nucleotides. It differs from DNA in the following ways:

a. The RNA molecule is a **single strand,** not a double strand like
DNA.

b. The sugar molecule in RNA is **ribose,** instead of the deoxyribose
in DNA.

c. The base **uracil** *(U)* takes the place of thymine.

2. Types of RNA. There are three types of RNA present in the cell:
messenger RNA (mRNA), **transfer RNA** (tRNA), and **ribosomal RNA.**

3. Synthesis of RNA. When the cell is between divisions, the DNA in
the nucleus is stretched out into a long, thin thread. The two strands of
the DNA separate, as in replication. Free RNA nucleotides attach themselves to the exposed bases of the DNA, forming strands of RNA that are
complementary to the DNA. Each gene produces a messenger RNA
molecule. Other regions of the DNA produce transfer RNA molecules.

4. The genetic code. The sequence of bases along each molecule of
messenger RNA specifies the sequence of amino acids that make up a
specific protein chain. Each amino acid is represented by a sequence of
three bases, called a **triplet code,** or **codon.**

5. Protein synthesis. Messenger RNA molecules move from the nucleus to the cytoplasm, where they become associated with ribosomes
(which are made partly of ribosomal RNA). The coded message of the
mRNA is "read" at the ribosome and is converted to a chain of amino
acids in the following way:

a. Transfer RNA. Each molecule of tRNA, which is much shorter
than a molecule of mRNA, has a segment at one end that becomes
attached to a particular amino acid that is present in the cytoplasm. The
other end of the tRNA molecule has an **anticodon** of three bases that
matches a codon on mRNA for that particular amino acid.

b. Translation of mRNA. At the ribosome, the tRNA molecule, with
its amino acid, temporarily bonds to its complementary codon on the
mRNA molecule. The mRNA molecule then moves past the ribosome to
the next codon, and another tRNA molecule bonds to it. The two amino

EXTENDED AREA—MODERN GENETICS

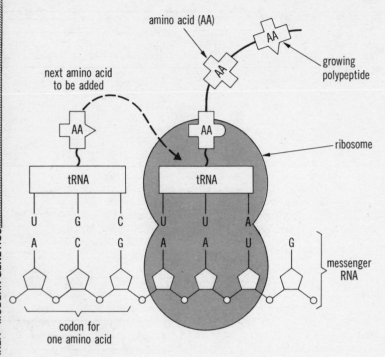

amino acid (AA)

next amino acid
to be added

growing
polypeptide

ribosome

messenger
RNA

codon for
one amino acid

Figure 5-11. RNA and the synthesis of proteins.

acids are then joined by an enzyme. The next mRNA codon is then read in the same way, and a third amino acid joins the other two. In this way, a chain of amino acids, in the order specified by the base sequence of the mRNA molecule, is formed. Each tRNA molecule is released to repeat its function as the mRNA molecule moves along past the ribosome.

6. One gene-one enzyme hypothesis. This hypothesis states that each enzyme that a cell manufactures is specified by a single gene, which is a particular sequence of DNA nucleotides. When the gene is active, it controls the production of that enzyme. A more accurate statement of the hypothesis is that each gene controls the production of one polypeptide chain, which becomes part of a particular enzyme or other protein. This is called the **one gene-one polypeptide hypothesis.**

7. DNA and the individuality of organisms. The form and function of each cell depends mainly on the enzymes and other proteins it contains. The form and function of a whole organism are the combined effects of all its cells. Since the organism's DNA is the source of the messages that determine the proteins made by the cells, the DNA determines the individuality of the organism.

QUESTIONS

1. Which is a five-carbon sugar found in an RNA molecule? (1) uracil (2) ribose (3) adenine (4) glucose

2. Which base is found in DNA but not in RNA? (1) adenine (2) cytosine (3) thymine (4) uracil

3. The sequence of nucleotides in a messenger RNA molecule is determined by the sequence of nucleotides in a (1) transfer RNA molecule (2) protein molecule (3) polysaccharide molecule (4) DNA molecule

4. In protein synthesis, the code for a particular amino acid is determined by (1) the one gene-many enzyme hypothesis (2) a sequence of three nucleotides (3) multiple alleles (4) the number of messenger RNA molecules

5. If the code for glutamic acid is ATG on the DNA molecule, this code on the transfer RNA molecule may be written as (1) ATG (2) CTG (3) AUG (4) GTA

6. To which organelles is messenger RNA attached? (1) chloroplasts (2) ribosomes (3) mitochondria (4) vacuoles

7. During protein synthesis, amino acids are picked up in the cytoplasm and positioned at the ribosomes by (1) unattached nucleotide molecules (2) polypeptide molecules (3) molecules of DNA (4) molecules of RNA

8. In protein synthesis, which sequence of bases in transfer RNA will pair with the sequence GGU found in messenger RNA? (1) CCT (2) CCA (3) AAC (4) UUA

9. Which is the correct sequence of code transfer involved in the formation of a polypeptide? (1) DNA, transfer RNA, messenger RNA (2) transfer RNA, DNA, messenger RNA (3) messenger RNA, transfer RNA, DNA (4) DNA, messenger RNA, transfer RNA

10. The position of an amino acid in a protein molecule is determined by the (1) concentration of amino acids in the cytoplasm (2) amount of ATP in the cell synthesizing the protein (3) sequence of nitrogenous bases in DNA (4) sequence of amino groups in the amino acid

11. "One-gene-one-polypeptide" is to gene action as "lock and key" is to (1) dehydration synthesis (2) enzyme specificity (3) spontaneous generation (4) the heterotroph hypothesis

E. GENE MUTATIONS

1. Definition. A **gene mutation** is any change in the base sequence of an organism's DNA.

2. Types. A gene mutation may be the result of the insertion of an extra base, the removal of a base, or the substitution of one base for another.

F. GENETIC RESEARCH

1. Cloning. The process of producing genetically identical offspring from a single cell of an organism is called **cloning.** Vegetative propagation of plants and regeneration of animals are examples of cloning that occur naturally. Clones of frogs have been produced experimentally from the nuclei of cells in the blastula stage of an embryo. By similar techniques, clones of mice have also been produced.

2. Bacterial transformation. When cultures of two strains of bacteria are mixed, portions of the DNA of one strain may enter the cells of the second strain. The bacteria of the second culture are then able to synthesize proteins that only the first strain could produce before the transfer. This process is called **bacterial transformation.**

3. Genetic engineering. By means of bacterial transformation and other techniques, it is possible to transfer genes from one organism to another, producing what is called **recombinant DNA.** The recipient organism then produces the protein specified by the transferred gene. This process, called **genetic engineering** or "gene splicing," has been used to produce strains of bacteria that can synthesize useful substances, such as insulin, growth hormone, and interferon. In the future, these techniques may make it possible to correct genetic defects in individuals.

G. POPULATION GENETICS

1. Definition. Population genetics is the study of gene frequencies, and the factors that affect them, in populations of sexually reproducing organisms.

2. A **population** consists of all the members of a particular species that inhabit a given region and interbreed within the region.

3. The **gene pool** of a population is the total of all the genes present in the population.

4. Gene frequency. The fraction of individuals of a population that possess a particular gene is called the **frequency** of that gene. It is usually stated as a percent or a decimal. For example, if 1/10 of the individuals in a population possess a certain gene (whether expressed or not), the frequency of that gene is 10% or 0.1.

5. Hardy-Weinberg Principle

a. Statement of the principle. The **Hardy-Weinberg Principle** states that under certain conditions the gene pool of a population will remain stable, that is, all gene frequencies will remain the same from generation to generation.

b. Conditions. The principle holds true only under the following conditions:

(1) The population is large.
(2) Mating within the population is random.
(3) There is no migration into or out of the population.
(4) No mutations are occurring in the population.

c. Significance of the principle. All four of the necessary conditions seldom occur in any population. As a result, the gene pool is not stable and gene frequencies change as time goes by. This leads to changes in the characteristics of the population and may result in the *evolution* of new species.

QUESTIONS

1. A base may be added to or deleted from a DNA molecule. Such changes in the base sequence of an organism's DNA are examples of (1) bacterial transformations (2) cytoplasmic inheritance (3) gene mutations (4) multiple alleles

2. Which process has taken place when the base sequence of a DNA molecule is altered? (1) replication (2) blending (3) segregation (4) mutation

3. The gene pool includes the sum total of all heritable genes for all traits within a given (1) species (2) niche (3) population (4) biome

4. According to the Hardy-Weinberg principle, in sexually reproducing populations the gene pool will remain stable if the population is large, if mating is random, and if (1) mutations do not occur (2) recessive characteristics are present in greater amount than dominant characteristics (3) the population migrates as environment changes (4) the species is hybrid for most traits

5. The Hardy-Weinberg principle is applicable only when (1) dealing with large populations (2) dealing with migratory species (3) there is a high rate of mutation (4) mating is nonrandom

6. Which will usually have least effect on the frequency of a trait in the human population? (1) migration of a population into a new area similar to the old environment (2) mutation and selection of alleles (3) migration of a population into an area already occupied by another population of the same species (4) migration of a population to a new environment followed by selection of genes with respect to the new environment

Base your answers to questions 7 through 9 on the graph below which shows the distribution of fur color in a rabbit population. The only alleles for fur color that exist in this population are those for white fur and brown fur.

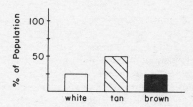

7. Which conclusion could best be made from the graph and the information given? (1) The gene for white fur is dominant. (2) The gene for brown fur is dominant. (3) The gene for tan fur is dominant. (4) Neither the gene for white fur nor the gene for brown fur is dominant.

8. What is the percentage of the two alleles for fur color in the rabbit population? (1) 20% white, 80% brown (2) 25% white, 75% brown (3) 50% white, 50% brown (4) 70% white, 30% brown

9. The distribution of fur color shown by the graph would most likely remain the same in the future for this population of rabbits if (1) the mating continued to be random (2) a beneficial mutation for fur color occurred (3) part of the population migrated (4) the population of rabbits were small

UNIT VI　EVOLUTION AND DIVERSITY

VI-1. EVOLUTION THEORY

A. BASIC PRINCIPLES. Evolution is any process of change through time. The **theory of organic evolution** proposes that existing forms of life have evolved from earlier forms over a long period of time. The diversity of living things as well as their unity may be the result of evolution.

B. SUPPORTING OBSERVATIONS. There are several different types of observations that support the theory of organic evolution as an explanation for the similarities and the differences among life forms, or species.

1. Geologic record. By means of radioactive dating, the ages of rock formations in many places on earth have been determined. The oldest rocks appear to be at least 4.5 billion years old. It is assumed that the earth itself is older than the oldest rocks. A timetable of the earth's geologic history, such as mountain building and ocean formation, has been constructed from the radioactive dating of rocks and minerals in the earth's crust. This geologic record combined with the fossil record (see below) has produced an apparent sequence of life forms from most simple to most complex during the history of the earth.

2. Fossil record

　a. A **fossil** is any remains or trace of a once-living organism.

　b. Formation of fossils

　　(1) Preservation of whole organisms. An organism may be preserved and protected against decay by being trapped in amber, frozen in ice, or buried in tar.

　　(2) Preservation of hard parts, such as shells and bones. In some cases the soft parts of an animal have decayed away, but the bones or shells have been preserved.

　　(3) Petrifaction. In some cases, the materials of a dead organism may be gradually washed away and replaced by minerals from the water. The result is a **petrified** replica of the structure of the organism in stone.

　　(4) Sedimentation. Most fossils are formed at the bottom of bodies of water in which sediments gradually settle and cover the bodies of dead organisms. The sediments harden in time and change to sedimentary rock. The buried organism may leave a trace in the form of an **imprint,** a **mold,** or a **cast** of its body.

　　(5) Other traces. Some animals, such as dinosaurs, have left footprints in mud, which later hardened to form fossils. Worms and other burrowing animals have left fossils in the form of tubes and tunnels in rock that hardened after the animals had burrowed through the materials.

　c. Fossil sequences. Generally, the upper layers of sedimentary rocks are assumed to have been laid down over the lower layers. Therefore, the upper layers are younger than the lower layers. Fossils found in the upper layers must therefore be younger than fossils found in deeper layers, if the layers have not been disturbed by movements of the earth's surface. Upper, younger layers usually contain fossils of more complex organisms than the lower, older layers. This indicates a gradual change from simpler organisms to more complex ones in the course of time. Similarities between different organisms found in upper and lower layers indicate a possible hereditary relationship between the organisms.

3. Comparative anatomy. A comparison of the detailed structure of parts of different organisms often shows an unexpected similarity. For example, the forelegs of frogs and horses, the arms of humans, the flippers of whales, and the wings of bats and birds all have the same number and arrangements of bones, even though these structures have different outward forms and functions. These are called **homologous structures.** They indicate that these vertebrates evolved from a common ancestor.

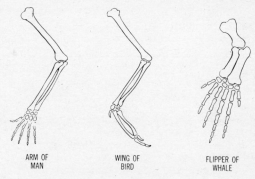

ARM OF MAN WING OF BIRD FLIPPER OF WHALE

Figure 6-1. Homologous structures.

4. Comparative cytology. Cell organelles, such as the cell membrane, ribosomes, and mitochondria, are similar in organisms of all kinds.

5. Comparative embryology. The development of embryos of organisms that are quite different in the mature form often shows a similar early pattern and similar structures in the early stages. All vertebrate embryos, for example, pass through stages that are very similar in structure and organization before differentiating into the special structures of the species. This is believed to be a carryover from the development pattern of a common ancestor.

6. Comparative biochemistry. The composition and structure of the biochemical compounds in different species can be compared. It is found that in species that seem to be closely related by other evidence, these compounds are also very similar in detail. For example, the closer the relationship between two species, the closer the similarity of the amino acid sequences in their proteins, such as hemoglobin and insulin. Another example is the similarity in structure of the hemoglobin molecules of animals and the chlorophyll molecules of plants.

QUESTIONS

1. A clear leaf print in a rock indicates that the rock is most probably (1) igneous (2) sedimentary (3) metamorphic (4) volcanic

2. In petrified fossils, the tissues of the organism (1) become amber (2) become marble (3) have been replaced by minerals (4) have been sealed in tar

3. The diagram at the right represents undisturbed layers of sedimentary rock. One of the layers contains fossils of species A and another layer contains fossils of species B as indicated. Based on the diagram, it is most probable that (1) species A was more abundant than species B (2) species A was smaller in size than species B (3) species B existed before species A (4) species B descended from species A

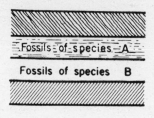

4. Support for the theory of evolution based on similarities in the structure of certain organisms is obtained from the study of (1) comparative biochemistry (2) comparative geography (3) comparative anatomy (4) comparative physiology

5. Biology classes often study plants and plantlike organisms in the following order: algae, fungi, mosses, ferns, gymnosperms. Which is the best reason for this order of study? (1) The order arranges the organisms in a series from smaller to larger forms. (2) It is logical to study organisms of decreasing complexity, from multicellular to unicellular. (3) It is easier to teach by beginning with the familiar before discussing less familiar organisms. (4) Fossil evidences indicate that this is the order in which the organisms appeared and developed.

6. The characteristic of 4 toes in the forefoot of the earliest known fossil horse and the single toe of the modern horse is an example of (1) variation (2) acquired characteristics (3) homologous structures (4) adaptation

7. Sheep possess hormones that can help humans to metabolize sugars. No hormones have been found in the common housefly that have the same effect on humans. From this, one may conclude that (1) common houseflies cannot metabolize sugars (2) sheep and humans had a common ancestor (3) sheep and humans have identical enzymes (4) sheep and humans appeared on the earth at the same time

8. Which is the best evidence to support the theory concerning the order of evolutionary development of vertebrates? (1) All vertebrates have capillaries connecting the veins and arteries. (2) The earliest fish fossils are over a million years old. (3) There is a sequence of vertebrate fossils in undisturbed sedimentary rock. (4) All vertebrates have four-chambered hearts.

9. Which are examples of homologous structures? (1) forelegs of a frog and arms of a human (2) flipper of a whale and tail of a monkey (3) wings of a bat and cilia of Paramecium (4) pseudopodia of Ameba and gills of a shark

10. The bony structure of a human's arm and hand most closely resembles the (1) wing of a grasshopper (2) wing of a butterfly (3) wing of a bat (4) fin of a shark

C. HISTORICAL DEVELOPMENT. Several theories have been proposed in the past to account for the diversity of species as well as their similarities.

1. Lamarck. Lamarck's theory of evolution proposed that changes in species occurred basically as the result of a striving of organisms for improvement. The main ideas of this theory were:

a. Use and disuse. New organs appear in a species as a result of a need for them, and they increase in size or effectiveness through repeated use. Organs that are not needed decrease in size or strength as the result of disuse.

b. Transmission of acquired characteristics. A trait acquired during the lifetime of an individual can be transmitted to its offspring. This includes improvements or strengthening of existing traits.

c. Evolution. Evolution of new species is the result of the accumulation of acquired characteristics transmitted through many generations.

2. Weismann. Weismann maintained that acquired characteristics cannot be inherited. In one of his experiments, he cut off the tails of mice in many successive generations. No change in the length of tails in offspring was observed.

3. Darwin. Darwin proposed that evolution occurred as the result of **natural selection,** a process resembling the artificial selection practiced by breeders of plants and animals. The main ideas of Darwin's theory are:

a. Overproduction. Within a population, more offspring are produced in each generation than can survive, because of limitations of living space and food supply.

b. Competition. The individuals of each generation compete for the available food and for opportunities to mate and reproduce.

c. Variation. Within each generation, some individuals are better fitted to survive than others, because of variations in characteristics.

d. Survival of the fittest. Those individuals better fitted to survive are more likely to live long enough to reproduce.

e. Transmission of favorable variations. The offspring of the fittest individuals will inherit the favorable variations that enabled their parents to survive and reproduce.

f. Evolution of species. The accumulation of favorable variations (adaptations) in this way will gradually lead to the appearance of new species better adapted to their environment.

4. DeVries. One weakness of Darwin's theory was that it did not explain how variations arose. DeVries discovered mutations and proposed that mutations were the source of new traits that permitted evolution to occur.

QUESTIONS

1. In his theory of evolution, Lamarck assumed that (1) useful characteristics which are acquired are inherited (2) the diversity of organisms depends upon genetic mutations (3) variations are produced by gene recombinations (4) new organs arise as a result of common ancestry

2. Which scientist most strongly supported the idea that evolutionary changes occurred because there was a need for them?   (1) De Vries   (2) Mendel   (3) Lamarck   (4) Darwin

3. The theory of evolution, based on the principle of natural selection, was proposed by   (1) Mendel   (2) Darwin   (3) Watson   (4) Lamarck

4. Which statement describes a part of Darwin's theory of evolution?   (1) Variation is not essential to evolution.   (2) Too few offspring are produced in any population.   (3) Organisms with favorable adaptations tend to survive.   (4) Unfavorable mutations cause an increase in populations.

5. Darwin's theory of evolution is based on the concept of   (1) use and disuse   (2) mutations   (3) natural selection   (4) hybridization

6. Charles Darwin believed the basic forces in evolution to be   (1) selection and mutation   (2) selection, use, and disuse   (3) selection and variation   (4) selection and fossil formation

7. With which statement would Darwin most likely have agreed?   (1) Competition among individuals of a species causes heritable variations.   (2) Organisms best adapted to a particular environment are the most likely to reproduce.   (3) Survival of any species is proportional to the inheritance of acquired characteristics.   (4) Variations are caused by natural selection.

8. The modern horse has fewer toes than its ancestors. It is generally believed that such changes are governed by   (1) natural selection   (2) chromosomal deletions   (3) reduction division   (4) use and disuse

9. If a species of insect lacks the variations needed to adapt to a changing environment, it will most likely   (1) acquire them through evolution   (2) become extinct   (3) evolve into a lower form   (4) evolve into a higher form

10. To which statement is De Vries' theory of mutations most directly applicable?   (1) The cactus plant, when introduced into Australia, spread very rapidly.   (2) Staphylococci that are resistant to penicillin have been discovered.   (3) Cells normally duplicate themselves exactly.   (4) The seeds of a wind-twisted pine grew into tall, straight trees in the sheltered valley.

D. MODERN THEORY OF EVOLUTION. The modern theory of evolution accepts Darwin's ideas of natural selection and uses present knowledge of genetics to account for variation.

1. Sources of variation. Random mutations that are occurring at regular rates in all populations are the main source of variation. Sexual reproduction produces and maintains additional variation by segregation and recombination of genes.

2. Natural selection

a. In an unchanging environment, traits that increase the chance of survival and reproduction in a given environment tend to be passed on and increase in frequency within a population. Traits that are unfavorable in the given environment tend to diminish in frequency.

b. In a changing environment, genes that have high survival value in the new conditions will tend to be selected and will increase in frequency. Genes that had high survival value in the former conditions, but have lower value in the new conditions, will be less likely to be transmitted. Their frequency in the gene pool will decrease.

c. Isolation. Two populations of the same species may become separated by a geographical **barrier,** such as a body of water or a mountain range. This is called **geographical isolation.** The two populations do not interbreed because of their isolation from each other. The gene pools of the two populations may then become different (diverge) as the result of different selective factors in the environment, different mutations that appear, or small differences in gene frequencies to begin with. The isolated populations may diverge so much that they lose the ability to interbreed successfully even if brought together. They have now developed **reproductive isolation** and are considered to be different species. Examples are Darwin's finches on the Galapagos islands. These finches are apparently derived from a mainland species, but they have evolved into separate species by geographic isolation on the various islands.

d. Large-scale geographic isolation. There is evidence that the continents were once a single land mass and then separated and drifted apart. Large groups of organisms on the different continents evolved along different lines because of this large-scale isolation. Examples are the marsupials of Australia. On other continents, placental mammals developed and displaced the marsupials by natural selection. The marsupials of Australia survived and evolved independently because they had no competition from placental mammals.

E. CHANGES IN SPECIES. The fossil record shows that over time, species have changed and new species have appeared. Changes in existing species have also been observed to occur. Examples include the appearance of new strains of bacteria **resistant** to antibiotics, such as the resistance of the gonorrhea organism to penicillin; insect variants resistant to insecticides, such as resistant roaches, mosquitoes, and flies; and **industrial melanism,** the appearance of dark-colored insects that blend against backgrounds darkened by soot. These changes are not *caused* by the new environmental factor; it merely acts as a selecting agent.

F. RATE OF CHANGE. Scientists are not agreed at this time about the rate at which evolutionary change has occurred in the past.

1. Gradualism. Some scientists believe that evolution occurs gradually, slowly, and continuously.

2. Punctuated equilibrium. Other scientists suggest that species tend to remain the same for long periods of time (many millions of years), with sudden, relatively brief intervals during which large and rapid changes produce many new species.

QUESTIONS

1. It is believed that evolution has occurred at a faster rate since the introduction of sexual reproduction. This belief is based on the fact that sexual reproduction (1) increases the chances for variations (2) occurs more rapidly than asexual reproduction (3) allows members of two different species to mate with each other, thereby producing entirely new species (4) involves the reproduction of only the fittest organisms

2. Fossil evidence indicates that many species have existed for only comparatively brief periods of time and have then become extinct. Which statement best explains the reason for their short existence? (1) These organisms lacked the energy to produce mutations.   (2) Humans modify plant and animal species through the knowledge of genetics.   (3) These organisms lacked genotypic variations having adaptive value.   (4) Within a species there is an increasing complexity of homologous structures that reduce the chance of survival.

3. Mutations provide a basis for   (1) abiogenesis   (2) reproduction   (3) formation of aggregates   (4) evolution

4. Modern biologists would not agree with Lamarck because they do not accept the concept of   (1) survival of the fittest   (2) overproduction of offspring   (3) mutation   (4) evolution of organs because of need

5. In addition to the basic ideas of Darwin, modern evolutionary theory includes the concept that   (1) gene recombinations result in variation   (2) all acquired characteristics are inherited   (3) life originally came from outer space   (4) life on Earth began on land

6. Within seven years after corn rootworm had first been controlled with certain insecticides, nearly all the corn rootworm descendants exhibited immunity to the usual doses of these insecticides. The most likely explanation of such immunity is that the insecticides   (1) cause the corn rootworm to be more resistant   (2) cause the corn rootworm to be less resistant   (3) function as factors of natural selection among random mutations   (4) isolate the corn rootworm from the effects of disease

VI-2. THE ORIGIN OF LIFE—HETEROTROPH HYPOTHESIS

According to current geologic theory, the earth formed by the condensation and solidification of a mass of gas in space. Life could not have been present when the earth first formed. It must have appeared later. Most scientists believe that life arose by natural processes from nonliving materials on the primitive earth and that these processes can be understood in terms of known principles of chemistry and physics. Any theory of the origin of life must start with certain assumptions about the conditions on the primitive earth. The theory is then constructed by logical deductions from those assumptions. One widely held theory is called the **heterotroph hypothesis.** According to this hypothesis, the first organisms were heterotrophs. They could not synthesize organic materials, but they lived, grew, and multiplied by using organic compounds made in the environment by natural phenomena.

A. PRIMITIVE CONDITIONS. The heterotroph hypothesis makes the following assumptions about conditions on the primitive earth.

1. Raw materials. The original atmosphere of the earth had no free oxygen. Its gases were free hydrogen and compounds of hydrogen, including ammonia (NH_3) and methane (CH_4). There was also an abundance of water (H_2O), which was present in the atmosphere as water vapor, and which condensed and fell as rain. The rain carried dissolved gases from the atmosphere into the oceans. Rain that fell on land areas dissolved minerals from the rocks and carried them into rivers and then into the oceans.

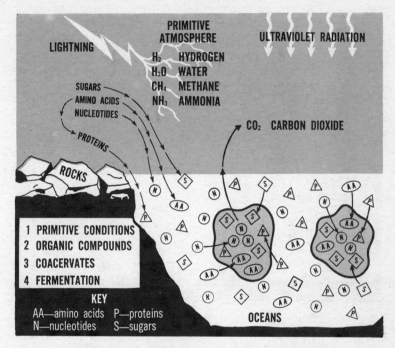

Figure 6-2. The heterotroph hypothesis (early stages).

2. Temperature. The earth, having just cooled from a liquid state, was much hotter than it is now. The oceans could be thought of as a "hot, thin soup."

3. Other energy sources. Besides the earth's heat, other sources of energy in the environment included lightning (electrical energy), solar radiation (light, ultraviolet rays, and x rays), and radioactivity in the rocks of the earth's crust.

B. SYNTHESIS REACTIONS. Energy from the environment acted to synthesize complex, high-energy organic molecules from the inorganic raw materials in the "hot, thin soup" of the oceans. These compounds included simple sugars, amino acids, and proteins. Such compounds have been produced in laboratory experiments in which the assumed primitive conditions have been simulated.

C. AGGREGATES OF ORGANIC MOLECULES. Certain organic molecules tended to cluster together and form aggregates separated from the surrounding liquid medium by a kind of membrane. These aggregates grew by absorbing new molecules from the surrounding waters.

D. REPRODUCTION. When some of the aggregates grew too large to absorb enough nutrients through their surface, they divided, or reproduced. Some of them developed organized structures that were retained

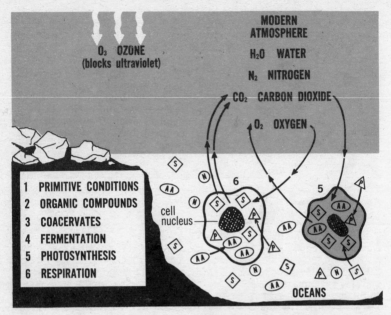

Figure 6-3. The heterotroph hypothesis (later stages).

and distributed equally when they reproduced. These aggregates can be considered to have been the first living organisms.

E. ANAEROBIC RESPIRATION. Some of these heterotrophic organisms probably developed a form of energy release similar to anaerobic respiration or fermentation. Carbon dioxide was a product of these reactions, and carbon dioxide gradually accumulated in the oceans and in the atmosphere.

F. DEVELOPMENT OF AUTOTROPHS. Eventually some of the organisms developed processes for using energy and carbon dioxide to synthesize their own organic nutrients. These organisms thus became the first autotrophs.

G. AEROBIC RESPIRATION. One of the products of autotrophic nutrition was free oxygen. As oxygen accumulated in the environment, organisms developed mechanisms for using the more efficient processes of aerobic respiration to release energy. Thus the pattern was set for the various types of nutrition among living forms today: autotrophs using either anaerobic or aerobic respiration, and heterotrophs using either anaerobic or aerobic respiration.

H. SUMMARY. The sequence of development of types of nutrition, according to the heterotroph hypothesis, was:

HETEROTROPHS → anaerobic respiration → CO_2 given off →

AUTOTROPHS → O_2 given off → aerobic respiration

QUESTIONS

1. According to the heterotroph hypothesis, the first molecules of sugar and amino acids in the primitive oceans were formed by (1) respiration (2) fermentation (3) hydrolysis (4) random synthesis

2. A current theory concerning the origin of life assumes that the earth's primitive atmosphere contained (1) hydrogen, ammonia, and methane (2) ammonia, oxygen, and methane (3) carbon dioxide, nitrogen, and methane (4) oxygen, nitrogen, and carbon dioxide

3. The heterotroph hypothesis suggests that (1) heterotrophic nutrition is the basis of all life (2) heterotrophs developed from previously existing autotrophs (3) living organisms arose as a result of photosynthesis (4) organic molecules developed before there were living organisms

4. According to the heterotroph hypothesis, the first living organisms probably were able to obtain energy directly from (1) methane in the atmosphere (2) hydrogen in the atmosphere (3) organic molecules in water (4) oxygen dissolved in water

Questions 5 and 6 are based on the heterotroph hypothesis.

5. According to this hypothesis, the first organisms could not have carried out photosynthesis because of the absence of atmospheric (1) water vapor (2) oxygen (3) nitrogen (4) carbon dioxide

6. This hypothesis assumes that energy from lightning was used directly to (1) add nitrogen to the early atmosphere (2) add carbon dioxide to the early atmosphere (3) enable heterotrophs to manufacture food (4) synthesize organic molecules

7. The evolution of photosynthetic forms of life made possible the metabolic process of (1) aerobic respiration (2) alcoholic fermentation (3) cellular synthesis (4) molecular dissociation

8. In the early history of the earth, as the number of green plants increased, which changes probably occurred in the atmosphere? (1) The amounts of oxygen and carbon dioxide increased. (2) The amounts of oxygen and carbon dioxide decreased. (3) The amount of oxygen increased and the amount of carbon dioxide decreased. (4) The amount of carbon dioxide increased and the amount of oxygen decreased.

UNIT VII   PLANTS AND ANIMALS IN THEIR ENVIRONMENT

VII-1. ECOLOGICAL ORGANIZATION

A. ECOLOGY. Ecology is the study of the interactions of plants and animals and their interrelationships with the physical environment. A basic concept of ecology is that no organism can be studied by itself, but only in relation to other organisms and the environment.

B. POPULATIONS. All members of a species living in a given area make up a **population.** A **species** is a group of organisms that are capable of interbreeding among themselves and producing fertile offspring under natural conditions. (Fertile offspring are individuals capable of reproduction.) For example, all the gray squirrels living in a certain forest make up the population of gray squirrels in that forest. All the dandelions growing in a field are the population of dandelions in that field.

C. COMMUNITIES. All the plant and animal populations of a given area make up a **community.**

D. ECOSYSTEMS
  1. Definition. In any community the living organisms interact with each other and with their nonliving, or physical, environment. This self-contained, interdependent system of living and nonliving things is called an **ecosystem.**
  2. Some characteristics of an ecosystem. An ecosystem must have a constant source of energy, populations of organisms able to store this energy in the form of organic compounds, a continuous cycling of materials between populations and their environment, and a flow of energy from one population to another.
  3. Examples of ecosystems. A forest or wilderness area uninhabited by humans is an example of a natural ecosystem. A farm community that produces all the food it needs, and makes all the other things it needs from materials found within the community, is an example of an ecosystem involving humans. A balanced aquarium is an artificial model of an ecosystem.
  4. Energy for ecosystems. The source of energy for almost all ecosystems is sunlight. A few ecosystems have recently been found on the ocean floors in which the source of energy is heat from the earth's interior.

E. THE BIOSPHERE. The portion of the earth in which life exists is called the **biosphere.** It includes the oceans, all the land areas and their soil, and the lower part of the atmosphere. The biosphere includes all the ecosystems of the earth.

QUESTIONS

1. The study of ecology would be of greatest importance to a person who wished to work in the field of (1) genetics (2) medicine (3) conservation (4) biochemistry

2. All of the members of a given species living in a given area constitute (1) a community (2) a biome (3) an ecosystem (4) a population

3. All the plants, animals, and protists living in a forest make up a (1) population (2) community (3) species (4) phylum

4. The living organisms and their nonliving environment functioning together are known as (1) a community (2) a population (3) an ecosystem (4) a biome

5. Which group of terms is arranged in the correct order from simple to complex? (1) biosphere, ecosystem, organism, community, population (2) organism, population, community, ecosystem, biosphere (3) population, organism, community, ecosystem, biosphere (4) organism, population, community, biosphere, ecosystem

6. A balanced aquarium is best described as (1) a biome (2) a biosphere (3) an ecosystem (4) a community

VII-2. CHARACTERISTICS OF ECOSYSTEMS

A. ABIOTIC ENVIRONMENT

1. Definition. The **abiotic environment** is the physical, or nonliving, part of the environment.

2. Abiotic factors in the environment. The ability of an organism to live and reproduce depends on certain physical and chemical (abiotic) factors in its environment. Some of these abiotic factors are: intensity of light; temperature range; amount of moisture; type of soil or rock for land organisms; availability of minerals and other inorganic substances; supply of gases, such as oxygen, carbon dioxide, and nitrogen.

3. Limiting factors. In any particular environment, each of the abiotic factors varies over a certain range. This range sets limits on the types and numbers of organisms that can live in that environment. For example, in a desert, the small amount of moisture available is a limiting factor that determines which plants and animals can survive there. Other examples of limiting factors are the low temperatures of regions at high latitudes or altitudes; the salt concentration in the oceans and the seashore regions; the low concentration of dissolved oxygen in warm waters.

B. BIOTIC ENVIRONMENT. The **biotic environment** is the living part of the environment. It includes all the interacting populations of living things. The living things of an ecosystem act as biotic factors in the environment. The biotic factors affect both the living and nonliving parts of the environment. They include not only the living organisms, but their parts, interactions, and waste products. Examples of effects of biotic factors in an environment are:

1. Autotrophs produce organic nutrients containing stored chemical energy.

2. Bacteria of decay (decomposers) return materials to the physical environment for reuse.

3. The consuming of one organism by another transfers energy within the ecosystem.

4. The branches and leaves of large trees limit the kinds of smaller plants that can live in the shade they produce.

5. Flowers are pollinated by the activities of insects.

C. NUTRITIONAL RELATIONSHIPS. Nutritional relationships are the interactions in an ecosystem that provide each organism with the nutrients it needs for maintenance, growth, and reproduction.

1. Autotrophic nutrition. In every ecosystem there are certain organisms that can synthesize their own food from inorganic materials and a source of energy from outside the system.

2. Heterotrophic nutrition. All other organisms of an ecosystem depend upon other organisms for their food. There are three types of food dependency:

a. Saprophytes use dead organic matter as a source of food. Most saprophytes are **decomposers**—they break down the organic remains of organisms and make them available as inorganic products to be reused by the autotrophs. The decomposers include the **bacteria of decay** and certain molds and other fungi. A few plants are also saprophytes, for example, Indian pipe, a flowering plant without chlorophyll and incapable of photosynthesis.

b. Herbivores are animals that eat plants. Examples are cattle, horses, sheep, deer, rabbits, and snails.

c. Carnivores are animals that eat other animals. They include:

(1) **Predators,** which kill and eat other living animals. Examples: lions, hawks, sharks, mantises.

(2) **Scavengers,** which eat dead organisms that they have not killed themselves. Examples: vultures, hyenas, crabs.

d. Omnivores are animals that eat both animals and plants. Examples: humans, bears, wood turtles, ants.

3. Symbiotic relationships. A relationship in which two organisms live together in a close nutritional relationship is called **symbiosis.** A symbiotic relationship may or may not be beneficial to both organisms. Some symbiotic relationships appear to be temporary. Some are not fully understood. Types of symbiosis are:

a. In **commensalism,** one organism obtains a benefit from the relationship and the other is not affected (represented as +, 0). Examples are remora and shark; barnacle and whale; orchids and large tropical trees. In each case the first organism benefits from the environment provided by the other, but has no effect on the other.

b. In **mutualism,** both organisms benefit (+, +). Examples are:

(1) In a **lichen** (a combination of an alga and a fungus), the alga provides food for both by photosynthesis, and the fungus provides moisture, minerals, and anchorage.

(2) Nitrogen-fixing bacteria in root nodules of legumes provide nitrates for the plant, while the plant provides glucose as food for the bacteria.

(3) Protozoa in the digestive tract of termites are able to digest wood eaten by the termites. The end products of this digestion are used by the termites, while the termites provide food for the protozoa.

c. In **parasitism,** the parasite benefits at the expense of the host (+, −). Examples are:

(1) *Athlete's foot fungus and humans:* The fungus obtains nutrients from the human skin, but causes itchy scales and swellings.

(2) *Tapeworm and certain animals:* The tapeworm inhabits the digestive tract, absorbing digested nutrients and depriving the host of their benefit.

(3) *Dodder or mistletoe on trees:* The parasitic plant sends its roots into the stems of the host plant and absorbs water, minerals, and other nutrients from the host.

QUESTIONS

1. Which abiotic factor might be an important part of a grassy field environment?   (1) daily and seasonal temperature changes   (2) the microorganism population   (3) species competition   (4) the number of food chains

2. According to population scientists, one of the factors responsible for limiting populations is the   (1) availability of food   (2) daily variation of environmental temperature   (3) time required for ecological succession   (4) lifespan of the members of the population

3. A characteristic of an autotrophic nutritional relationship is the conversion of   (1) radiant energy into chemical energy   (2) free nitrogen into nitrates   (3) rock into soil   (4) plant protein into animal protein

4. The fact that most bacteria are saprophytes means that they live by   (1) feeding on other living things   (2) feeding on dead organic matter   (3) making food by photosynthesis   (4) changing carbon dioxide to food

5. Plant-eating animals such as cows are known as   (1) saprophytes   (2) herbivores   (3) carnivores   (4) omnivores

6. On the highway, one often sees crows feeding on dead animals. As a result of this nutritional pattern, crows may be classified as   (1) predators   (2) herbivores   (3) producers   (4) scavengers

7. Animals that ingest both plants and animals are known as   (1) omnivores   (2) carnivores   (3) herbivores   (4) saprophytes

8. Which pair of terms would most likely apply to the same organism?   (1) heterotroph, herbivore   (2) heterotroph, autotroph   (3) autotroph, parasite   (4) producer, predator

Base your answers to questions 9 and 10 on the paragraph below.

A tree in a forest dies and falls to the forest floor. Mosses, algae, molds, termites, microorganisms, worms, spiders, and mice are some of the organisms living on the decaying log.

9. All of the living organisms on the log make up a   (1) substratum   (2) community   (3) population   (4) material cycle

10. What type of organisms derive their energy most directly from the log?   (1) bacterial viruses   (2) mosses   (3) algae   (4) decomposing bacteria

11. The symbiotic relationship between two organisms in which one organism is benefited and the other is unaffected is known as   (1) mutualism   (2) commensalism   (3) parasitism   (4) saprophytism

12. If bacteria in the digestive tract perform a function useful to the host, the relationship would be known as (1) parasitism (2) phototropism (3) mutualism (4) saprophytism

13. Barnacles often attach themselves to whales and receive free transportation to many areas of the ocean. This relationship is an example of (1) parasitism (2) mutualism (3) commensalism (4) competition

14. A type of nutritional relationship in which both symbionts benefit from the association is (1) commensalism (2) mutualism (3) parasitism (4) saprophytism

15. The relationship between certain termites and protozoans that inhabit their digestive tracts benefits both organisms. This is an example of (1) parasitism (2) saprophytism (3) mutualism (4) commensalism

16. Some bacteria which live in the large intestine of humans produce B-complex vitamins which are useful to the human. This relationship between the bacteria and humans is an example of (1) parasitism (2) mutualism (3) commensalism (4) saprophytism

17. The remora fish probably has no effect on the shark to which it attaches itself, but the remora benefits in several ways. Which type of relationship is this? (1) commensalism (2) mutualism (3) predation (4) parasitism

18. Some seed plants, such as dodder, lack chlorophyll and have leaves that are tiny scalelike structures. These plants most likely derive their nourishment by (1) insect-eating (2) dehydration (3) photosynthesis (4) parasitism

19. The four terms below are used to identify various nutritional relationships. Which term includes all the others? (1) parasitism (2) commensalism (3) symbiosis (4) mutualism

D. ENERGY FLOW. All organisms need energy for their life activities. This energy is obtained from their food. The consumption of food is thus a transfer of energy. The energy pathways through an ecosystem from one organism to another are represented by food chains and food webs.

1. Food chains. A **food chain** starts with a green plant or other autotroph that converts the radiant energy of sunlight into the chemical energy of organic compounds (food). This energy is then passed along through a series of animals, each of which eats the organism before it in the chain and is eaten by the animal after it. This sequence of organisms forms a food chain. An example is:

grass *eaten by* grasshopper *eaten by* frog *eaten by* hawk

2. Food webs. Most animals eat more than one kind of plant or animal and may be eaten, in turn, by more than one kind of animal. Therefore, the food relationships and energy flow in any natural ecosystem are more complex than the simple food chain. There are many interactions and interconnections among the food chains of a community. These interactions are described as a **food web.** In every food web there are several levels of organisms.

a. Producers. Food for a community starts as organic compounds synthesized by green plants or other autotrophs. The autotrophs in any community are called the **producers.**

b. Consumers. Organisms that feed directly upon green plants are called **primary,** or **first-level, consumers.** The primary consumers are **herbivores.** Animals that eat primary consumers are called **secondary,** or **second-level, consumers.** In most food webs there are higher-level consumers, such as third-level predators that eat second-level consumers, and fourth-level consumers that eat third-level consumers. All animals of the second level or higher are **carnivores** (meat-eaters). Food relationships in a food web are complex and may skip over a level. For example, some second-level consumers eat plants and first-level consumers. They are **omnivores** (eaters of both plants and animals).

c. Decomposers. The organic wastes and the remains of dead organisms are broken down to simpler substances by organisms called **decomposers.** The decomposers use the energy stored in the organic materials and produce simple compounds that are returned to the environment. These can then be reused by other organisms in the community. Most decomposers are **bacteria of decay.**

3. Pyramid of energy. In a food web, only a small part of the energy at any level is transferred to the next higher level in usable form. There is much more energy at the producer level than at the primary consumer level, and much more energy at the primary level than at the secondary level. This reduction in usable energy at each feeding level of an ecosystem can be represented as a **pyramid of energy.** The energy that is not transferred is converted to heat and lost by radiation from the earth. Thus an ecosystem needs a constant supply of energy to maintain itself.

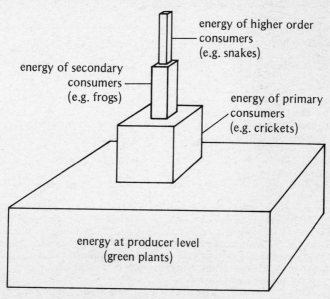

Figure 7-1. The pyramid of energy in an ecosystem.

4. Pyramid of biomass. The amount of living tissue that can be supported at each feeding level depends on the amount of energy available at that level. Therefore, the total mass of the living organisms (the **biomass**) at each level is much less than the mass at lower levels. In any community, the biomass of the herbivores is much less than the biomass of the producers, and the biomass of the carnivores is much less than the biomass of the herbivores. These relationships can be represented by a **pyramid of biomass.** The pyramid of biomass explains the scarcity and high cost of meat and animal products as compared with vegetable foods in many human societies.

QUESTIONS

1. What is the original source of all energy in an ecosystem? (1) absorbed sunlight (2) wind velocity (3) temperature change (4) organic growth

2. In a food chain consisting of the corn plant→mice→hawks, the principal function of the corn is to (1) capture energy from the environment (2) provide material for organic decay (3) furnish hiding places for the mice (4) release energy from the soil

3. The flow of energy in an ecosystem is represented by
(1) seeds→sparrows→hawks→bacteria
(2) sparrows→bacteria→hawks→seeds
(3) hawks→seeds→bacteria→sparrows
(4) sparrows→seeds→hawks→bacteria

4. All food chains begin with a (1) dependent organism (2) saprophytic plant (3) photosynthetic plant (4) herbivorous animal

5. Practically all species of organisms may be consumed by more than one other species. This situation is known as (1) a food web (2) a food cycle (3) an autotrophic response (4) a heterotrophic response

6. Food webs are an example of one type of (1) environment (2) succession (3) interdependence (4) habitat

7. The best description of a primary consumer is that it (1) captures light energy to make food (2) utilizes carbohydrates which it ingests (3) is generally a food source for producers (4) changes inorganic compounds to carbohydrates

8. In a food web, herbivores are known as (1) primary consumers (2) secondary consumers (3) producers (4) decomposers

9. In a community composed of deer, trees, grass, and mountain lions, the mountain lions would be classified as (1) decomposers (2) producers (3) first level consumers (4) second level consumers

10. Which must be present in an ecosystem if the ecosystem is to be maintained? (1) producers and carnivores (2) producers and decomposers (3) carnivores and decomposers (4) herbivores and carnivores

11. A consumer-producer relationship is best illustrated by (1) foxes eating mice (2) leaves growing on trees (3) rabbits eating clover (4) tapeworms living in foxes

12. Organisms that convert complex compounds into simple compounds that are then returned to their environment for use by other organisms are best classified as (1) consumers (2) producers (3) decomposers (4) autotrophs

13. Which sequence illustrates a generalized food chain in a natural community?
(1) autotroph→herbivore→secondary consumer
(2) autotroph→herbivore→autotroph
(3) heterotroph→herbivore→secondary consumer
(4) secondary consumer→autotroph→carnivore

Base your answers to questions 14 and 15 on the diagram below and on your knowledge of biology. The diagram illustrates the relationships between the organisms in a certain pond.

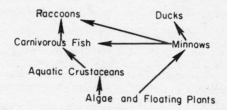

14. In addition to sunlight, another factor needed to make this a self-sustaining ecosystem would be the presence of (1) producers (2) primary consumers (3) decomposers (4) higher order consumers
15. In this pond community, which organisms are secondary consumers? (1) aquatic crustaceans and raccoons (2) carnivorous fish and aquatic crustaceans (3) ducks and minnows (4) ducks and carnivorous fish
16. A disease kills all of the rabbits in an area. Populations of which type would be the first to be harmed? (1) producers (2) primary consumers (3) secondary consumers (4) decomposers
17. In a food web, the greatest concentration of chemical bond energy is stored by the (1) first level consumers (2) second level consumers (3) producers (4) decomposers
18. The ecological roles played by organisms may be represented graphically in the form of pyramids. This representation recognizes the fact that (1) environments seldom support a maximum population (2) energy transfer is not 100% efficient (3) climax communities are subject to change (4) population pressure may produce migration

Answer questions 19 and 20 on the basis of the paragraph below and on your knowledge of biology. Write the number of the word or expression that best answers each question.

When a green leaf is exposed to sunlight under conditions favorable to photosynthesis, approximately 1% of the radiant energy received is transformed into chemical energy which becomes stored in carbohydrates. However, only a very small portion of this energy is available for use by animals.

19. The principal reason that such a small percentage of the chemical energy is available to animals is probably that (1) animals require enzymes to digest carbohydrates (2) plants use some of the energy themselves (3) chemical substances never release stored energy (4) animals lack chlorophyll

20. A second reason which helps account for the small amounts of energy available for animals' consumption is probably that (1) animals excrete a large percentage of the digestible carbohydrates that they eat (2) too much energy released quickly is harmful to animals (3) some of the energy-containing substances may be in forms which animals cannot use (4) carbohydrates are unstable and many disintegrate before animals can eat them

21. In the food chain below, what are the most abundant organisms?
corn plants→field mice→garter snakes→red-tailed hawks
(1) corn plants (2) field mice (3) garter snakes (4) red-tailed hawks

22. In a lake containing algae, minnows, trout, and small crustaceans, which organism would probably be present in largest numbers? (1) minnows (2) small crustaceans (3) algae (4) trout

23. The size and relationships among populations within a community are frequently represented in the form of a pyramid because (1) a species of prey outnumbers its predators (2) producer populations are smaller than consumer populations (3) decomposers continually recycle energy to the environment (4) herbivores are less numerous than carnivores

E. MATERIAL CYCLES. Although an ecosystem needs a continuous supply of energy from outside itself, its raw materials are continuously cycled and reused.

1. The carbon-hydrogen-oxygen cycle. Carbon, hydrogen, and oxygen are cycled by the processes of respiration and photosynthesis. In respira-

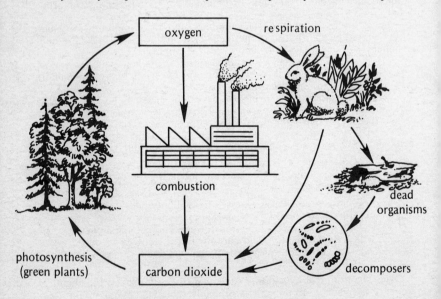

Figure 7-2. The oxygen and carbon cycles.

tion, the carbon and hydrogen in organic compounds react with oxygen to produce carbon dioxide and water. In photosynthesis, water is broken down to hydrogen and oxygen, and the hydrogen is combined with carbon dioxide to produce organic compounds.

2. The water cycle. Besides being cycled chemically through respiration and photosynthesis, water is also cycled physically between the vapor and liquid states. By transpiration and evaporation, liquid water enters the atmosphere as water vapor. By condensation and precipitation, it returns to the liquid state (rain, dew) or the solid state (snow, sleet, hail, frost). Water in the solid state becomes reusable by organisms when it melts to liquid water.

3. The nitrogen cycle. Green plants and other autotrophs need a supply of nitrogen in the form of **nitrates** (compounds containing the NO_3 group), from which they synthesize plant proteins. Animals obtain nitrogen in the form of proteins either from plants or from other animals that eat plants. The bacteria of decay convert nitrogenous wastes and remains to nitrates for reuse by plants.

a. Nitrogen-fixing bacteria. Part of the nitrogen cycle involves the free nitrogen of the atmosphere. **Nitrogen-fixing bacteria** convert free nitrogen to nitrates, which enter the soil as soluble nutrients that can be absorbed by plant roots. Many nitrogen-fixing bacteria are found in nodules on the roots of plants called **legumes,** such as peas, beans, and clover.

b. Decomposers (bacteria of decay) convert nitrogenous wastes into **ammonia** (NH_3).

c. Nitrifying bacteria convert ammonia into nitrates.

d. Denitrifying bacteria break down nitrogen compounds into free nitrogen, which returns to the atmosphere.

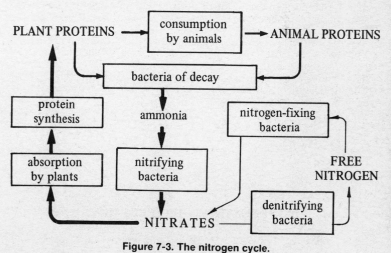

Figure 7-3. The nitrogen cycle.

QUESTIONS

1. An ecosystem is self-sustaining if (1) there is a cycling of materials between organisms and their environment (2) there is a greater number of consumers than producers (3) more animals than plants are present (4) equal numbers of plants and animals are present

2. In every natural community the autotrophic plants not only provide the basic food supply but also (1) provide carbon dioxide for the animals (2) release oxygen into the atmosphere (3) create extensive areas of shade (4) convert organic nitrogen into ammonia

3. Photosynthetic organisms depend upon the metabolic activities of other organisms for a continuing supply of (1) carbon dioxide (2) oxygen (3) water (4) enzymes

4. The concentration of carbon dioxide in the atmosphere remains relatively constant at about 0.04% as a result of established equilibrium between the processes of (1) assimilation and excretion (2) oxidation and photosynthesis (3) photosynthesis and assimilation (4) respiration and reproduction

5. Oxygen that is used in the process of animal respiration returns to the environment combined with carbon or (1) hydrogen (2) nitrogen (3) sulfur (4) phosphorus

6. Which would best be demonstrated by using a snail, some algae, and some water in a sealed glass jar? (1) development of osmotic pressure (2) Redi's experiment (3) fixation of nitrogen (4) carbon-oxygen cycle

7. Plants absorb nitrogen in the form of (1) amino acids (2) urea (3) nitrates (4) free nitrogen

8. Which organisms are chiefly involved in the recycling of dead matter? (1) algae (2) viruses (3) nitrogen-fixing bacteria (4) bacteria of decay

9. In which group are some of the members capable of utilizing free nitrogen? (1) viruses (2) insects (3) bacteria (4) yeasts

10. In the nitrogen cycle, nitrogen from the atmosphere is combined chemically with other elements as a result of the action of (1) bacteria (2) viruses (3) amino acids (4) yeasts

11. Atmospheric nitrogen is converted to usable nitrates by (1) nitrogen-fixing bacteria (2) nitrifying bacteria (3) denitrifying bacteria (4) decay bacteria

12. The forming of nitrogen compounds from free nitrogen is called (1) denitrification (2) lipid synthesis (3) nitrogen gas synthesis (4) nitrogen fixation

13. When bacteria of decay attack proteins, which is an important product of the bacterial activity? (1) ammonia (2) cellulose (3) lactic acid (4) vinegar

VII-3. ECOSYSTEM DEVELOPMENT

A. SUCCESSION. Ecosystems develop and change over periods of time. The most evident changes that occur are in the makeup of the communities of organisms living in the ecosystem or in a particular geographical region. The replacement of one type of community by another in a continuous sequence over time is called **ecological succession.**

1. Pioneer organisms are the first plants to populate a particular location. Lichens are the pioneer organisms on bare rock.

2. Changes in the environment. Pioneer organisms change the environment so that other organisms are able to live in the same area. For example, lichens start the processes that change rock to **soil,** in which other plants can grow. Each new population causes changes in the environment, which allow other populations to develop and to replace the earlier ones.

3. Plant successions. A typical sequence of plant populations that dominate an area in turn might be: pioneer organisms, grasses, shrubs, conifers, and deciduous trees.

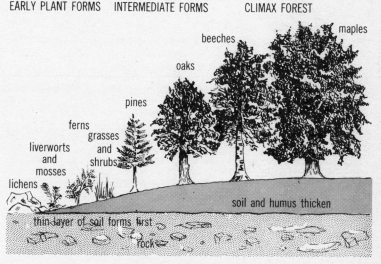

EARLY PLANT FORMS   INTERMEDIATE FORMS   CLIMAX FOREST

maples

beeches

oaks

pines

ferns

grasses
and
shrubs

liverworts
and
mosses

lichens

soil and humus thicken

thin layer of soil forms first

rock

Figure 7-4. Plant succession.

4. Animal successions. The plants, or **flora,** of a region are the producers and the source of food for the primary level of animal consumers. The animal species, or **fauna,** of a region depend on the kinds and amounts of plants in the community. As the plant community changes, the animal community that depends on the plants also changes.

5. Types of communities. At any given stage of succession in a community, there are certain dominant plant types, which determine the other kinds of organisms that can exist together under the prevailing abiotic and biotic conditions. Types of communities are identified by the dominant plant species and chief characteristics of the environment. Examples are:

a. *Sphagnum bog*—an old, shallow lake with no outlet or inlet, on which a mat of sphagnum (peat) moss is the dominant plant.

b. *Mangrove swamp*—a muddy tidal flat or coastal region populated by mangroves, which are a large, tropical evergreen type of tree.

c. *Pine barrens*—large area of sandy or peaty soil in which a species of pine tree is the dominant plant.

6. Climax communities. Ecological succession finally leads to a community of populations that does not change any further. A self-perpetuating community in which the populations do not change, and remain in balance with one another, is called a **climax community.** Oak-hickory climax communities are a common example at low elevations in New York State, and hemlock-beech-maple communities are common at higher elevations.

7. Changes in climax communities. A climax community persists until a major catastrophe changes or destroys it. A new succession then starts, which may end in a different climax community if the abiotic factors were permanently altered. The new succession may take hundreds or thousands of years to be completed. An example of catastrophic destruction of a climax community is the volcanic eruption of Mount St. Helens in Washington that occurred in 1980. A new succession has started in the ash-covered soil on the sides of the mountain.

B. COMPETITION. At any given time, the organisms of a community must share the resources of the environment, such as living space, water, light, oxygen, and minerals. **Competition** is the conflict between individual organisms seeking to obtain a sufficient amount of these resources.

C. NICHES. Each species in a community uses the resources of the environment and obtains food in its own particular way. The particular way in which a species relates to and uses the environment is called its **niche.** A niche is often described as the *role* of a species in the community. A niche can be described by the kind of food an organism needs, the places it lives and reproduces in, the time of day it is active, etc. If two species try to occupy the same niche in a community, the competition for the same resources usually results in one species being eliminated and the other dominating that niche. There is normally only one species per niche in a community.

QUESTIONS

1. A rocky island appears as oceanic waters recede. Which of the following forms of vegetation would probably appear first on the bare rocks? (1) lichens   (2) weeds   (3) shrubs   (4) pioneer trees

2. Lichens on bare rock and wind-blown weeds in a burned-over area are known as pioneer organisms because they (1) are the last to grow in a given area   (2) exhibit mutualism   (3) initiate the nitrogen cycle (4) will start an ecological succession

3. The orderly, progressive changes which result in establishing a climax community are referred to as (1) adaptive radiation   (2) community reaction   (3) ecological succession   (4) population stratification

4. Which statement best describes the climax stage of an ecological succession? (1) It will be populated only by plants.   (2) It persists until there are drastic changes in the environment.   (3) It represents the initial phases of evolution.   (4) It will change rapidly from season to season.

5. The climax community is best described as a community that (1) is in a state of balance or dynamic equilibrium (2) contains more animals than plants (3) contains pioneer organisms that drastically modify the environment (4) once attained, remains forever

6. In a forest community, the dominant species are (1) grasses (2) trees (3) fungi (4) shrubs

7. Between which organisms would competition for food be most intense? (1) lions and zebras (2) sheep and cows (3) snakes and frogs (4) mushrooms and ferns

8. Competition by two species for the same ecological niche generally results in (1) the sharing of the niche by the two species (2) one species taking possession of the niche (3) both species leaving the area (4) interbreeding between the two species

9. Many forested regions were once barren rock areas. The sequence of stages most likely to account for this change would be
(1) annual herbs—woody shrubs—lichens—mosses
(2) lichens—mosses—annual herbs—woody shrubs
(3) woody shrubs—mosses—lichens—annual herbs
(4) mosses—annual herbs—woody shrubs—lichens

VII-4. BIOMES

A. DEFINITION. There are large regions of the earth that have certain general climatic conditions. The climax communities tend to be very much alike throughout each of these climatic regions. A large region of the earth characterized by a particular type of climax community is called a **biome**.

B. TERRESTRIAL BIOMES. The biomes of the land areas of the earth are called **terrestrial biomes**.

1. Environmental factors. The abiotic factors that determine the type of land biome include (a) average annual temperature, (b) annual temperature range (highest and lowest), (c) intensity and duration of solar radiation, and (d) annual precipitation. These factors make up the **climate** of a region. The earth is divided into climate zones that depend largely on latitude north or south of the equator. However, climate is also affected by altitude and by nearness of large bodies of water.

2. Types of terrestrial biomes. Each type of terrestrial biome is characterized by a particular kind of climax vegetation. Some biomes are named by their climax vegetation. Some of the major land biomes are described in Table 7-1.

3. Effects of altitude. An increase in altitude generally has the same effect on climate as an increase in latitude (greater distance from the equator). At any given latitude, the changes in communities at higher altitudes resemble the changes that would be observed at sea level at higher latitudes. For example, the vegetation at moderate altitudes near the equator resembles the deciduous forests found at sea level in the mid-latitudes. This relationship is represented in Figure 7-5.

TABLE 7-1. CHARACTERISTICS OF THE MAJOR TERRESTRIAL BIOMES.

Biome	Climate	Vegetation
tundra	long, very cold winters; short growing season, during which only the topsoil thaws	lichens, mosses, grasses, sedges, shrubs
taiga	cold winters with much snow; growing season about 4 months, during which ground thaws completely	coniferous trees (pines, firs, spruces)
temperate deciduous forest	cold winters, hot, humid summers; abundant rainfall	deciduous forests of oak, maple, hickory, beech, chestnut, birch; many other types of trees, flowering plants, ferns, and mosses
grassland	temperate to tropical; moderate rainfall, insufficient to support trees	chiefly grasses and wildflowers
desert	hot days, cool nights; very little rainfall, insufficient for grasses	sparse growth of flowering plants specially adapted to require little water; e.g., cactus
tropical rain forest	constant, high temperatures throughout the year; frequent and abundant rainfall, very humid	large, broad-leaved trees, vines, epiphytes (plants not rooted in soil)

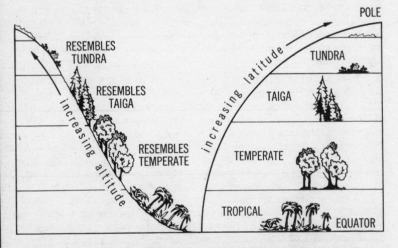

Figure 7-5. Similarity between altitudinal and latitudinal life zones. The right half of the drawing illustrates the differences in characteristic plant forms of sea-level biomes at various latitudes. The left half of the drawing illustrates the fact that increasing altitude has the same effect on the biome as increasing latitude. Thus, very high mountain tops in the tropics resemble the taiga and tundra of the polar regions.

C. AQUATIC BIOMES. Biomes consisting of areas covered by water are called **aquatic biomes.** The oceans, which cover more than 70% of the earth's surface, make up the **marine biome,** the largest ecosystem on the earth. The following are general characteristics of aquatic biomes:

1. Availability of water is not a limiting factor.

2. Temperatures do not vary much, because water can absorb and release large quantities of heat with relatively little change in temperature compared to land masses.

3. The abiotic factors that vary most and affect the kinds and numbers of organisms include oxygen, carbon dioxide, temperature, light, and suspended or dissolved materials.

4. Light for photosynthesis is limited to the regions near the surface, as light is not transmitted to the deeper regions.

5. Aquatic animals need to be adapted to absorb oxygen dissolved in the water. They must also have adaptations to maintain water balance in their cells, depending on the concentration of salts in the water environment.

D. THE MARINE BIOME. The oceans of the world are considered to be a single biome with the following characteristics:

1. A stable aquatic environment.

2. Helps to stabilize temperatures by absorbing and holding solar heat in summer and releasing it in winter in each hemisphere.

3. Is a habitat for a large number of different organisms.

4. Maintains a constant supply of mineral salts dissolved from the land masses and carried to the ocean by rivers.

5. Provides most of the world's supply of food nutrients by photosynthesis in shallow coastal waters and in the upper zone of the open ocean.

E. FRESH-WATER HABITATS. Most of the world's fresh-water areas are relatively small, separate bodies of water, such as lakes. Most lakes are ecosystems that undergo succession, leading to filling in and conversion to land areas and a terrestrial climax community. Only large lake systems, such as the Great Lakes of the United States, are stable enough to be considered fresh-water biomes.

QUESTIONS

1. The chief distinguishing characteristic of a biome is its (1) altitude (2) latitude (3) climax vegetation (4) ecosystem

2. Normally, which abiotic factor would have the least influence on the succession of plants in a land biome? (1) the average temperature (2) the amount of sunlight (3) the water content of the soil (4) the nitrogen content of the air

3. In the Northern Hemisphere, which is the sequence of biomes as latitude increases? (1) taiga, tundra, tropical rain forest, temperate deciduous forest (2) temperate deciduous forest, tundra, tropical rain forest, taiga (3) tundra, taiga, temperate deciduous forest, tropical rain forest (4) tropical rain forest, temperate deciduous forest, taiga, tundra

4. A person could best identify the type of terrestrial biome in an unfamiliar area by (1) examining a sample of soil (2) observing the climax vegetation (3) measuring the temperature and humidity (4) counting the different types of animals

5. Which biome contains large coniferous forests? (1) grasslands (2) taiga (3) tundra (4) rain forest

6. In which biome would the climax vegetation be most similar to the pioneer organisms on bare rock? (1) tundra (2) taiga (3) grasslands (4) temperate deciduous forest

7. The climax trees in a taiga forest are (1) spruce and fir (2) beech and maple (3) oak and hickory (4) apple and walnut

8. The climax organism growing above the tree line on a mountain would be the same as the climax organism found in the (1) taiga (2) tundra (3) tropical forest (4) desert

Base your answers to questions 9 through 12 on the diagram below and your knowledge of biology.

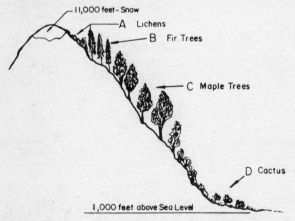

9. The major biome of New York State is most like the zone located in the diagram at point (1) A (2) B (3) C (4) D

10. The zone of living things located at point A is called a (1) deciduous forest (2) tundra (3) taiga (4) snow zone

11. When studying the animal life on the mountain, a person would usually observe that (1) representative species are present in each plant zone (2) only small animals are present in zones A and B (3) similar species are present in all the plant zones (4) identical species are present in zones A and D

12. Which is a correct statement of an ecological concept? (1) No life is normally found above 8,500 feet above sea level. (2) Vegetation at lower altitudes is similar to the vegetation at higher latitudes. (3) A plant succession starts at the bottom of the mountain and reaches a climax at the top. (4) An increase in altitude has the same general effect on plant associations as an increase in latitude.

13. Which world biome has the smallest change in temperature? (1) tropical rain forest (2) taiga (3) desert (4) tundra

14. Which biome is considered to be the most stable? (1) tropical rain forest (2) tundra (3) marine (4) grassland

15. The earth remains at a relatively low temperature because the water in the oceans absorbs heat (1) slowly and loses it slowly (2) rapidly and loses it rapidly (3) slowly and loses it rapidly (4) rapidly and loses it slowly

16. The quantity of aerobic life present in any body of water is limited chiefly by the (1) reproductive adaptations of the various species (2) numbers of species that can adapt to a water environment (3) amount of salt concentration in the water (4) amount of oxygen dissolved in the water

17. The great majority of animals in a marine environment live near the surface of the water because their survival is related to the process in plants known as (1) photosynthesis (2) respiration (3) diffusion (4) homeostasis

18. As the distance increases from the surface of a body of water to its extremely deep regions, the (1) amount of living matter is likely to increase (2) variety, but not the amount, of living organisms increases (3) amount of living matter decreases (4) amount of living matter remains the same

VII-5. HUMANS AND THE BIOSPHERE

A. EFFECTS OF HUMANS ON THE ENVIRONMENT. Unlike other species, humans exert a powerful influence on their environment and can change it and have changed it in many ways. These human effects on the environment have both positive (desirable) and negative (undesirable) aspects.

B. NEGATIVE ASPECTS. Many human activities upset the natural balance of ecosystems. Often, this has long-term undesirable results for humans as well as the other organisms of the community.

1. Human population growth. The human population is now growing at a rapid rate, partly because of medical advances that have lengthened the average life span. A growing population needs an increasing food supply as well as more living space. Attempts to increase the food supply by use of fertilizers and expansion of cultivated areas have had negative effects on many surrounding ecosystems.

2. Overhunting. Human hunting, trapping, and fishing activities have removed many species of animals from their habitats much faster than they could be replaced by natural breeding rates. This has led to the extinction or endangerment of these species. Animals now extinct because of human activities are the dodo bird and the passenger pigeon. The blue whale is an example of an endangered species. When species become extinct or rare, humans lose the future benefit for which the animals were hunted in the first place.

3. Importation of organisms. Humans have transferred organisms into communities where they did not naturally exist. In some cases, the transported organisms had no natural enemies or other checks on their increase in the new habitat. They therefore multiplied in large numbers, displaced other desirable species, and disrupted existing ecosystems. Examples of organisms imported into the United States that then caused undesirable effects are the Japanese beetle, the starling, the gypsy moth, the Mediterranean fruit fly, and the organism that causes Dutch elm disease.

4. Exploitation of wildlife. Many species of flora and fauna have been hunted or gathered to satisfy human demand other than the need for food. Examples include the hunting of African elephants and the Pacific walrus for the ivory of their tusks; the capture of Colombian parrots to be sold as pets; the cutting down of tropical rain forest trees to make plywood. The result has been severe depletion of the numbers of these organisms.

5. Poor land use management. The growth of cities and suburbs has occurred at the expense of surrounding farmlands and natural ecosystems. The result is less land available for food production and fewer areas for recreation. At the same time, the increasing demand for food has led to overcropping of agricultural land and failure to use cover crops and other soil protection measures. Soil nutrients have been depleted and topsoil lost as a result, leading to lower productivity of the land.

6. Adverse effects of technology. The great expansion of industry and technology has had undesirable effects on the environment, including pollution of the water, air, and land.

a. Water pollution. Chemical wastes from homes, factories, mines, and power plants have polluted the waters in many areas. Phosphates, heavy metals, and PCB's are examples of harmful pollutants. Heat discharged into waterways by factories and power plants is also a form of water pollution that has undesirable effects on the fish and other life in rivers and lakes.

b. Air pollution. Exhaust gases and particulate matter from automobiles have been a major cause of air pollution in urban and suburban areas. Exhausts from factory smokestacks have also polluted the air. Polluted air is harmful to humans who must breathe it. Another undesirable effect of air pollution is the condition called **acid rain.** Oxides of sulfur and nitrogen react with water vapor to form acids in the air. These acids are brought to earth in precipitation. In many areas, lakes have become so acid as a result of acid rain that much of their wildlife has died. Acid rain also has a corrosive effect on buildings and machinery.

c. Pesticides and herbicides. Many chemical agents used to destroy insects and other pests that attack crops, or to prevent the growth of weeds, have entered the soil, the air, and the water supply, with undesirable effects on food webs.

d. Waste disposal. The disposal of solid wastes has become a major problem. Among these wastes are the large number of cans, bottles, and plastic containers in which foods and other products are sold. Another serious waste disposal problem is that of the radioactive wastes produced by nuclear power plants.

C. POSITIVE ASPECTS. Human societies and governments have come to recognize the dangers of past practices. We have increasing understanding of ecological interactions, and we are better able to predict and control undesirable effects of human activities on the environment.

1. Population control. Many governments of countries with high birth rates have adopted policies that encourage people to have fewer children. Effective methods of controlling human reproduction have been and are being developed.

2. Conservation of resources. There are many programs being instituted to prevent soil depletion and erosion, to conserve water and energy, and to recycle metals.

3. Pollution controls. Many laws have been enacted that impose controls on the major sources of air and water pollution. New techniques are also being developed to dispose of wastes in ways that do not harm the environment.

4. Species preservation. Wildlife refuges and national parks are designed to preserve habitats for species endangered by the conversion of wild areas to industrial and residential use. Game laws and fisheries also prevent extinction of wildlife species by overhunting and fishing. Bisons, egrets, whooping cranes, bald eagles, and peregrine falcons are among the animals whose populations are growing again after dropping to very low numbers.

5. Use of biological controls. New methods of pest control avoid the use of chemical poisons that often affect desirable as well as undesirable species, that disrupt food webs, and that pollute the land and water. These new biological controls include methods that prevent fertile matings of insect pests, that use species-specific sex attractants to trap and kill the insects, and that use natural parasites of specific insects to reduce their numbers by disease. The gypsy moth, the Mediterranean fruit fly, and the Japanese beetle have been subjected to such biological controls in recent years.

6. State environmental protection laws. New York State has enacted laws that provide for studies of the environmental effect of major projects involving land use before the projects can be authorized. The State Environmental Quality Review Act (SEQR) and the Freshwater Wetlands Act are examples.

D. THE FUTURE. The standard of living of humans has undoubtedly been raised by the development and use of resources and increased technology. However, we now realize that this improvement has come at the expense of the environment. Expansion and growth will come to a halt if we ignore the ecological consequences. Awareness of ecological principles, careful use of our energy and other resources, and concern for the welfare of future generations will insure that the richness of our life and the richness of the environment can endure into the future.

QUESTIONS

1. Although humans have been enormously successful in modifying their environment, many of these modifications have seriously upset the balance of nature. This can be attributed to the lack of realization that (1) humans are supreme in power (2) humans can adapt to more environmental conditions than any other species (3) human abilities are superior in all areas (4) humans do not depend on environmental factors for survival

2. The chief drawback to the use of pesticides is that such substances (1) are usually more expensive than the damage done by the pests they eliminate (2) usually cause genetic changes in the plants being treated

(3) may stimulate rapid evolution among the pest organisms   (4) reduce the usable production of crop plants

3. Methods of agriculture have created serious insect problems, primarily because these methods   (1) increase soil erosion   (2) provide concentrated areas of food for insects   (3) aid the absorption of water   (4) grow crops in areas where formerly only insects could survive

4. Japanese beetles do relatively little damage in Japan because in Japan they   (1) are kept in check by natural enemies   (2) are kept in check by effective insecticides   (3) hibernate during the winter months   (4) have gradually adapted to the environment

5. Which method of controlling insect pests is least likely to disturb the balance of nature?   (1) control by quarantine   (2) biological control   (3) environmental control by humans   (4) chemical control

6. Dumping excessive amounts of raw sewage directly into a river tends to reduce its dissolved oxygen content. This change in dissolved oxygen content will most likely cause   (1) an increase of aquatic organisms that carry on aerobic respiration   (2) an increase of aquatic organisms that carry on anaerobic respiration   (3) a decrease in the concentration of minerals in the river water   (4) a decrease in the temperature of the water as a result of thermal pollution

7. When scientists try to control the screwworm by exposing it to cobalt-60 radiation, they are trying to   (1) make the male flies sterile   (2) destroy the flies directly by radiation   (3) produce mutant flies which are not parasites   (4) increase the breeding rate of the screw flies' natural enemies

8. Human attempts to prevent some species from becoming totally extinct have succeeded in the case of the   (1) passenger pigeon   (2) dodo bird   (3) grizzly bear   (4) great auk

PRACTICE TESTS FOR EXTENDED AREAS
(Part II of the Regents Examination)

PRACTICE TEST 1
Biochemistry

1. Which structural formula represents an amino acid?

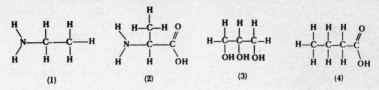

(1)   (2)   (3)   (4)

2. The structural formulas below represent two molecules.

These molecules are normally joined by the removal of (1) H and OH (2) N (3) O (4) R and NH_2

Base your answers to questions 3 through 6 on the structural formulas below, which represent organic molecules.

(A)   (B)   (C)

(D)   (E)

3. Which two molecules contain a carboxyl group? (1) B and C (2) C and D (3) D and E (4) A and E

4. Which molecules are the building blocks of certain fats? (1) A and D (2) B and C (3) A and C (4) B and E

5. Which two molecules are sugars? (1) A and B (2) B and C (3) C and D (4) D and E

6. Which molecule might be part of an enzyme molecule? (1) A (2) B (3) E (4) D

7. Which kind of reaction is represented by the equation below?
(1) hydrolysis   (2) photosynthesis   (3) dehydration synthesis   (4) nitrogen fixation

$$\underset{\overset{|}{H}}{\overset{\overset{H}{|}}{H-N}}-\overset{\overset{H}{|}}{\underset{\overset{|}{H}}{C}}-\overset{\overset{O}{\parallel}}{C}-OH \; + \; \underset{\overset{|}{H}}{\overset{\overset{H}{|}}{H-N}}-\overset{\overset{H}{|}}{\underset{\overset{|}{H}}{C}}-\overset{\overset{O}{\parallel}}{C}-OH \longrightarrow \underset{\overset{|}{H}}{\overset{\overset{H}{|}}{H-N}}-\overset{\overset{H}{|}}{\underset{\overset{|}{H}}{C}}-\overset{\overset{OH}{|}}{C}-\overset{\overset{H}{|}}{\underset{\overset{|}{H}}{N}}-\overset{\overset{H}{|}}{C}-\overset{\overset{O}{\parallel}}{C}-OH \; + \; H_2O$$

8. At 20°C the optimum reaction rate of a certain enzyme occurs at a pH of 7. A greater reaction rate could most probably be attained by increasing (1) the temperature to 30°C and keeping the pH at 7 (2) both the temperature and the pH (3) the pH and keeping the temperature at 20°C (4) the pH and decreasing the temperature

9. Chlorophyll is important in photosynthesis because chlorophyll (1) reflects green light energy (2) reflects red light energy (3) converts light energy into chemical bond energy (4) converts the chemical bond energy of glucose into the chemical bond energy of ATP

10. Water prepared with oxygen-18 is supplied to a plant in a well-lighted, controlled environment. Upon analysis a short time later, the O^{18} would probably be found in (1) glucose only (2) starch only (3) carbohydrates, proteins, and fats (4) the air surrounding the plant

11. A scientist uses the isotope carbon-14 to trace the path of carbon through the reactions of photosynthesis. In which sequence would the carbon-14 most likely be found? (1) water—free oxygen—glucose (2) carbon dioxide—pyruvic acid—glucose   (3) carbon dioxide—3-carbon compounds—glucose (4) ammonia—nitrates—plant protein

12. To start cellular respiration, muscle tissue requires a supply of (1) carbon dioxide and water (2) glucose and ATP (3) pyruvic acid and citric acid (4) oxygen and chlorophyll

Base your answers to questions 13 and 14 on the following reactions:

(A) glucose + 2 ATP $\xrightarrow{\text{enzymes}}$ 2 pyruvic acid + 4 ATP

(B) 2 pyruvic acid + oxygen $\xrightarrow{\text{enzymes}}$ carbon dioxide + water + 36 ATP

13. The total process shown by equations A and B is important to life because it (1) converts light energy into chemical energy (2) converts light energy into heat energy (3) converts chemical bond energy into a form usable by cells (4) requires no energy to initiate the process

14. The process shown by equation B occurs in the organelle known as the (1) ribosome (2) mitochondrion (3) endoplasmic reticulum (4) nucleolus

Base your answers to questions 15 through 17 on the cellular metabolic process that is represented in the diagram below.

15. This process is useful to animal cells because it is their chief source of (1) oxygen (2) glucose (3) enzymes (4) ATP

16. Why do some bacteria carry on only the anaerobic phase of this process even though oxygen gas is present? (1) They lack the enzymes needed for the aerobic reactions. (2) They lack the ability to transport oxygen gas through their membranes. (3) They store pyruvic acid for their energy needs. (4) They produce carbon dioxide and water in other reactions.

17. What is the net number of ATP molecules produced by this entire process from one molecule of glucose? (1) 32 (2) 2 (3) 36 (4) 42

Base your answers to questions 18-20 on the equation below.

18. The type of reaction represented by this equation is called (1) hydrolysis (2) carbon fixation (3) glycolysis (4) dehydration synthesis

19. This reaction occurs during the process of (1) protein synthesis (2) aerobic respiration (3) digestion of carbohydrates (4) photosynthesis

20. The products of this reaction are (1) lipids (2) amino acids (3) peptides (4) monosaccharides

PRACTICE TEST 2
Human Physiology

1. Which two nutrients are not able to provide energy for cell use? (1) water and minerals (2) water and proteins (3) carbohydrates and proteins (4) fats and sugar

2. The calorie content of a food refers to its amount of (1) fat (2) carbohydrate (3) digestible material (4) energy

3. Which does blood absorb while flowing through blood vessels in the small intestine? (1) cellulose (2) starch (3) proteins (4) amino acids

4. Constipation is most likely to result from a deficiency in the diet of (1) minerals (2) roughage (3) water (4) digestible carbohydrates

5. A blocking of the flow of blood to the heart muscle causes (1) high blood pressure (2) a heart attack (3) a stroke (4) atherosclerosis

6. A person obtains passive immunity by receiving antibodies extracted from the blood of an animal. Such immunity is of short duration because (1) after the person recovers, there is no need for the antibody (2) the injection has to be weak (3) the antibody, being a foreign substance, is soon eliminated (4) the toxin and the antibody have neutralized each other

7. Actively acquired immunity develops when a disease-causing organism stimulates the immune system to form (1) toxins (2) toxoids (3) specific albumins (4) specific antibodies

8. Assume that a drop of anti-A serum and a drop of anti-B serum are placed side by side on a slide. A drop of blood of unknown type is added to each drop of serum. If the blood cells do not clump in either the anti-A or the anti-B serum, the blood of unknown type is probably type (1) A (2) B (3) AB (4) O

9. A transplanted organ may be rejected and destroyed by the recipient's body because (1) the donor has a different blood type (2) the tissues of the transplanted organ act as antigens (3) the recipient's blood lacks the proper antibodies (4) the tissues surrounding the transplant have different cell types

10. An allergic reaction that causes contraction of the bronchioles and difficulty in breathing is (1) asthma (2) emphysema (3) bronchitis (4) atherosclerosis

11. Failure of the human body to metabolize calcium properly is most closely associated with malfunctioning of the (1) parathyroids (2) thyroid (3) pancreas (4) testes

12. The most important function of specialized cells of the pancreas is (1) absorption (2) excretion (3) secretion (4) respiration

13. The islets of Langerhans are most closely associated with (1) diabetes (2) cretinism (3) giantism (4) kidney disease

Questions 14 through 18 pertain to certain human hormones. For each question, select the number of the hormone, chosen from the list below, which is most closely associated with that statement. (An answer may be used more than once or not at all.)

Hormones
(1) Adrenaline
(2) TSH
(3) Insulin
(4) Estrogen

14. This hormone directly influences the development of the female secondary sex characteristics.

15. This hormone stimulates activities in the thyroid gland.

16. This hormone promotes the outflow of sugar from the blood into the muscles.

17. This hormone contributes in greatest measure to the regulation of heartbeat, blood sugar levels, and blood clotting rates.

18. This hormone is secreted by the pituitary gland.

For each description in questions 19 through 23, select the number of the human body structure, chosen from the list below, to which that phrase refers. (An answer may be used more than once or not at all.)

Human Body Structures
(1) Cerebellum
(2) Parathyroid
(3) Kidneys
(4) Liver
(5) Medulla oblongata
(6) Mitochondria

19. Originates the impulses that control the breathing rate.

20. The organelle that contains the enzymes involved in aerobic respiration.

21. Major site where glucagon stimulates the release of glucose into the blood.

22. Principal site of urea synthesis.

23. Controls the metabolism of calcium, which is necessary for nerve function.

PRACTICE TEST 3
Reproduction and Development

1. Which statement best describes cells formed during cleavage? (1) They contain X-chromosomes but never Y-chromosomes. (2) They contain more yolk than the zygote from which they are formed. (3) They are smaller than the fertilized egg cell. (4) They are found in mature ovaries.

2. From which embryonic layer does the nervous system arise in vertebrates? (1) mesoderm (2) ectoderm (3) endoderm (4) gastroderm

3. Overproduction is essential to the survival of a given species of fish because (1) fish usually have a limited food supply (2) fish eggs have a limited supply of yolk (3) their fertilized eggs develop externally and have little protection (4) large numbers of offspring are essential to provide sufficient variations

4. A shell surrounding the embryo is an adaptation for (1) internal development (2) external development in water (3) external development on land (4) storing food for the developing embryo.

5. In mammals, which structure is composed of tissues from both the embryo and the parent ? (1) oviduct (2) allantois (3) umbilical cord (4) placenta

6. Which group of organisms produces eggs with the least amount of stored food? (1) mammals (2) amphibians (3) birds (4) fish

Questions 7 through 11 describe structures associated with mammalian reproduction and development. For each description in questions 7 through 11, write the number preceding the name of the structure, chosen from the list below, that is most closely associated with that description.

Structures
(1) Allantois
(2) Amnion
(3) Gonad
(4) Oviduct
(5) Placenta
(6) Uterus
(7) Yolk sac

7. Meiotic division normally occurs in this structure.

8. This structure is formed from a combination of maternal and embryonic tissues.

9. Internal fertilization usually takes place in this structure.

10. This structure becomes modified by hormonal action in preparation for the implantation of an early embryo.

11. This structure contains a watery environment for internal embryonic development.

12. Which statement describes the gastrula stage of embryonic development in the frog? (1) Embryonic germ layers are formed. (2) The embryo is ready to leave the uterus. (3) A solid ball of cells is formed. (4) Placental tissue is formed.

13. From which embryonic germ layer do blood vessels, muscles, and gonads arise? (1) ectoderm (2) endoderm (3) epiderm (4) mesoderm

14. Most animals reproducing in a water environment carry on (1) internal fertilization without protection of the zygote (2) internal fertilization with protection of the zygote (3) external fertilization without protection of the zygote (4) external fertilization with protection of the zygote.

15. Which is the correct order of events in the reproductive cycle of the human female? (1) growth of follicle, breakdown of corpus luteum, ovulation (2) menstruation, ovulation, rupture of follicle (3) growth of follicle, rupture of follicle, ovulation (4) rupture of follicle, menstruation, ovulation

Base your answers to questions 16 through 18 on the reproductive system of a pregnant female shown below.

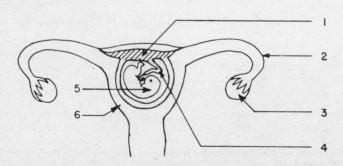

16. Through which structure are materials exchanged between the bloodstreams of the mother and the developing embryo? (1) 1 (2) 2 (3) 3 (4) 5

17. In which structure is the zygote normally formed? (1) 1 (2) 2 (3) 5 (4) 6

18. Within which structure does meiotic cell division occur? (1) 1 (2) 6 (3) 3 (4) 4

19. In which structure is a developing embryo normally implanted? (1) oviduct (2) uterus (3) ovary (4) vagina

20. Identical twins may develop as a result of fertilization of (1) one egg by one sperm (2) one egg by two sperms (3) two eggs by one sperm (4) two eggs by two sperms

21. If a human female produces two healthy egg cells during her monthly cycle and both are fertilized, the result of this will be the development of (1) one zygote and the crowding out of the other (2) fraternal twins (3) identical twins (4) Siamese twins

Base your answers to questions 22 through 24 on the diagram below, which represents the development of a fertilized egg.

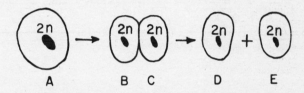

22. Cell A represents a (1) zygote (2) blastula (3) gastrula (4) polar body

23. Which process occurs when cell A divides and forms cells B and C? (1) meiosis (2) cleavage (3) fertilization (4) differentiation

24. Cells D and E represent (1) two sperms (2) two eggs (3) cells that could develop into identical twins (4) cells that could develop into fraternal twins

25. Which structure makes nutrients and oxygen directly available to the embryo? (1) uterus (2) oviduct (3) placenta (4) ovary

26. Gestation is most closely associated with (1) birth (2) death (3) prenatal development (4) fertilization

27. Which structure is associated with embryonic development in both birds and humans? (1) amnion (2) placenta (3) umbilical cord (4) large yolk

PRACTICE TEST 4
Modern Genetics

1. Addition, deletion, and translocation are types of (1) polyploidy (2) genetic mutation (3) chromosomal alteration (4) nondisjunction

2. One of the problems of controlling genetically related diseases is that (1) people don't like to talk about them (2) it is often difficult to detect the presence of the causative gene in a heterozygous individual (3) their mutation rates are very low (4) they are very rare

3. Which disease results from the genetic inability to synthesize a single enzyme? (1) diabetes (2) color blindness (3) PKU (phenylketonuria) (4) Down's syndrome

4. During the replication of a DNA molecule, bonds are broken between the (1) nitrogenous bases (2) phosphate groups (3) 5-carbon sugars (4) sugars and phosphates

Base your answers to questions 5 through 7 on the diagram below and your knowledge of biology.

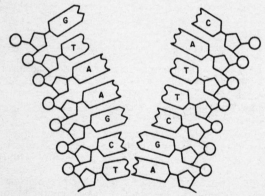

5. The molecule represented by the diagram would most likely be found in (1) plant cells only (2) animal cells only (3) both plant and animal cells (4) neither plant nor animal cells

6. A change in the sequence of the nucleotides shown in the diagram could result in (1) a gene mutation (2) blending inheritance (3) inbreeding (4) polyploidy

7. The diagram represents one step in the replication of a molecule of (1) RNA (2) ATP (3) ADP (4) DNA

8. With which cellular activity is the replication of DNA most closely associated? (1) mitosis (2) transport (3) polysaccharide synthesis (4) aerobic respiration

9. After the replication of a DNA molecule is completed, each of the two daughter DNA strands is usually composed of (1) fragments from both strands of the parent DNA molecule (2) one nucleotide strand exactly like one of the parent DNA nucleotide strands (3) nucleotides like the parent DNA molecule except uracil is substituted for thymine (4) nucleotides slightly different from the parent DNA molecule

10. Which substance is present in some of the nucleotides of DNA molecules, but not in those of RNA molecules? (1) adenine (2) cytosine (3) thymine (4) ribose

11. One difference between DNA molecules and RNA molecules is that only the (1) DNA contains cytosine and guanine (2) RNA contains ribose and uracil (3) RNA molecules are found in the nucleus (4) DNA carries the genetic code

Base your answers to questions 12 and 13 on the diagram below of nucleic acids and on your knowledge of biology.

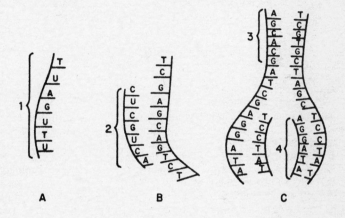

12. Which number indicates a newly synthesized strand of DNA? (1) 1 (2) 2 (3) 3 (4) 4

13. Which number indicates a strand of messenger RNA being synthesized? (1) 1 (2) 2 (3) 3 (4) 4

14. If the sequence of purines and pyrimidines in a segment of a DNA strand were cytosine, guanine, adenine, thymine, adenine, then the sequence in a complementary strand of newly made messenger RNA would be (1) cytosine, uracil, adenine, guanine, uracil (2) guanine, cytosine, uracil, adenine, uracil (3) uracil, adenine, cytosine, uracil, guanine (4) guanine, cytosine, thymine, adenine, thymine

15. During protein synthesis, which substance attaches to a particular amino acid molecule and positions it in a polypeptide chain? (1) transfer RNA (2) messenger RNA (3) DNA (4) ADP

16. If all necessary enzymes are present, which event would occur last in the process of protein formation? (1) formation of messenger RNA from the original DNA base sequence (2) transfer of amino acids from cytoplasm to the ribosomes (3) movement of messenger RNA from the nucleus to the ribosomes (4) formation of a polypeptide chain

17. In all living cells, deoxyribonucleic acid controls cellular activities by (1) determining the order of amino acids in protein molecules (2) regulating osmotic pressure on each side of the cell membrane (3) varying the rates of cellulose synthesis and hydrolysis (4) coordinating the active transport of centrioles into and out of cells

18. A defect in the genetic code is carried from the nucleus to the ribosomes by molecules of (1) ATP (2) PGAL (3) messenger RNA (4) transfer RNA

19. Biochemically, gene mutations are considered to be any change that alters the sequence of (1) nitrogenous bases in an organism's DNA (2) phosphates in ATP molecules (3) sugars in transfer RNA molecules (4) hydrogren bonds in messenger RNA

Base your answers to questions 20 through 22 on the representation below of a change in a portion of the base sequence in a DNA molecule.

$$\text{A } \textcircled{T} \text{ C G A T} \xrightarrow{\text{X-ray}} \text{A } \textcircled{A} \text{ C G A T}$$

20. The change that is represented may best be interpreted as a (1) gene mutation (2) nucleic acid replication (3) nucleotide synthesis (4) gene replication

21. In humans, a change similar to the one shown may cause an individual to be afflicted with (1) Down's syndrome (2) polyploidy (3) phagocytosis (4) sickle-cell anemia

22. An important characteristic of this type of change is that it most often (1) involves many chromosomes at once (2) is an advantage to an organism (3) may be passed on to offspring (4) requires a change in the environment

23. The gene pool of a population consists of only the (1) heritable genes in the population (2) mutated genes in the population (3) dominant genes in the population (4) recessive genes in the population

24. Which factor would limit variation within a population? (1) mutation (2) segregation and recombination of genes (3) the introduction of new members of the same species (4) reproductive isolation

25. The Hardy-Weinberg principle can be applied to a population of organisms that reproduces by (1) budding (2) parthenogenesis (3) mating (4) fission

26. Albinism in corn plants, which is determined by a recessive gene, prevents the plant from carrying on photosynthesis. Nevertheless, albinos continue to appear among corn plants because when (1) albinos are crossed, all of their offspring are albinos (2) albinos and homozygous green plants are crossed, some of their offspring are albinos (3) heterozygous green plants are crossed with each other, all of their offspring are albinos (4) heterozygous green plants are crossed with each other, some of their offspring are albinos

PRACTICE TEST 5
Ecology

1. Which pair of organisms exhibits the type of symbiosis known as commensalism? (1) remora and shark (2) alga and fungus in a lichen (3) athlete's foot fungus and humans (4) lamprey eel and trout

2. Which is a good example of mutualism? (1) protozoa in the intestinal tract of termites (2) fleas in the hair of dogs (3) barnacles on the back of a sea turtle (4) trichina in the muscles of hogs

3. Certain bacteria living in a human's large intestine help to produce vitamin K. This relationship is an example of (1) animal parasitism (2) plant parasitism (3) commensalism (4) mutualism

4. Considering their nutritional requirements, bacteria of decay would be classified as (1) saprophytes (2) producers (3) parasites (4) predators

5. The yucca moth pollinates the yucca cactus flower while depositing her eggs on the flower. The moth larvae that hatch then feed on some of the seeds developing within the flower. The flower can only be pollinated by this species of moth. This relationship between moth and flower is one of (1) commensalism (2) mutualism (3) parasitism (4) saprophytism

6. In most natural communities, the distribution of organisms in terms of their total mass and their contribution to food chains can be compared to the structure of a (1) web (2) pyramid (3) sphere (4) niche

7. In a pond populated by all four of these organisms, which would normally be present in greatest numbers? (1) algae (2) frogs (3) water lilies (4) bass

Base your answers to questions 8 through 10 on the food chain shown below and your knowledge of biology.

algae→water fleas→shrimp→
small fish→herring→humans

8. At which stage in the food chain will the greatest amount of energy be found? (1) algae (2) water fleas (3) herring (4) humans

9. Which are the first carnivorous organisms in the food chain? (1) algae (2) herring (3) shrimp (4) humans

10. At which stage in the food chain will the greatest number of animal organisms be found? (1) shrimp (2) water fleas (3) small fish (4) herring

11. In the nitrogen cycle, which organisms are usually associated with the conversion of free nitrogen into nitrates? (1) nitrogen-fixing bacteria (2) bacteria of decay (3) soil molds (4) nitrifying bacteria

12. Which process enables some bacteria to use nitrogen from the atmosphere in order to synthesize amino acids and proteins? (1) ammonification (2) nitrogen-fixation (3) denitrification (4) nitrification

13. Bacteria living in the nodules on the roots of leguminous plants are an evolutionary adaptation that aid the plant by (1) converting inorganic molecules to carbohydrates (2) converting carbon dioxide to free oxygen (3) producing nitrates from free nitrogen (4) producing waxy materials

14. In the nitrogen cycle, the materials produced by the nitrifying bacteria are used by plants to synthesize (1) simple sugars (2) fatty acids (3) starches (4) proteins

15. Cattails growing near the shores of ponds help in the succession from pond to forest by forming an organic material called   (1) clay   (2) humus   (3) nodules   (4) sand

16. Before the climax condition is reached during ecological succession, a community causes changes in the environment. These changes usually   (1) lead to a forest climax community in all ecosystems   (2) make conditions less favorable for some species in that community   (3) make conditions less favorable for later communities   (4) lead to a pioneer community

17. Which factor would usually be expected to increase competition among the chipmunk population in a certain area?   (1) an epidemic of rabies among chipmunks   (2) an increase in the number of chipmunks killed on the highways   (3) an increase in the number of hawks that prey upon chipmunks   (4) a temporary increase in the chipmunk reproduction rate

18. Whether a land ecosystem supports a climax community of a deciduous forest or a grassy prairie depends chiefly upon the   (1) annual rainfall   (2) longitude but not latitude   (3) yearly changes in the length of the growing season   (4) monthly variations in temperature

19. Which world biome contains the fewest number of different plant and animal species?   (1) tropical rain forest   (2) temperate deciduous forest   (3) taiga   (4) tundra

20. That many desert plants have leaves that are merely spines or thorns is most likely related to the fact that   (1) annual rainfall in the desert is less than 10 inches   (2) desert animals do not require shade   (3) spines and thorns lack chlorophyll   (4) the roots of desert plants are much longer than their stems.

21. Which zone of vegetation is found at the highest altitude?   (1) coniferous forests   (2) low herbs and shrubs   (3) mosses and lichens   (4) deciduous forests

22. Plankton is the name given to the algae, protozoa, and other forms of microscopic life that grow in great numbers on and near the surface of the ocean. Which statement describes the most important role of plankton in nature?   (1) It serves as the basis of food chains for oceanic life.   (2) It serves directly as the basic diet for all fish.   (3) It is symbiotic to landforms of microscopic life.   (4) It insulates the marine environment, thereby preventing rapid heat loss.

23. The largest and most stable biome is the   (1) tropical forest biome   (2) desert biome   (3) marine biome   (4) taiga biome

24. As compared to plant life on land, plant life in the oceans is limited, primarily because in the oceans   (1) light does not penetrate to great depths   (2) salt in the water destroys most plant life   (3) plants and their seeds are the chief source of food for the smaller animals   (4) a limited amount of CO_2 is available for photosynthesis

25. One major difference between most marine and fresh-water animals is their   (1) respiratory gas requirements   (2) methods of locomotion   (3) methods of autotrophic nutrition   (4) adaptations for maintaining water balance

LABORATORY SKILLS
AND READING COMPREHENSION

Part III of the Regents Examination in Biology consists of five groups of questions, with 5 questions in each group. The student must answer the questions in three of these five groups. Four of the five groups are concerned with laboratory skills, the construction of data tables and graphs, and the interpretation of experimental results. However, one group of questions tests the student's ability to understand and draw conclusions from a reading passage dealing with a biological topic.

LIST OF REQUIRED LABORATORY SKILLS

The Regents Syllabus in Biology identifies 15 skills that the students of biology should be able to demonstrate. Some of these skills are judged during student performance of the required laboratory work. All of the skills are subject to testing on the Regents examination. The required skills are listed below.

1. Formulate a question or define a problem, and develop a hypothesis to be tested in an investigation.

2. Given a laboratory problem, select suitable lab materials, safety equipment, and appropriate observation methods.

3. Distinguish between controls and variables in an experiment.

4. Identify parts of a light microscope and their functions, and focus in low and high power.

5. Determine the size of microscopic specimens in micrometers.

6. Prepare wet mounts of plant and animal cells, and apply staining techniques using iodine or methylene blue.

7. Identify cell parts under the compound microscope, such as the nucleus, cytoplasm, chloroplasts, and cell wall.

8. Use and interpret indicators such as pH paper, Benedict's (Fehling's) solution, iodine (Lugol's) solution, and bromthymol blue.

9. Use and read measurement instruments, such as metric rulers, Celsius (centigrade) thermometers, and graduated cylinders.

10. Dissection of plant and animal specimens for the purpose of exposing major structures for suitable examination. Suggestions of specimens include seeds, flowers, earthworms, grasshoppers, etc.

11. Demonstrate safety skills involved in heating materials in test tubes or beakers, use of chemicals, and handling of dissection instruments.

12. Collect, organize, and graph data.

13. Make inferences and predictions based upon data collected and observed.

14. Formulate generalizations or conclusions of the investigation.

15. Assess the limitations and assumptions of the experiment, and determine the accuracy and repeatability of the experimental data and observations.

BASIC INFORMATION FOR LABORATORY SKILLS

Questions relating specifically to laboratory skills appear in Part III of the Biology Regents Examination. The following information will be helpful in answering the questions on this part of the examination.

A. USING THE METRIC SYSTEM

1. Metric units. You should be familiar with the following metric units of measurement.

Quantity	Unit	Abbreviation
Length	meter	m
Volume	liter	l or L
Mass	gram	g

2. Metric prefixes. Metric units are made larger or smaller by the use of prefixes attached to the unit name. The following prefixes are the ones you need to know.

Prefix	Multiplies Unit by	Example	Meaning
centi-	1/100	centimeter (cm)	1/100 meter (0.01 m)
milli-	1/1000	milliliter (mL)	1/1000 liter (0.001 L)
micro-	1/1,000,000	micrometer (μm)	1/1,000,000 meter (0.000001 m)
kilo-	1000	kilogram (kg)	1000 grams (1000 g)

3. Metric equivalents. You should be familiar with the following equivalent measurements.

1 meter = 100 centimeters
1 m = 100 cm

1 centimeter = 1/100 meter
1 cm = 0.01 m

1 centimeter = 10 millimeters
1 cm = 10 mm

1 millimeter = 1/10 centimeter
1 mm = 0.1 cm

1 millimeter = 1000 micrometers
1 mm = 1000 μm

1 micrometer = 1/1000 millimeter
1 μm = 0.001 mm

1 liter = 1000 milliliters
1 L = 1000 mL

1 milliliter = 1/1000 liter
1 mL = 0.001 L

1 milliliter = 1 cubic centimeter
1 mL = 1 cm^3

4. Reading metric scales. The measuring instruments you use in the laboratory are marked in metric units. In most cases, the scale is marked with a series of lines, or **graduations.** Usually, every tenth graduation is numbered, indicating the number of units represented by that graduation. The graduations between the numbered marks then represent one-tenth the difference between the numbered graduations. Sometimes there are only five graduations between numbered marks. Each graduation then represents two tenths (0.2) of the difference between numbered graduations. Study the following examples of metric scales you should be familiar with.

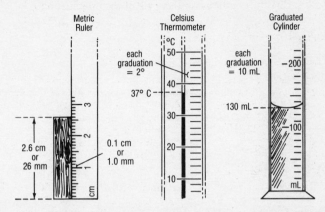

B. STAINING. Lugol's iodine solution and methylene blue are stains commonly used to make cell structures visible under the microscope. The structures that become easier to see include the nucleus, nucleoli, cytoplasm, vacuoles, and when present, chloroplasts and cell wall.

C. CHEMICAL TESTS. Among the chemical tests you should be familiar with are the use of indicators for determining pH (see page 21) and the simple tests for nutrients.

a. pH indicators

Indicator	Color in Acid	Color in Base
Litmus paper	red	blue
Bromthymol blue	yellow	blue

Bromthymol blue is sensitive to a change from slightly basic to slightly acid, or the reverse. It is therefore useful for detecting an increase or decrease in carbon dioxide concentration, for carbon dioxide in water forms a slightly acid solution.

b. Tests for nutrients

Nutrient	Test	Result
Sugar	Add Benedict's solution (blue), heat to boiling	Blue solution turns green, yellow, orange, or brick red
Starch	Add iodine (Lugol's) solution	Blue-black color appears
Protein	Add biuret solution (light blue)	Solution turns pink or purple

QUESTIONS

1. While observing a specimen mounted on a slide under a microscope, a student moves the slide in the direction of arrow A. As seen through the microscope, the image will appear to move in the direction of arrow   (1) A   (2) B   (3) C   (4) D

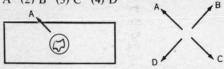

2. A student observed a paramecium under the low-power objective of a microscope (100×) and then under high power (400×). The image of the paramecium under low power, compared to the image of the same paramecium under high power, would be   (1) smaller and in a darker field of view   (2) smaller and in a brighter field of view   (3) larger and in a darker field of view   (4) larger and in a brighter field of view

3. When a thin section of living plant tissue was mounted on a slide and observed under a microscope, it appeared that some of the cells were without nuclei. Which is the most likely explanation for this observation?   (1) Cell nuclei can be seen only with the phase microscope. (2) Some nuclei were not in the plane of the section.   (3) The cells had insufficient light to form nuclei.   (4) The tissue section did not contain nuclei.

4. A student places a drop of water containing paramecia on a slide. He snaps the high-power objective in place and focuses the microscope. Although he scans the slide for several minutes, he is unable to see any paramecia. Which is the best course of action for him to take first in order to see the paramecia?   (1) Wash the slide off and try another drop of water.   (2) Use some substance to slow the paramecia and continue scanning.   (3) Put the low-power objective in place and scan under low power.   (4) Put stain in the water and scan again.

5. Which may be observed by viewing the chloroplasts in the cell of an elodea plant under a microscope?   (1) excretion   (2) photosynthesis   (3) protoplasmic streaming   (4) cellular respiration

6. The diameter of the high-power field of a microscope is 0.5 millimeter. The diameter of a cell that would fill the field would be approximately   (1) 0.5 micrometer   (2) 5.0 micrometers   (3) 50 micrometers   (4) 500 micrometers

7. A student calibrated a microscope with a millimeter scale and found that the low-power field had a diameter of 1 millimeter. She then observed an elodea leaf with the microscope and counted 50 elodea cells in a row across the diameter of the low-power field. The average length of these elodea cells was   (1) 20 micrometers   (2) 50 micrometers   (3) 200 micrometers   (4) 500 micrometers

8. A microscope has a 10× eyepiece and a 10× and 40× objective. The measured diameter of its low-power field is 1.2 millimeters. The diameter of its high-power field is   (1) 120 micrometers   (2) 12,000 micrometers   (3) 300 micrometers   (4) 400 micrometers.

9. Five cubic centimeters of Benedict's solution or Fehling's solution were placed in a test tube and 8 drops of urine were added. The tube was then put in boiling water for 5 minutes. The solution turned brick red. This test indicated that the urine contained   (1) mineral salts   (2) sugar   (3) nitrogen   (4) starch

Base your answers to questions 10 through 12 on the following information:

The apparatus below is to be used in an experiment to show that exhaled air contains more carbon dioxide than inhaled air. (Bromthymol blue turns yellow when carbon dioxide is bubbled through it.)

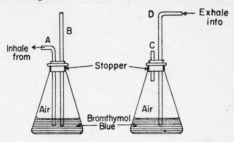

10. Which error was made in setting up the apparatus? (1) Tube A should not extend into the bromthymol blue. (2) Tube B should not extend into the bromthymol blue. (3) Tube C should extend into the bromthymol blue. (4) Tube D should not extend into the bromthymol blue.

11. If the apparatus is used correctly, the bromthymol blue will (1) turn yellow in the inhale flask only (2) turn yellow in the exhale flask only (3) turn yellow in both flasks (4) remain blue in both flasks.

12. Which liquid could be substituted for bromthymol blue? (1) iodine solution (2) limewater (3) ammonium hydroxide (4) Benedict's solution

Base your answers to questions 13 through 15 on the following information and your knowledge of biology.

If heavy rains occur while apple orchards are in bloom, the apple crop the following fall is usually much smaller than would normally be expected.

13. The information given above is best described as (1) an inference (2) a hypothesis (3) a prediction (4) an observation

14. A likely reason for the small crop after heavy rains during the flowering season is that (1) heavy rains reduce the normal activity of most insects (2) water that collects in the ovules prevents fertilization (3) sunlight is necessary for photosynthesis (4) wet weather results in the growth of harmful molds

15. The completed statement in question 14 is best described as (1) an observation (2) a hypothesis (3) a conclusion (4) an assumption

16. Tomato seeds will not germinate in the ripe fruit. This seems to indicate that something in the fruit prevents germination. An experiment to check this would be to moisten tomato seeds with tomato juice. The best control for this experiment would be to moisten (1) other kinds of seeds with water (2) other kinds of seeds with tomato juice (3) tomato seeds with water (4) tomato seeds with hormones

Base your answers to questions 17 through 19 on the experiment described below:

>   Fifty clover seeds are surface-sterilized in an antiseptic solution. Half are planted in sterile soil in pot A; the other half are first mixed with *Rhizobium* nitrogen-fixing bacteria and then planted in sterilized soil in pot B.

17. The plants in pot A are   (1) experimental   (2) controls   (3) variables   (4) hypotheses

18. The variable in this experiment is   (1) the seeds in pot A   (2) the seeds in pot B   (3) the availability of nitrogen   (4) sterility

19. An assumption of this experiment is that   (1) all the seeds will germinate   (2) sterilization kills seeds   (3) nitrogen is needed for plant growth   (4) seeds will germinate in sterilized soil

20. The length of the leaf in the drawing is   (1) 1.07 cm   (2) 1.7 cm   (3) 10.7 cm   (4) 107 mm

21. The volume of the liquid in the graduate is   (1) 10.3 mL   (2) 13 mL   (3) 14 mL   (4) 105 mL

22. The temperature registered by the thermometer is   (1) 73°C   (2) 76°C   (3) 78°C   (4) 80°C

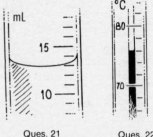

Ques. 21   Ques. 22

Base your answers to questions 23 and 24 on the information below:

>   The following curves describe the growth of two species of protozoa in a single container. Species A serves as food for its natural enemy, species B.

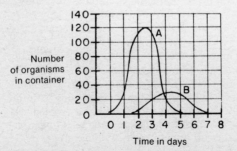

Time in days

23. Which statement best describes these curves?

(1) Species B begins growth when its food, species A, becomes plentiful; species A dies when species B has consumed it; species B dies for lack of food.

(2) Species B begins its growth when species A begins to decrease in number; species A decreases in number because species B is decreasing.

(3) Species A increases in number because species B is not plentiful; species B becomes plentiful because species A has died.

(4) Growth of species B is not dependent on the growth of species A.

24. It can be predicted that, if species A were to become even more numerous on the second day, then the number of species B on the fourth day would   (1) decrease in proportion to A's increase   (2) decrease slightly   (3) remain the same as on the curve   (4) increase

Base your answers to questions 25 and 26 on your knowledge of biology and the two graphs below. The first graph shows the number of days of snow cover from 1940 to 1960 and the second graph shows the percentage of white mice in a population of white mice and brown mice during the same period.

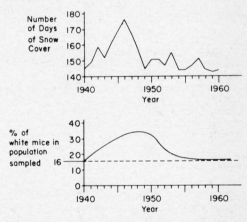

25. The appearance of the maximum percentage of white mice occurred   (1) before the maximum number of days of snow cover   (2) at the same time as the maximum number of days of snow cover   (3) after the maximum number of days of snow cover   (4) both before and after the maximum number of days of snow cover

26. Which statement is supported by the data in the graphs?   (1) The percentage of brown mice was greatest during the years of longest snow cover.   (2) The percentage of mice with white fur was greatest during the years of longest snow cover.   (3) The total number of mice in the population was greatest during years of least snow cover.   (4) The actual number of brown mice was greatest during the years of longest snow cover.

27. When using a gas burner to heat materials in a test tube, it is very important to (1) avoid boiling (2) leave the flame burning at all times to prevent escape of gas (3) be careful where you point the open end of the test tube (4) use the cooler yellow flame rather than the hot blue flame

Base your answers to questions 28 through 32 on the activities described in the paragraph below and on your knowledge of biology.

A tomato plant was placed under a sealed bell jar and exposed to light. Carbon dioxide containing radioactive carbon was introduced into the bell jar as shown in the diagram.

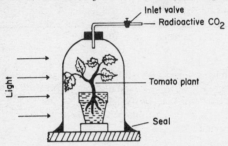

After an hour the inlet valve was closed. Later the entire plant was removed from the soil and cleaned by rinsing in water. A Geiger counter indicated radioactivity in the roots. These roots were then dried and chopped into very small pieces. They were sprinkled into an aquarium containing a hungry goldfish that was not radioactive. Four days later, the fish was removed from the aquarium and a tissue section from the fish was tested with a Geiger counter. The counter indicated an above-normal count.

28. Which cycle is primarily being studied by means of this investigation? (1) oxygen (2) carbon (3) nitrogen (4) water

29. A control setup for this investigation would be identical to the one described except for the replacement of the (1) tomato plant with a geranium plant (2) goldfish with a tadpole (3) radioactive CO_2 with atmospheric CO_2 (4) soil with distilled water

30. By which process was the radioactivity incorporated into the material that was transported to the roots? (1) growth (2) nitrification (3) mitosis (4) photosynthesis

31. What would have resulted if the plant had been kept in complete darkness during this investigation? (1) The roots would not have become radioactive. (2) Respiration would not have occurred. (3) Transport in the plant would not have occurred. (4) The radioactivity would have killed the plant.

32. This investigation suggests that, when plants are eaten by animals, some plant materials may be (1) changed to animal tissue (2) separated into molecules before being digested (3) eliminated by the animal in a form that allows the plants to grow again (4) used in regulating the animal's digestive processes

Base your answers to questions 33 through 36 on the photograph below, which shows an enlarged microscropic view of a cell in an animal embryo.

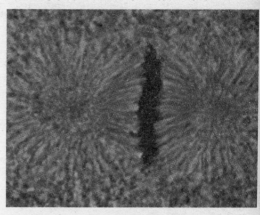

Photograph by Carolina Biological Supply Company

33. The process occurring in this cell is (1) photosynthesis (2) replication (3) meiosis (4) mitosis

34. The stage of the process represented by this photograph is called (1) interphase (2) metaphase (3) synapsis (4) nondisjunction

35. The vertical line of dark structures near the middle of the photograph consists of a (1) cell plate (2) nuclear membrane (3) chromatid (4) complete set of doubled chromosomes

36. One result of the process occurring in this cell is (1) exchange of nuclear material (2) variation of offspring (3) formation of two cells with the same hereditary information (4) reduction in the number of chromosomes

Base your answers to questions 37 through 40 on the passage below and your knowledge of biology.

ANIMAL FEEDS AND BACTERIAL RESISTANCE TO ANTIBIOTICS

In recent years it has become a widespread practice to add subtherapeutic doses of antibiotics to animal feeds as a means of promoting weight gain. It is feared that this use of antibiotics has contributed to the spread of antibiotic resistance among pathogenic bacteria that then infect humans.

A possible example of this effect was uncovered in a recent investigation at the Centers for Disease Control. The investigation centered on 18 cases of human diarrheal disease that occurred about the same time in several Midwest states. The disease was caused by the bacterium *Salmonella newport*. Bacteria obtained from the patients were resistant to several antibiotics, including tetracycline, and they all carried the same plasmid. (A plasmid is a circlet of DNA outside the main bacterial chromosome. Many plasmids are known to carry genes that confer resistance to antibiotics.)

Several months before this outbreak, diarrheal disease had occurred among cows at a dairy farm in South Dakota. *Salmonella* bacteria isolated from the infected cows showed the same resistance pattern and the same plasmid as did the bacteria from the human patients. Adjacent to this dairy farm is a beef feedlot where cattle had been fed tetracycline. The investigators were able to determine that nearly all the victims of the salmonellosis had eaten hamburger made from beef that came from these feedlot animals.

Among the conclusion drawn from this investigation are that (1) it is possible for antibiotic-resistant bacteria to develop in animals fed with antibiotics, and (2) the resistant bacteria can be transmitted to humans through the food chain and cause disease.

37. The purpose of adding antibiotics to animal feed is to   (1) make the animals grow faster   (2) reduce the cost of the feed   (3) build disease immunity in the animals   (4) improve the nutritive value of beef
38. In this investigation, antibiotic-resistant bacteria were found in (1) humans only   (2) cows only   (3) humans and cows   (4) beef cattle only
39. Antibiotic resistance in the bacteria studied in this investigation was   (1) a hypothesis   (2) an inference   (3) an observation   (4) a variable
40. Resistance to tetracycline in the bacteria was probably produced by a gene   (1) on the bacterial chromosome   (2) in the intestines of the cattle   (3) transmitted through the food chain   (4) on a plasmid

Base your answers to questions 41 through 44 on the information below and on your knowledge of biology.

A laboratory investigation was performed to determine the effect of temperature on the rate of action of an enzyme. Ten grams of chopped hard-boiled egg white was placed into each of six identical test tubes. The test tubes were then filled with a dilute solution of gastric protease and hydrochloric acid. The tubes were stoppered, and each was placed in an environment at a different constant temperature and mechanically agitated for one hour. At the end of that time, the egg white remaining in each tube was filtered out and dried, and its mass was measured. The observations are shown in the data table below.

DATA TABLE

Temperature (in °C)	Mass of Undigested Egg White (in grams)	Percentage of Egg White Digested
5	9.5	
15	7.0	
25	5.0	
35	4.0	
45	7.5	
55	10.0	

41. Calculate the percentage of egg white that was *digested* in each case and enter it in the data table.
42. Construct a graph showing the relationship between percentage of egg white digested and temperature. Label each axis of the graph and mark it with an appropriate scale. Plot the data and connect the points.
43. The results of this experiment indicate that gastric protease digests protein (egg white) most rapidly at a temperature of   (1) 5°C (2) 25°C   (3) 35°C   (4) 45°C or higher
44. Normal human body temperature is 37°C. The results of this experiment indicate that when body temperature rises above normal, the rate of protein digestion probably   (1) increases   (2) decreases   (3) fluctuates widely   (4) is not affected

Base your answers to questions 45 through 47 on the information below and on your knowledge of biology.

A student was working on an investigation to measure the relative activity of an enzyme at various pH values. He collected the following data:

pH 2, enzyme activity 10; pH 8, enzyme activity 50; pH 12, enzyme activity 10; pH 4, enzyme activity 20; pH 6, enzyme activity 40; pH 10, enzyme activity 40.

45. Organize the data above in a Data Table with two columns, following the directions below:

a. Label each column of the Data Table with an appropriate heading.

b. Fill in the two columns so that the pH values are increasing.

46. Using the information in the Data Table you prepared, construct a graph, following the directions below:

a. Label and make an appropriate scale on each axis.

b. Plot the data and connect the points.

47. Using a complete sentence, describe the conditions of acidity or alkalinity under which the enzyme is most effective.

Base your answers to questions 48 through 50 on the drawings below, which show a piece of onion epidermal tissue stained with iodine solution and observed with a compound microscope.

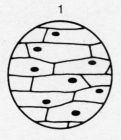

1

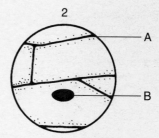

2

A

B

48. Name the structures labeled *A* and *B*.

49. Using a complete sentence, state the function of structure *B*.

50. Using a complete sentence, describe the adjustment of the microscope that was made to change from view 1 to view 2.

51. Four pieces of laboratory equipment are shown below. Write the name of the piece of equipment shown that should be used to obtain the most accurate measure of the volume of a liquid.

100°C

0°C

Base your answers to questions 52 through 54 on the four sets of laboratory materials listed below and on your knowledge of biology.

Set *A*
Light source
Colored filters
Beaker
Test tubes
Test tube stand

Set *B*
Scalpel
Forceps
Scissors
Pan with wax bottom
Pins
Stereomicroscope
Goggles

Set *C*
Droppers
Benedict's solution
Iodine
Test tubes
Starch solution
Sugar solution
Test tube holder
Heat source
Goggles

Set *D*
Compound light microscope
Glass slides
Water
Forceps

52. Which set should a student select in order to test for the presence of a carbohydrate in food?

53. Which set should a student select to determine the location of the aortic arches in the earthworm?

54. Which set should a student use to observe chloroplasts in elodea (a green waterplant)?

Base your answers to questions 55 through 57 on the diagram below of a compound microscope.

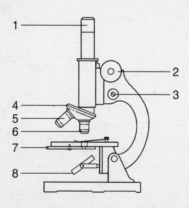

55. Write the number and the name of the part that is used for focusing under low power only.

56. Write the number of the low-power objective.

57. Using a complete sentence, name and state the function of part number 7.

58. Using a complete sentence, name an indicator you have used in biology this year, and tell what that indicator detects or measures.

Base your answers to questions 59 through 61 on the diagram below which represents a partially dissected earthworm and on your knowledge of biology.

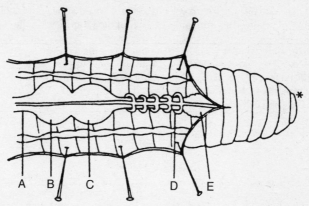

59. Select one letter from the diagram and write that letter and the name of the structure it represents.

60. Using one or more complete sentences, describe a function for the structure selected in question 59.

61. Which term best describes the region of the earthworm indicated by the *? (1) posterior (2) lateral (3) anterior (4) ventral

For each statement in questions 62 through 64 write the *number* of the laboratory procedure, chosen from the list below, that best applies to that statement.

Each procedure uses a sample of peeled raw potato whose dimensions are 2 cm × 2 cm × 2 cm.

Laboratory Procedures

(1) Place 2 drops of methylene blue solution on the potato sample.

(2) Place 2 drops of iodine (Lugol's) solution on the potato sample.

(3) Weigh the potato sample; place the sample in a beaker of distilled water for 30 minutes; remove the sample from the beaker and reweigh.

(4) Weigh the potato sample; heat the sample for 5 hours in an oven at 80°C; remove the sample from the oven and reweigh.

62. This procedure demonstrates the effects of osmosis.

63. This procedure would be used to detect the presence of starch in the potato sample.

64. This procedure provides information which can be used to determine the total water content of the potato sample.

Base your answers to questions 65 through 67 on the information below and on your knowledge of biology.

An investigation was conducted to test the effects of varying salt concentrations on potato cells. A student sliced a piece of raw potato into five 10-gram samples. Four of the samples were then placed in separate beakers, *A–D*, whose contents are indicated in the data table below. The fifth sample was placed in an empty beaker, *E*, and sealed. After 24 hours, the samples were removed from the beakers. The condition of each sample was then compared to the sample taken from the empty beaker. The data table shows these observations.

Key: Degree of Firmness

*least firm   *****most firm

Data Table

Beaker	Contents	Condition of Potato Sample After Removal from Beaker
A	pure water	*****
B	1% salt solution	***
C	4% salt solution	**
D	6% salt solution	*
E	empty	****

Directions (65–67): Your answers to the following questions must be written in complete sentences.

65. In this investigation, what is the purpose of the potato sample placed in the empty beaker?

66. State one variable in this investigation.

67. Name the process which resulted in the condition of the potato sample in beaker *A*.

Base your answers to questions 68 through 72 on the reading passage below and on your knowledge of biology.

The Great Lakes

The ecological balance of the Great Lakes has been seriously altered by human civilization, which has disrupted species in food chains from the producers (microscopic plankton) to the predator fish. This disruption has caused a reduction in the natural game fish populations of the lakes.

For example, the Atlantic salmon was formerly found in Lake Ontario. The salmon's passage to Lake Erie was blocked by

Niagara Falls. This fish was a prize catch for fishermen, but no Atlantic salmon have been caught in Lake Ontario since 1890. Soil that eroded from farmland covered the salmon's gravel spawning grounds with silt, trees that shaded the streams where the young salmon lived were torn down as forests were cleared, and dams built for sawmills prevented the salmon from traveling upstream to spawn.

As the population of Atlantic salmon and other deepwater fish declined, two alien marine species—the alewife and the sea lamprey—appeared in Lake Ontario. These intruders most likely entered the lake by way of the Hudson River, the Erie Canal, and the Oswego River. The lack of predators and the abundant food supply led to a rapid increase in the populations of these species until they were the dominant species in the lake. Furthermore, the completion of the Welland Canal linking Lake Erie and Lake Ontario in 1932 gave these species access to the remainder of the Great Lakes. By the early 1970's, about half of the fish caught throughout the Great Lakes were alewives. The sea lamprey's increasing population devastated the desirable fish in the lakes, harming the fishing industry.

Government agencies such as the United States Fish and Wildlife Service took action at this point to restore the game fish to the lakes and return sport fishing to this region. They developed a lampricide that proved fatal to the young sea lampreys, but had no harmful effects on other species. They also started stocking the lakes with predator game fish such as coho salmon, chinook salmon, and steelhead trout. As a result of these actions, the populations of the alewife and the sea lamprey have both decreased, and sport fishing has returned to Lake Ontario.

68. Which would most likely have occurred if the microscopic plankton had been removed from Lake Ontario when Atlantic salmon were abundant? (1) Predator fish would have thrived.   (2) Game fish would have increased their spawning activities.   (3) Food chains would have been disrupted. (4) The water level in the lake would have increased.

69. Which fish species was *not* introduced into the Great Lakes for sport fishing? (1) coho salmon   (2) chinook salmon   (3) alewife   (4) steelhead trout

70. Which graph represents the effect of the spread of human civilization on the population of Atlantic salmon in Lake Ontario?

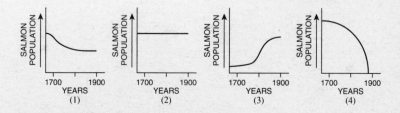

Directions (71–72): Your answers to the following questions must be written in complete sentences.

71. State one way humans contributed to the change in the Atlantic salmon population in Lake Ontario.

72. Explain the role humans played in the appearance of the alewife and the sea lamprey in Lake Erie.

Base your answers to questions 73 through 77 on the passage below and on your knowledge of biology.

Acid Deposition

Acid rain is a complex environmental puzzle. In large areas of Canada and the northeastern United States, people are concerned about its possible effects.

Many scientists do not use the term *acid rain*; instead they refer to "acid deposition," a more complex but more accurate name. Acid deposition can mean two things: (1) sulfur and nitrogen pollutants in the air react with water in the atmosphere and form acid precipitation, or (2) sulfur and nitrogen pollutants are directly deposited on the surface of the earth where they react with water, forming acid substances. Either way, the increased acidity changes the chemistry of both land and water environments. Two main causes of acid deposition are the burning of fossil fuels (such as coal, oil, and gasoline) and natural sources (such as volcanoes and bacterial decay).

Water in pollution-free environments is actually slightly acidic. It has an average pH of 5.6. So a pH of 5.6 is a standard that may be used to judge whether water in the enviornment (rain, lakes, etc.) is truly more acidic than usual.

In cases of acid deposition, pH values from 3 to 5 are common, with some as low as 1.5. An important factor is *where* the acid deposition occurs. Other substances in the environment can neutralize the acid. For example, in one area the acid might be neutralized by the presence of calcium compounds or ammonia.

Evidence shows that acid deposition has an adverse effect on the environment. In lakes with increasing acidity, scientists have observed a decrease in the fish population. The acidity appears to reduce the fishes' ability to reproduce and the ability of the young fish to survive. It also seems to decrease the productivity of plankton* and to encourage the growth of more acid-resistant types of plants. On land, increased acidity can damage foliage (trees, etc.) and change the chemistry of the soil.

In summary, it appears that acid deposition is a complex and serious environmental problem. It may have adverse effects on the environment if left unchecked.

---

*plankton—*Free-floating, usually microscopic organisms found near the surface of the water*

73. Which substance may neutralize acidic conditions in the environment? (1) carbon dioxide (2) calcium carbonate (3) nitrogen (4) sulfur

74. Which of the following is *not* a possible source of acid deposition? (1) automobile exhaust (2) a volcanic eruption (3) a water-powered electric generating plant (4) burning of coal in industry

75. Acid deposition can serve as (1) a selective agent in the environment (2) a biotic factor in the environment (3) an agent to produce alkaline soil (4) a growth accelerator for fish

Directions (76–77): Your answers to the following questions must be written in complete sentences.

76. What measurement made in the water of a lake would indicate that acid deposition may be occurring?

77. Why is acid deposition a more accurate term than acid rain for the causes of increasing acidity of the environment?

Base your answers to questions 78 through 82 on the passage below and on your knowledge of biology.

HIV and AIDS

Acquired immunodeficiency syndrome (AIDS) is a fatal disease that has spread to over 120 countries in the world. The disease is caused by human immunodeficiency virus (HIV), an infectious virus which may be spread through the exchange of body fluids during sexual contact with an infected person or through the sharing of contaminated needles by drug abusers. Once in the bloodstream, HIV attaches to the surface of white blood cells called helper T-lymphocytes. Helper T-lymphocytes normally assist B-lymphocytes in producing antibodies against foreign antigens. Foreign antigens can be in the form of bacteria, viruses, or toxins. Helpter T-lymphocytes also direct killer T-cells to attack cells of the body that have already been infected by many types of viruses as well as cells that are part of transplanted organs.

After HIV attaches to a helpter T-lymphocyte, HIV injects its nucleic acid, RNA, into the cell. HIV is called a retrovirus because its RNA directs the synthesis of DNA within the host lymphocyte with the help of an enzyme called reverse transcriptase. The DNA made from the viral RNA becomes incorporated into the DNA of the nucleus of the lymphocyte. This DNA can direct the formation of new HIV within the cell that reduces the effectiveness of the helper T-cell in the immune system. The infected lymphocyte is eventually destroyed and the newly made viruses are released into the bloodstream to infect other cells. As the number of certain helper T-cells in the body decreases, the immune system becomes less and less able to resist other diseases.

Directions (78–82): Your answers to the following questions must be written in complete sentences.

78. After human immunodeficiency virus has entered the bloodstream, what is the next step in the sequence leading to the development of AIDS?

79. State one normal function of the helper T-lymphocyte.

80. What is the normal function of killer T-cells?

81. What is the role of the RNA of the invading HIV when it is released into the host cell?

82. Why do many AIDS patients die from other diseases such as pneumonia?

Base your answers to questions 83 through 87 on the passage below and on your knowledge of biology.

Lyme Disease

Since 1980, the number of reported cases of Lyme disease in New York State has been increasing. The vector (carrier) of Lyme disease is the small deer tick, *Ixodes dammini*. The disease is spread from infected animals to ticks that bite these animals. Humans bitten by these parasitic ticks may then become infected.

The symptoms of Lyme disease do not always occur immediately after a tick bite. An individual may develop a skin rash several days to weeks after being bitten by a tick. Flu-like symptoms such as headaches, muscle aches, joint pain, and fever may also develop. Generally, these symptoms clear up and the individual may not seek medical help. Also, in some cases there may be no symptoms other than a sudden onset of arthritis. However, in a small number of cases, if the infection is not treated, it may lead to chronic arthritis, disorders of the heart and nervous system, or in a few cases, death. A blood test can help to confirm a diagnosis, and antibiotics are effective in treating the infection.

People may take preventive action by frequently checking themselves and their pets for ticks, tucking pant legs into socks when walking through woods, wearing light-colored clothing to aid in spotting a tick, and using insect repellent.

83. Based on the reading passage, what is the vector for Lyme disease? (1) dog ticks (2) deer ticks (3) dogs (4) deer

84. The vector described in the reading passage is an example of (1) a parasite (2) a predator (3) an autotroph (4) a saprophyte

Directions (85–87): Your answers to the following questions must be written in complete sentences.

85. State one way people might protect themselves from getting Lyme disease.

86. State two symptoms that may occur if a person has Lyme disease.

87. State one danger of ignoring any symptoms that may develop after a tick bite.

GLOSSARY

abiotic factor: A physical factor of the environment, such as water, air, light, or temperature.

absorption: The passage of materials across a cell membrane into the cell; the process by which usable materials are taken into an organism.

acid: A compound that produces an excess of hydrogen ions in a water solution.

active site: The region on an enzyme where the reaction it catalyzes takes place.

active transport: A process in which the movement of materials across a cell membrane requires the expenditure of cellular energy.

adaptation: An inherited trait or modification that improves the chance of survival and reproduction of an organism in a given environment.

addition: The breaking-off of a segment of a chromosome and its attachment to the homologous chromosome.

adenine: A nitrogenous base found in DNA and RNA.

ADP (adenosine diphosphate): The lower-energy compound remaining after one phosphate group is removed from ATP.

adrenal gland: An endocrine gland that secretes hormones that help the body deal with stress.

adrenaline (epinephrine): A hormone produced by the medulla of the adrenal gland; a neurotransmitter produced by some neurons.

adult: The stage in the development of an animal at which it becomes capable of reproduction.

aerobic respiration: Respiration carried on in the presence of free oxygen, in which glucose is completely oxidized to carbon dioxide and water.

aging: The natural processes by which all organisms gradually become less efficient in the performance of the life functions.

air sac: The structure at the end of a bronchiole where gas exchange takes place.

allele: One of the two or more forms of the gene for a specific trait.

allergy: A disorder caused by the release of histamine by the body cells following an antigen-antibody reaction.

alveolus (pl., **alveoli**): A cavity in an air sac that is the respiratory surface in the lung.

amino acid: The structural unit of proteins; contains a carboxyl group ($-COOH$), an amino group ($-NH_2$) and a side chain.

amnion: In both shelled eggs and mammals, a fluid-filled extraembryonic sac that surrounds the embryo; provides a watery environment and protects the embryo.

amylase: An enzyme that breaks down starch.

anaerobic respiration: Respiration in the absence of free oxygen, in which glucose is partially oxidized.

anal pore: The opening through which indigestible wastes are ejected from a paramecium.

anaphase: The stage of mitosis during which the daughter chromosomes move to opposite poles.

anemia: A disorder in which the blood contains too few red blood cells or insufficient hemoglobin.

anterior: Pertaining to the front, or head, end of a bilaterally symmetrical animal.

anther: The saclike structure of a stamen in which pollen grains are produced.

antibody: A protein produced by lymphocytes, that reacts with a specific foreign substance, or antigen, and inactivates it.

anticodon: A sequence of three bases on tRNA that is complementary to a mRNA codon and specifies the amino acid that the tRNA carries.

antigen: Any substance that can cause a response of the immune system.

anus: The opening of the digestive tube through which undigested materials are eliminated from the body.

aorta: The single blood vessel running along the dorsal surface of the grasshopper; the major artery carrying oxygenated blood away from the heart.

aortic arch: A heartlike blood vessel in the earthworm.

apical meristem: Meristematic tissue that produces lengthwise growth of plant roots and stems.

appendix: A small pouch found where the small intestine joins the large intestine.

arteriole: The smallest type of artery.

artery: A blood vessel that carries blood away from the heart to the organs and tissues of the body.

asexual reproduction: A type of reproduction in which there is only one parent; all offspring are genetically identical to the parent.

associative neuron: See interneuron.

aster: A star-shaped structure formed during mitosis by fibers extending from the centriole.

atom: The smallest particle of an element that has the properties of that element; the unit of which elements are made.

ATP (adenosine triphosphate): The compound in which energy released by cellular respiration is stored.

atrium: One of the upper, thin-walled chambers of the heart; auricle.
auricle: See **atrium.**

autonomic nervous system: A division of the peripheral nervous system consisting of involuntary motor fibers from the brain and spinal cord that serve the internal organs of the body.

autosome: A chromosome other than a sex chromosome.

autotroph: An organism capable of synthesizing its needed organic nutrients from inorganic substances.

autotrophic nutrition: A type of nutrition in which the organism does not require preformed organic substances from its environment.

auxin: A hormone that affects the growth of plant tissues.

axon: A long, thin fiber that carries nerve impulses away from the cell body of a neuron.

base: A compound that produces an excess of hydroxyl ions when dissolved in water.

bile: The secretion of the liver that breaks down globules of fats and oils into small droplets (emulsification).

binary fission: The simplest form of asexual reproduction, in which the parent organism divides into two approximately equal parts.

biodegradable: Able to be broken down by bacteria and other decay organisms into simpler substances.

biome: A large geographical region showing a particular type of climax vegetation.

biosphere: The portion of the earth in which living things exist.

biotic factor: An organism in an environment and its effects on other living things.

bladder: The organ that temporarily stores urine after it has left the kidneys.

blastula: A stage of development in which the embryo consists of a single layer of cells surrounding a fluid-filled cavity.

blending inheritance: See **incomplete dominance.**

brain: A group of specialized nerve cells that control and coordinate the activities of a nervous system.

breathing: The movement of air into and out of the lungs.

bronchial tube: One of the branches of a bronchus.

bronchioles: The finest branches of the bronchial tubes.

bronchus (pl., **bronchi**): A cartilage-ringed tube that branches from the trachea and enters a lung.

bud: An outgrowth of the parent organism; in plants, the bud gives rise to a new shoot; in protists and animals, the bud gives rise to a new, smaller individual organism.

budding: A type of asexual reproduction in which the parent organism divides into two unequal parts.

bulb: A short underground stem with leaves and stored food that can give rise to new plants by vegetative reproduction.

calorie: The amount of heat needed to raise the temperature of 1 g of water 1°C; the unit for measuring the energy content of foods.

cambium: A meristematic tissue that increases the diameter of stems and roots.

capillary: A microscopic blood vessel that connects the smallest arteries to the smallest veins.

capillary action: The upward movement of a liquid in a tube of narrow diameter.

carbohydrate: A compound of carbon, hydrogen, and oxygen in which the ratio of hydrogen to oxygen is 2:1.

carbon cycle: The pathways by which carbon is circulated through the biosphere.

cardiac muscle: A type of striated, involuntary muscle tissue found in the heart.

carnivore: An animal that feeds on other animals.

cartilage: A type of flexible connective tissue.

cast: A type of fossil formed when a mold becomes filled with minerals and hardens, producing a copy of the external features of an organism.

catalyst: A substance that increases the rate of a particular chemical reaction without being changed itself.

cell: The basic unit of structure and function in living things; the smallest unit in living things that shows the characteristics of life.

cell body: The part of a nerve cell that contains the nucleus and is the site of the metabolic activities of the cell; cyton.

cell membrane (plasma membrane): The structure that separates the interior of a cell from the surrounding environment and controls the passage of materials into and out of the cell.

cell plate: A structure formed during telophase in a plant cell that divides the cell in half and becomes part of the new cell walls of the daughter cells.

cell wall: The rigid structure, often composed of cellulose, that encloses the cells of plants and various microorganisms.

cellular respiration: The process by which energy stored in food is released by cells.

central nervous system: The division of the nervous system that includes the brain and the spinal cord (or, in simple animals, the nerve cord).

centrifuge: A device in which materials of different densities can be separated from one another by whirling them at high speed in a tubular container.

centriole: A cylindrical organelle found near the nucleus in animal cells that is involved in cell division.

centromere: The region of attachment of two sister chromatids.

cerebellum: A part of the brain located below the rear part of the cerebrum; coordinates voluntary movements.

cerebrum: The largest part of the human brain.

chemical bond: A force of attraction between atoms that holds them together in compounds.

chemical transmitter: See **neurotransmitter.**

chitin: The polysaccharide that makes up the exoskeleton of arthropods.

chlorophyll: The major photosynthetic pigment of plants and algae.

chloroplast: A plastid that contains chlorophyll and is a site of photosynthesis.

chorion: The membrane that surrounds the embryo and the other extraembryonic membranes in mammals, birds, and reptiles.

chromatid: One of the two strands of a doubled chromosome.

chromatin: In nondividing cells, the material of the chromosomes in the form of long, thin threads.

chromatography: A process used to separate and analyze mixtures of chemical substances.

chromosomal alteration: A change in chromosome structure, resulting in new gene combinations.

chromosome: During cell division, a rodlike structure in the nucleus on which the genes are located.

cilium (pl., **cilia**): A hairlike organelle on the surface of a cell, with the capacity for movement.

circulation: The movement of materials within a cell or between parts of an organism.

cleavage: In a fertilized egg, the first series of cell divisions, which occur without growth and which continue until the cells of the embryo are reduced to the size of most cells of the adult organism.

climax community: A mature, stable community that is the final stage of an ecological succession.

clone: A group of individual organisms that have identical genetic makeups.

closed circulatory system: A circulatory system in which blood is always confined in vessels.

coacervate: According to the heterotroph hypothesis, an aggregate of large proteinlike molecules; thought to have developed into the first forms of life on the primitive earth.

codominance: The expression of both alleles of a heterozygous pair; a condition in which neither allele of a pair is dominant over the other.

codon: A group of three bases in a mRNA sequence that specifies a particular amino acid.

coenzyme: A nonprotein, organic substance necessary to the functioning of a particular enzyme.

color blindness: A sex-linked trait in which an individual cannot perceive certain colors.

commensalism: A type of symbiotic relationship in which one organism benefits from the association and the other is not affected.

community: All the different populations within a given area.

complete protein: The protein content of a food that provides all the essential amino acids.

compound: A substance made of two or more kinds of atoms combined in definite proportions.

compound microscope: A microscope with two lenses or lens systems — an ocular and an objective.

concentration gradient: The difference in concentration between a region of greater concentration and a region of lesser concentration.

conditioned response: The simplest type of learned behavior.

conducting tissue: The xylem and phloem of a plant; vascular tissue.

constipation: A condition in which undigested material moves through the large intestine too slowly, so that too much water is extracted, the feces become hard, and elimination is infrequent or difficult.

consumer: A heterotroph; an organism that obtains nutrients from other organisms.

contractile vacuole: In protists, a specialized cytoplasmic structure that collects excess water from the cell and then expels it into the environment by active transport.

control: The setup in a controlled experiment in which no change is made.

controlled experiment: An experiment set up in duplicate, with a single factor changed in one of the setups.

corm: A short underground stem containing stored food; it can give rise to new plants by vegetative reproduction.

coronary circulation: The subdivision of the systemic circulation that supplies blood to the muscle of the heart.

corpus luteum: The progesterone-secreting yellow body in the ovary, formed when LH causes a ruptured follicle to fill with cells.

cortisol: A hormone secreted by the adrenal cortex that affects the metabolism of carbohydrates, proteins, and fats.

cotyledon: A modified leaf of the plant embryo, which often provides nourishment for the developing seedling.

covalent bond: A chemical bond formed by the sharing of electrons.

crop: In many invertebrates, a thin-walled organ that temporarily stores food from the esophagus.

cross: In genetics, the mating of two organisms with contrasting traits.

crossing-over: The process in which pieces of homologous chromosomes are exchanged during synapsis in the first meiotic division.

cross-pollination: The transfer of pollen from an anther on one plant to a stigma on another plant.

cutting: Any vegetative part of a plant used to produce a new plant by artificial vegetative reproduction.

cyclosis: A type of circulation occurring inside a cell, in which there is a streaming motion of the cytoplasm.

cyton: See **cell body.**

cytoplasm: The watery material between the nucleus and the cell membrane of a cell.

cytosine: A nitrogenous base found in DNA and RNA.

dark reactions: The series of reactions in photosynthesis in which carbon fixation occurs and which do not require light.

deamination: A step in the chemical breakdown of amino acids in which the amino group ($-NH_2$) is removed.

decomposer: An organism of decay.

deficiency disease: A disease or disorder resulting from the lack of a necessary nutrient in the diet.

dehydration synthesis: A type of reaction in which two molecules are bonded together by the removal of a water molecule.

deletion: A type of chromosomal alteration in which a portion of a chromosome, and the genes it contains, is lost.

denaturation: A distortion in the shape of an enzyme molecule caused by high temperature and making it unable to function as a catalyst for its substrate.

dendrite: A short, branched part of a neuron specialized for receiving nerve impulses and transmitting them to the cell body.

denitrifying bacteria: Bacteria that convert nitrates and ammonia to nitrogen gas, which is released into the atmosphere.

deoxyribose: A 5-carbon sugar found in DNA.

desert: A biome in which there is too little rainfall to support trees or grasses; shows great variation in temperature between day and night.

development: A complex series of changes that occur after fertilization and eventually give rise to the adult organism.

diaphragm: The muscle that forms the floor of the chest cavity.

diarrhea: A condition in which undigested material moves through the large intestine too rapidly, so that insufficient water is extracted, the feces are watery, and elimination is excessively frequent.

diastole: The period of relaxation during the heartbeat cycle.

dicot: A plant whose seeds have two cotyledons.

differentiation: The series of changes that transforms unspecialized embryonic cells into the specialized cells, tissues, and organs that make up an organism.

diffusion: The movement of molecules or particles from an area of greater concentration to an area of lesser concentration.

digestion: The breakdown of complex food materials into simpler forms that can be used by the organism.

dihybrid cross: A genetic cross in which two pairs of contrasting traits are studied.

dipeptide: A type of molecule formed when two amino acids are joined by a peptide bond.

diploid (2n) number: The full number of chromosomes characteristic of the species.

disaccharide: A double sugar formed by joining two monosaccharides by dehydration synthesis.

disjunction: The separation of homologous pairs of doubled chromosomes during meiosis.

DNA (deoxyribonucleic acid): The nucleic acid that contains the hereditary information; the genetic material.

dominance: The principle of genetics stating that when organisms pure for contrasting traits are crossed, all their offspring will show the dominant trait.

dominant trait: The trait that appears in the offspring of a cross between two pure individuals showing contrasting forms of the trait.

dorsal: Pertaining to the upper side or the back of a bilaterally symmetrical animal.

dorsal vessel: A major blood vessel of the earthworm that runs along the top of the digestive tract.

double helix: The structure of the DNA molecule, formed by the coiling of two parallel strands.

Down's syndrome: A genetic disorder caused by the nondisjunction of chromosome 21, and resulting in the presence of an extra chromosome; Mongolism.

ductless gland: A gland of the endocrine system.

ecological succession: The process by which an existing community in an ecosystem is gradually replaced by another community.

ecology: The branch of biology that deals with all the interactions between organisms and their environment.

ecosystem: The interaction of a community with its physical environment.

ectoderm: The outer layer of cells in a simple animal or embryo; one of the germ layers of the embryo.

effector: A muscle or gland.

egestion: The elimination of undigested material from the digestive tract.

egg cell (egg): The female gamete.

electron: A negatively charged particle found in the space outside the nucleus of an atom.

electron microscope: A microscope that uses an electron beam rather than light, and electromagnetic lenses, to produce very great magnifications.

electrophoresis: A technique used to separate and analyze mixtures of chemical substances whose particles have an electrical charge.

element: A substance made entirely of one kind of atom.

embryo: An organism in the early stages of development.

embryo sac: A seven-celled structure in the ovule of a flower in which fertilization occurs.

emphysema: A disease of the lungs in which the tissue loses elasticity and the walls of the alveoli break down.

emulsification: The process of breaking fats and oils into tiny droplets.

end product: The final substance produced by the digestion of a nutrient.

endocrine gland: A gland that secretes hormones directly into the blood; a duct-less gland.

endoderm: The inner layer of cells in a simple animal or embryo; one of the germ layers of the embryo.

endoplasmic reticulum: A system of membrane-enclosed, fluid-filled canals that form a network through the cytoplasm of a cell.

endoskeleton: A skeleton composed of bone and cartilage located within the body walls.

endosperm: The tissue that develops from the endosperm nucleus, often serving as a food supply for the plant embryo.

enzyme: A protein that acts as a catalyst, increasing the rate of a specific chemical reaction.

enzyme-substrate complex: The temporary union of an enzyme and its substrate.

epicotyl: The part of a plant embryo above the point of attachment of the cotyledons; gives rise to the terminal bud, leaves, and upper part of the stem.

epidermis: In plants, a protective tissue that forms the outer layer of leaves, green stems, and roots. In animals, the outer layer of skin consisting of layers of tightly packed epithelial cells.

epiglottis: A flap of tissue that covers the trachea during swallowing so that food passes only into the esophagus.

equatorial plane: In mitosis, the region midway between the poles of the cell.

erosion: The removal of soil by the action of wind and/or water.

esophagus: The tube that is the passageway for food from the mouth to the stomach.

essential amino acid: An amino acid that the body is unable to synthesize and must obtain from the protein in its food.

estrogen: A hormone secreted by the ovaries that promotes development of female secondary sex characteristics and regulates the reproductive cycle.

evolution: The theory that life arose by natural processes at an early stage of the earth's history and that complex organisms developed from simple organisms by a process of gradual change.

excretion: The process by which the wastes of cellular metabolism are removed from an organism.

exoskeleton: A skeleton found on the outside of the body, enclosing the soft parts.

extensor: A muscle that extends a joint.

external fertilization: The process in which eggs are fertilized outside the body of the female.

extracellular digestion: Digestion that occurs outside a cell under the action of enzymes secreted by the cell.

eyepiece: See **ocular**.

Fallopian tube: See **oviduct**.

fatty acid: A type of organic molecule that consists of a carbon chain with at least one carboxyl group attached to it; one of the end products of the digestion of lipids (fats).

feces: Undigested and undigestible food material that is solidified in the large intestine and then eliminated from the body.

feedback: An interaction in which a change in some quantity has an effect on the factor that originally caused the change.

fermentation: Following glycolysis, the conversion of pyruvic acid to an end product with no further release of energy.

fertilization: The union of an egg cell nucleus and a sperm cell nucleus to form a zygote.

fetus: The developing baby after about the second month of pregnancy.

fiber: See **roughage**.

fibrin: A protein that forms a meshwork of strands over a wound in the blood-clotting process.

fibrinogen: A soluble plasma protein that is converted into insoluble fibrin strands during the blood-clotting process.

filament: The stalklike structure that supports the anther in a stamen.

filtration: The process in which substances pass from the blood into the nephron of the kidney.

first-level consumer: A herbivore in a food chain; a primary consumer.

flagellum (pl., **flagella**): A hairlike organelle at the surface of a cell, with the capacity for movement.

flexor: A muscle that bends a joint.

follicle: A structure in the human ovary in which the mature egg develops.

follicle-stimulating hormone: See **FSH**.

food chain: A series of organisms through which food energy is passed in an ecosystem.

food vacuole: A vacuole in which food is digested in microorganisms and simple animals.

food web: Interconnected food chains in an ecosystem.

fossil: The remains or traces of an extinct organism.

fraternal twins: Two individuals formed when two eggs are fertilized at the same time; twins that are genetically different.

fruit: A structure that develops from the ovary and other associated flower parts after fertilization and that contains the seeds.

FSH (follicle-stimulating hormone): A hormone secreted by the anterior pituitary that stimulates the development of eggs in the ovaries.

gall bladder: The organ that stores bile produced by the liver.

gamete: A monoploid sex cell; a sperm cell or egg cell.

gametogenesis: The process by which gametes develop in the gonads.

ganglion: A group of cell bodies and associative neurons that switch, relay, and coordinate nerve impulses.

gastric juice: The digestive secretion of glands in the stomach, containing hydrochloric acid and pepsin.

gastrula: In animal development, an embryo undergoing gastrulation, which results in the formation of the second germ layer.

gastrulation: The process in which the cells on one side of a blastula push in to form the two-layered gastrula.

gene: A distinct unit of hereditary material found in chromosomes; a sequence of nucleotides in DNA that codes for a particular polypeptide.

gene frequency: The percentage of individuals in a population carrying a certain gene.

gene linkage: See **linked genes.**

gene mutation: A change in the sequence of the bases in a gene, that changes the structure of the polypeptide that the gene codes for.

gene pool: The total of all the genes in a population.

gene splicing: See **genetic engineering.**

genetic engineering: The process of producing altered DNA, usually by breaking a DNA molecule and inserting new genes.

genetics: The branch of biology concerned with the ways in which hereditary information is transmitted from parents to offspring.

genotype: The genetic makeup of an individual.

genus: A group of closely related species.

geographic isolation: The first stage of speciation, in which interbreeding of organisms within a species is prevented by a natural barrier.

geotropism: The growth response of a plant to the force of gravity.

germination: The development of a seed when supplied with water and other necessary conditions.

gestation period: The length of a pregnancy.

GH: See **growth hormone.**

gizzard: In many invertebrates, a thick-walled grinding organ that crushes food released from the crop.

gland: An organ that produces certain substances that are released into ducts or into the blood.

glomerulus: A cluster of capillaries in the nephron of a kidney.

glucagon: The hormone secreted by the pancreas that increases the blood glucose level.

glucose: A monosaccharide that is the main source of energy for respiration in most organisms.

glycerol: An alcohol that reacts with fatty acids to form fats; one of the end products of the digestion of lipids (fats).

glycogen: A polysaccharide that is the main food storage compound in animals.

glycolysis: The series of reactions in which a glucose molecule is converted into two molecules of pyruvic acid with a net gain of 2 ATP.

goiter: An enlargement of the thyroid gland, often due to a deficiency of iodine.

Golgi body: An organelle consisting of stacks of membranes forming flattened sacs in the cytoplasm, which serves as a storage center for proteins synthesized by a cell.

gonad: In animals, a specialized organ in which gametes develop.

gradualism: In the theory of evolution, the idea that evolution proceeds by a series of small, gradual, and continuous changes.

grafting: A type of artificial vegetative propagation accomplished by permanently joining a part of one plant to another plant.

grana: Stacks of lamellae in a chloroplast that contain the pigments for photosynthesis.

grassland: A biome in which there is not enough rainfall to support trees and the dominant form of vegetation is grasses; prairie.

growth: The process by which living organisms increase in size.

growth hormone (GH): A hormone secreted by the anterior pituitary that controls the growth of the body.

guanine: A nitrogenous base found in DNA and RNA.

guard cell: In leaves, a specialized epidermal cell that regulates the opening and closing of the stomates.

gullet: The part of the paramecium where food particles enter the cell.

habit: Learned behavior that becomes automatic.

habitat: The particular part of the environment in which an organism lives.

haploid: See **monoploid.**

Hardy-Weinberg law: The principle that under certain conditions the gene frequencies in sexually-reproducing populations do not change.

heart: The organ that pumps blood through a circulatory system.

heart attack: A blockage of the blood flow in one of the coronary arteries, resulting in damage to the portion of the heart muscle in the affected region.

hemoglobin: A red, iron-containing respiratory pigment that increases the oxygen-carrying capacity of the blood.

hemophilia: A hereditary disease in which one or more of the clotting factors are missing from the blood.

herbivore: A heterotroph that feeds only on plants.

hermaphrodite: An individual organism that possesses both testes and ovaries.

heterotroph: An organism that cannot synthesize its own nutrients and must obtain them ready-made.

heterotroph hypothesis: The hypothesis that the first organic compounds were formed by natural chemical processes on the primitive earth and that the first lifelike structures developed from coacervates and were heterotrophs.

heterotrophic nutrition: A type of nutrition in which the organism requires pre-formed organic substances from its environment or its food.

heterozygous: Having two different alleles for a trait.

high blood pressure: See **hypertension.**

homeostasis: The maintenance of a stable internal environment in an organism.

homologous chromosomes: A pair of chromosomes having the same size and shape and carrying alleles for the same traits.

homologous structures: Structures found in different kinds of organisms that have the same basic arrangement of parts and a similar pattern of embryonic development.

homozygous: Having two identical alleles for a trait.

hormone: A substance secreted by a gland directly into the bloodstream that produces a specific effect on a particular tissue.

host: In parasitism, the organism in which the parasite lives and from which it obtains nutrients.

humus: The dark, rich organic matter in topsoil formed from the decay of dead plants and animals.

hybrid: An individual that is heterozygous for a trait.

hydrolysis: The process by which molecules are broken apart by the addition of water molecules.

hypertension: A condition in which the blood pressure remains much above normal throughout the heartbeat cycle; high blood pressure.

hypocotyl: The part of a plant embryo below the attachment of the cotyledons, which gives rise to the lower portion of the stem and the roots.

hypothesis: A possible explanation of an observed set of facts.

ICF: See **intercellular fluid.**

identical twins: Two individuals formed when one fertilized egg divides in half at an early stage of development, producing two organisms with the same genetic makeup.

immunity: The ability of the body to resist a particular disease.

implantation: The attachment of the embryo to the uterine lining.

imprint: A type of fossil formed when an impression in mud made by a living thing is preserved when the mud is transformed into rock.

impulse: A region of electrical and chemical change that passes along the nerve cell membrane.

inborn immunity: Immunity to a disease that is present at birth.

incomplete dominance: A type of inheritance in which the dominant allele of a contrasting pair is not fully expressed in a heterozygous individual and the phenotype is intermediate between the pure dominant and the pure recessive phenotypes; blending inheritance.

incomplete protein: Protein that does not contain all the essential amino acids.

independent assortment: The principle of genetics stating that different traits are inherited independently of one another.

indicator: A substance that changes color when the pH goes above or below a certain value.

industrial melanism: The development of dark-colored organisms in a population exposed to industrial air pollution.

inference: A hypothesis or conclusion based on the results of an experiment.

ingestion: The taking in of food from the environment.

inorganic compound: A compound that does not contain carbon and hydrogen.

instinct: A complex, inborn behavior pattern.

insulin: A hormone secreted by the pancreas that lowers blood glucose levels.

intercellular fluid (ICF): The colorless, watery fluid that bathes all the cells of the body.

internal fertilization: The process in which eggs are fertilized within the body of the female.

interneuron: A neuron that relays impulses from one neuron to another.

interphase: The stage of the cell reproductive cycle lasting from the end of one cell division to the beginning of the next.

intestine: The organ in which digestion and absorption of food occurs; often called small intestine.

intracellular digestion: Digestion that occurs in vacuoles in the cytoplasm of a cell.

inversion: A type of chromosomal alteration in which a portion of a chromosome is reversed, resulting in the reversal of the order of the genes in the segment.

involuntary muscle: Muscle that is not under conscious control; smooth muscle.

ion: An atom or group of atoms with an electrical charge.

ionic bond: The force of attraction between two ions in a chemical compound.

islets of Langerhans: The endocrine portion of the pancreas, consisting of clusters of hormone-secreting cells.

isotope: An atom that differs from other atoms of the same element by the number of neutrons in its nucleus.

joint: A point in the skeleton where bones meet.

juvenile hormone: In a caterpillar, a hormone that prevents the transformation of the larva into more mature forms.

karyotyping: A technique for examining the chromosome makeup of an individual.

kingdom: A group of related phyla; the largest category in systems of classification.

lacteal: A small lymph vessel found in the center of a villus.

lamellae: The system of double membranes inside a chloroplast.

large intestine: The portion of the digestive tract, leading to the rectum, in which no digestion occurs, water is absorbed, and the feces are formed.

larva: An early developmental stage of some animals; must undergo metamorphosis to reach the adult form.

larynx: The voice box; connects the pharynx with the trachea.

lateral meristem: Meristem tissue that produces growth in the diameter of roots and stems; cambium.

latitude: Distance north or south of the equator.

layering: A type of artificial vegetative propagation, accomplished by covering part of a growing plant with soil.

leukocyte: See **white blood cell.**

ligament: A tough, fibrous band of connective tissue that holds the bones together at a movable joint.

light reactions: In photosynthesis, a series of reactions requiring light in which water is split and ATP and $NADPH_2$ are produced.

limiting factor: A condition of the environment that limits the growth of a population, such as limited availability of food, water, space, or some other necessity.

linked genes: Genes located on the same chromosome; they are not independently assorted, but instead are generally distributed together during meiosis.

lipase: An enzyme that breaks down lipids.

lipid: An organic compound, other than a carbohydrate, consisting of carbon, hydrogen, and oxygen; a fat, oil, or wax.

litmus paper: A pH indicator that turns red in an acid solution and blue in a basic solution.

locomotion: Self-generated movement from one place to another.

lung: In vertebrates, an organ specialized for the exchange of gases between the blood and the atmosphere.

lymph: The fluid inside the lymph vessels.

lysosome: A small, saclike organelle that contains hydrolytic enzymes.

magnification (magnifying power): The amount of enlargement of an image that a lens or a microscope produces.

Malpighian tubule: The excretory organ of grasshoppers and other insects.

maltase: An enzyme that breaks down maltose and other disaccharides to glucose.

mammary gland: An exocrine gland in female mammals that secretes milk for the nourishment of young after they are born.

marine biome: A community of organisms inhabiting salt water.

marsupial: Nonplacental mammals in which the fetus completes its development in a pouch on the mother's body.

medulla: In the brain, the part beneath the cerebellum and continuous with the spinal cord; controls involuntary activities. The middle region of the kidney.

meiosis: Cell division that occurs only in sex cells and that produces monoploid cells; reduction division.

menopause: The cessation of the menstrual cycle.

menstrual cycle: The hormone-controlled cycle in the human female in which an egg matures and is released from the ovary and the uterus prepares to receive it.

menstruation: The shedding of some of the uterine lining, the unfertilized egg, and a small amount of blood through the vagina, which occurs about once a month in the human female.

meristematic tissue: The only tissue of a mature plant capable of cell division; meristem.

mesoderm: The germ layer between the endoderm and ectoderm.

messenger RNA (mRNA): The type of RNA strand that carries the code for a polypeptide from DNA in the nucleus to the ribosomes in the cytoplasm, where it is translated into amino acid sequences during protein synthesis.

metabolism: All the chemical reactions of the life processes of an organism.

metamorphosis: The series of changes that certain types of organisms undergo as they develop from an egg to an adult.

metaphase: The stage of mitosis during which the chromosomes line up at the equatorial plane and the chromatids separate.

microdissection: Operations done under a microscope on living cells, using very small instruments.

micrometer: One-millionth of a meter; also called micron.

micropyle: A small opening in the ovule through which the pollen tube grows.

microtome: An instrument used to slice thin sections of a specimen for viewing with a microscope.

microtubule: A long, cylindrical organelle found in cilia and flagella.

migration: The movement of animals from one region or community to another.

mineral: An inorganic substance found naturally in the earth's crust.

mitochondrion: An oval, membrane-enclosed organelle in which most of the reactions of cellular respiration occur.

mitosis: The process by which the nucleus of a cell divides, producing two nuclei with the diploid chromosome number.

mitotic cell division: Cell division in which the nucleus divides by mitosis.

model: In science, any representation of an object or process that helps to explain its properties and behavior.

mold: A type of fossil formed when sediment in which an organism is embedded hardens, preserving the shape of the organism after its remains decompose. A kind of fungus.

molecule: An uncharged group of atoms held together by covalent bonds.

Monera: A kingdom including the simplest types of one-celled organisms, in which there is no membrane-enclosed nucleus; the bacteria and blue-green algae.

Mongolism: See **Down's syndrome.**

monocot: A plant whose seeds have one cotyledon.

monoploid (n): Having half the diploid number of chromosomes; haploid.

monosaccharide: The simplest type of carbohydrate, with the empirical formula CH_2O; a simple sugar.

motile: Capable of locomotion.

motor neuron: A neuron that carries impulses from the spinal cord and brain toward an effector.

mRNA: See **messenger RNA.**

mucus: A lubricant secreted by cells in the linings of the respiratory and digestive systems.

multiple alleles: Three or more different forms of a gene, each producing a different phenotype.

multiple birth: The birth of more than one child from the same pregnancy.

multiple-gene inheritance: The type of inheritance in which two or more pairs of genes affect the same characteristic.

muscle: A tissue consisting of cells with the capacity to contract and exert a pull.

mutagenic agent: A material or environmental factor capable of causing mutations to occur.

mutation: The appearance of a new allele on a chromosome.

mutualism: A symbiotic relationship in which both organisms benefit from their association.

natural selection: The idea that organisms with favorable variations are better able to survive and reproduce than organisms not as well adapted.

negative feedback: A type of feedback that tends to oppose an initial change and thus maintains the stability of the quantities involved.

nephridium: The organ of excretion in the earthworm.

nephron: The functional unit of the kidney.

nerve: A bundle of axons that are bound together by connective tissue.

nerve cell: A neuron.

nerve net: In the hydra, an interconnected network of nerve cells through which impulses can travel in any direction.

neuron: A cell specialized for the transmission of impulses; the functional unit of the nervous system.

neurotransmitter: A substance released by the synaptic knob into the synaptic cleft that initiates impulses in adjacent neurons.

neutral: Neither acidic nor basic; a neutral solution has a pH of 7.

neutralization: The reaction of an acid and a base to produce a neutral solution.

neutron: An electrically neutral particle found in the nuclei of atoms.

niche: The particular way in which a species functions in an ecosystem.

nitrifying bacteria: Bacteria that can convert nitrites to nitrates.

nitrogen cycle: The pathways by which nitrogen is circulated through the biosphere.

nitrogen-fixing bacteria: Bacteria that can produce nitrogen compounds from the gaseous nitrogen of the atmosphere.

nondisjunction: The failure of homologous chromosomes to separate normally during meiosis, producing offspring with one more or one less chromosome than normal.

nonplacental mammal: A mammal in which no placenta forms during development of the embryo and the necessary nutrients are supplied by the yolk of the egg.

nucleic acid: An organic compound with a very large molecule made up of repeating units called nucleotides, which form the genetic code for transmitting hereditary information; DNA or RNA.

nucleolus: A dense, granular body, found in the nucleus of cells, that is a site of RNA production.

nucleotide: The basic unit of DNA, containing a sugar, a phosphate group, and one of the four nitrogenous bases.

nucleus: In a cell, a large, dense, membrane-enclosed body that controls the cell's metabolism and reproduction. In an atom, the central core of the atom, containing protons and neutrons.

nutrient: A substance that can be used in metabolism for energy, for growth and repair, or for regulation.

nutrition: The process by which materials are taken from the environment into an organism and changed into usable forms.

objective: The lens of a compound microscope that is close to the specimen and forms an image that is further enlarged by the ocular.

ocular: The lens of a compound microscope that is placed close to the eye and through which the image of the specimen is observed.

omnivore: A heterotroph that feeds on both plants and animals.

one-gene-one-polypeptide hypothesis: The hypothesis that every gene directs the synthesis of a particular polypeptide chain; originally called the one-gene-one-enzyme hypothesis.

open circulatory system: A circulatory system in which blood is not always enclosed in blood vessels, but flows into open spaces to bathe the tissues.

oral groove: The opening in the paramecium through which food is ingested.

organelle: A specialized structure in the cytoplasm of a cell that carries out a specific function.

organic compound: A compound that contains carbon along with hydrogen; found in nature only in the bodies and products of living organisms.

organism: An individual living thing.

osmosis: The diffusion of water across a semipermeable membrane from a region of high concentration of water to a region of low concentration of water.

ovary: In animals, the female gonad, which produces egg cells; in the flower, the structure at the base of the pistil in which fertilization occurs and which develops into a fruit.

oviduct: The tube leading from the ovary to the uterus.

ovulation: The release of an egg from an ovary.

ovule: In seed plants, a structure within the ovary that contains the egg cell nucleus and that develops into the seed after fertilization.

ovum: Egg cell.

oxidation: A type of chemical reaction in which an atom or molecule loses electrons or hydrogen atoms.

oxidation-reduction reaction: A reaction in which one substance is oxidized and another substance is reduced.

pancreas: A combination of exocrine and endocrine glands that secrete digestive juice and the hormones insulin and glucagon.

pancreatic juice: The digestive secretion of the pancreas containing amylase, proteases, and lipases.

parasite: A heterotroph that obtains nutrients from the organism in or on which it lives.

parasitism: A symbiotic relationship in which one organism benefits from the association and the other is harmed.

parathormone: A hormone secreted by the parathyroid glands that regulates calcium and phosphate metabolism.

parathyroid glands: Four small glands embedded in back of the thyroid that secrete parathormone.

parthenogenesis: The development of an unfertilized egg into an adult animal without fusion with a sperm nucleus.

passive transport: A process by which materials move across cell membranes without the expenditure of cellular energy.

penis: In mammals, the male organ through which the urethra passes to the outside of the body and through which urine and sperm pass out of the body.

pepsin: A digestive enzyme in gastric juice.

peptide bond: The bond formed between two amino acids by dehydration synthesis.

peripheral nervous system: The division of the nervous system that includes all the neurons and nerve fibers outside the brain and spinal cord.

peristalsis: The alternate waves of relaxation and contraction in the walls of the alimentary canal.

perspiration: The excretion of water by the sweat glands in the skin, which then reaches the surface through the pores and evaporates; also, the water released through the pores.

petal: One of the leaflike structures in the flower, inside the sepals and surrounding the reproductive organs.

petrifaction: The process by which the body of a dead organism is slowly replaced by dissolved minerals.

pH: A unit that indicates the concentration of hydrogen ions in a solution; a measure of the acidity or alkalinity of a solution.

phagocytosis: The process in which large particles or small organisms are ingested into a cell.

phenotype: The physical trait that appears in an individual as a result of its genetic makeup.

phenylketonuria (PKU): A genetic disease in which an enzyme necessary for the normal breakdown of the amino acid phenylalanine is missing, causing brain damage and mental retardation.

pheromone: A type of animal secretion that serves as a means of communication between members of the same species.

phloem: The tissue that conducts food and other dissolved materials throughout the plant.

phosphate: An inorganic compound containing phosphorus in the form of the PO_4^{-3} ion.

photosynthesis: The process by which organic nutrients are synthesized from inorganic compounds in the presence of light in autotrophic organisms.

phototropism: The growth of a plant toward a light source.

phylum: The largest or most inclusive group within a kingdom.

pigment: A substance that absorbs light of particular wavelengths.

pinocytosis: The process in which liquids or very small particles from the surrounding medium are taken into a cell.

pioneer organism: One of the first organisms to inhabit an area.

pistil: The female reproductive organ of flowering plants.

pistillate flower: A flower that contains pistils but no stamens.

pituitary gland: The endocrine gland attached to the hypothalamus that controls the activities of many other endocrine glands in the body.

PKU: See **phenylketonuria.**

placenta: In mammals, a temporary organ through which the embryo receives food and oxygen from the mother's body and gets rid of wastes.

placental mammal: A mammal in which a placenta forms during development of the embryo.

plasma: The liquid portion of blood, consisting mostly of water and dissolved proteins.

plasma membrane: See **cell membrane.**

platelet: A small, round or oval blood cell fragment that triggers the blood-clotting process.

pole: In cell division, the two regions from which the spindle fibers radiate and toward which the chromosomes move during anaphase.

pollen grain: The small sporelike structure containing the male monoploid gamete produced by the anther in flowering plants.

pollen tube: The extension of the pollen grain through which the sperm nuclei pass from the pollen grain to the ovule of a flower.

pollination: The transfer of pollen from an anther to a stigma of a flower.

pollution: The addition of anything to the environment that makes it less fit for use.

polymer: A large molecule consisting of chains of repeating units.

polypeptide: A chain of amino acids joined by peptide bonds.

polyploidy: A condition in which the cells have some multiple of the normal chromosome number.

polysaccharide: A long chain of repeating sugar units formed by joining simple sugars by dehydration synthesis.

population: A group of organisms of the same species living together in a given region and capable of interbreeding.

population genetics: The study of the changes in the genetic makeup of populations.

precipitation: The release of water from the atmosphere in such forms as rain, snow, dew, and fog.

predator: A carnivore that attacks and kills its prey and feeds on their bodies.

pregnancy: The condition in which an embryo is developing in the uterus of a female mammal.

primary consumer: An animal that feeds on plants; a herbivore.

primary succession: Succession that occurs in an area that had no previously existing life.

producer: An organism that produces organic compounds from inorganic compounds; an autotroph.

progesterone: A hormone secreted by the ovaries that helps to regulate the menstrual cycle and maintains the uterus during pregnancy.

prophase: The stage of mitosis in which the chromatids and spindle appear, and the nuclear membrane disappears.

protease: An enzyme that breaks down proteins.

protein: A compound consisting of one or more chains of amino acids.

Protista (protists): Simple, mostly one-celled organisms in which a membrane-enclosed nucleus is present.

proton: A positively charged particle found in the nucleus of all atoms.

pseudopod: A temporary projection of the cell surface in amebas and similar cells.

puberty: The stage of development in which a human individual begins to produce gametes and becomes capable of reproduction; the onset of sexual maturity.

pulmonary circulation: The pathways in which blood flows between the heart and the lungs.

punctuated equilibrium: In the theory of evolution, the idea that evolution proceeds by sudden, major changes in types of species occurring at widely spaced intervals of time.

pupa: The resting stage of metamorphosis in which the tissues of an insect are organized into the adult form.

pure: Homozygous for a trait.

pyramid of biomass: The relative mass of organisms at each feeding level in an ecosystem.

pyramid of energy: The amount of available energy at each feeding level in an ecosytem.

pyruvic acid: A 3-carbon compound formed by glycolysis.

radioactivity: The process in which an atom changes to another isotope or element by giving off charged particles and/or radiation.

radioisotope: A radioactive isotope.

receptor: A specialized structure in a nervous system that is sensitive to a certain type of stimulus.

recessive gene: Gene whose phenotype is not expressed if the dominant allele is also present.

recombinant DNA: DNA that has been altered by genetic engineering.

rectum: Structure in which undigested food (feces) is stored prior to elimination from the body.

recycling: The process of reusing materials rather than discarding them as waste.

reduction: A type of chemical reaction in which an atom or molecule gains electrons or hydrogen atoms.

reduction division: See **meiosis.**

reflex: An involuntary, automatic response to a given stimulus not involving the brain.

reflex arc: The pathway over which the nerve impulses travel in a reflex.

regeneration: The regrowth of lost body parts by an animal.

regulation: The processes by which an organism maintains a stable internal environment in a constantly changing external environment.

replication: Duplication, especially of DNA.

reproduction: The process by which living things produce new organisms of their own kind.

reproductive isolation: The loss of the ability to interbreed successfully by two groups of a population that have been separated geographically for a sufficiently long time.

resolution (resolving power): The ability of a microscope to show two points that are close together as separate images; sharpness of detail in an image.

respiration: The process by which organisms obtain the energy they need by releasing chemical energy stored in nutrients.

respiratory surface: A moist surface through which the exchange of respiratory gases takes place.

response: Any change in or action by an organism resulting from a stimulus.

Rh factor: One of a group of antigens found on the surface of red blood cells.

rhizoids: In fungi, rootlike hyphae that penetrate the food source, secrete digestive enzymes, and absorb the digested nutrients.

rhizome: A thick, horizontal stem containing stored food, which forms new plants by vegetative reproduction.

ribonucleic acid: See **RNA.**

ribose: A 5-carbon sugar found in RNA.

ribosomal RNA (rRNA): A type of RNA formed by DNA in the nucleolus and found in the ribosomes.

ribosome: An organelle that is the site of protein synthesis in a cell.

RNA (ribonucleic acid): The nucleic acid that carries out instructions coded in DNA.

root: A structure adapted for anchoring a plant in soil and absorbing water and dissolved substances.

root hair: A hairlike extension of a root epidermal cell that increases the surface area for absorption.

roughage: Bulky, indigestible material in food; also called fiber.

rRNA: See **ribosomal RNA.**

runner: A horizontal stem with buds that forms independent plants by vegetative reproduction.

saliva: The secretion of the salivary glands.

salivary gland: A gland that secretes saliva into the mouth.

salt: A compound produced by a neutralization reaction between an acid and a base.

saprophyte: An organism that obtains nutrients by breaking down the remains of dead plants and animals.

scavenger: A carnivore that feeds on dead animals that it finds.

scrotum: A sac of skin outside the body wall in which the testes of the male are located.

secondary consumer: A carnivore that feeds on plant-eating animals (primary consumers) in a food chain.

secondary sex characteristic: A characteristic, such as body hair, muscle development, broadened pelvis, or voice depth, controlled by the male and female sex hormones, but not essential to the reproductive process.

secondary succession: Succession that occurs in an area in which an existing community has been partially destroyed and its balance upset.

second-level consumer: See **secondary consumer.**

secretion: A substance manufactured by a cell for use by the organism for some purpose other than as a source of energy.

sedimentary rock: A type of rock formed from layers of particles that settled to the bottom of a body of water, in which many fossils are usually found.

seed: In seed plants, the structure formed from the ovule following fertilization that contains the plant embryo and nutrients.

seed coat: A tough, protective covering around a seed that develops from the wall of the ovule.

segregation: In genetics, the separation of alleles during meiosis; the presence of only one allele for a particular trait in each gamete.

selection: A technique in which only those animals and plants with the most desirable traits are chosen for breeding.

selectively permeable membrane: See **semipermeable membrane.**

self-pollination: Pollination in which pollen grains either fall or are transferred from an anther to a stigma on the same plant.

semen: The fluid mixture in which sperm pass out of the male body through the urethra.

semipermeable membrane: A membrane that allows the passage of some materials but not others.

sense organ: See **receptor.**

sensory nerve: A nerve containing the axons of sensory neurons only.

sensory neuron: A neuron that carries impulses from a receptor toward the spinal cord and brain.

sepal: A leaflike structure at the base of a flower, outside the petals.

sessile: Living attached to some object; not motile.

seta (pl., **setae**): A tiny bristle on the body segments of some animals, used in locomotion.

sex chromosomes: The two unmatched chromosomes that determine the sex of an individual; represented as X and Y.

sex gland: A gland in which gametes are produced; ovary or testis.

sex-linked trait: A trait that is controlled by a gene found on one of the sex chromosomes.

sexual reproduction: A form of reproduction in which a new individual is produced by the union of the nuclei of two specialized sex cells, usually produced by two separate parent organisms.

sickle-cell anemia: A genetic disease in which the red blood cells have an abnormal hemoglobin molecule and an abnormal shape.

simple microscope: A magnifying glass.

simple sugar: A monosaccharide.

skeletal muscle: Muscle attached to bone that is involved in locomotion and voluntary movement; striated muscle.

skeleton: The hard structures that give support and shape to the body of an organism.

small intestine: See **intestine.**

smooth muscle: Muscle whose cells do not show striations (parallel lines) under the microscope; involuntary muscle.

somatic nervous system: The division of the peripheral nervous system that contains sensory and motor neurons that connect the central nervous system to skeletal muscles, skin, and sense organs.

speciation: The formation of new species.

species: All organisms of one kind that can interbreed in nature.

sperm cell (sperm): The male gamete.

sperm nuclei: The two nuclei that travel down the pollen tube and enter the ovule.

spinal column: In vertebrates, the series of vertebrae connected by cartilage discs that surround and protect the spinal cord; backbone.

spinal cord: The large nerve connected to the brain at its anterior end and passing through the spinal column; a part of the central nervous system.

spindle: A cone-shaped structure formed by fibers during mitosis.

spiracle: The opening through which air enters and leaves the body of a grasshopper.

spore: A small, resistant reproductive cell that can give rise to a new organism under favorable conditions.

sporulation: Spore formation.

stain: A substance used to distinguish structures of cells under the microscope.

stamen: The male reproductive organ of a flower.

staminate flower: A flower that contains stamens but no pistils.

starch: A polysaccharide that is the main food storage compound in plants.

stigma: An enlarged, sticky knob on the top of a stigma that receives the pollen.

stimulus: Any factor that causes a receptor to trigger impulses in a nerve pathway.

stolon: A runner.

stomach: The organ in which food is temporarily stored and partially digested.

stomate: An opening in the epidermis of leaves that allows the exchange of respiratory gases between the internal tissues of the plant and the atmosphere.

striated muscle: Muscle tissue whose cells show striations (parallel lines) under the microscope.

style: In flowers, the supporting structure of a pistil, at the upper end of which is the stigma.

substrate: The substance upon which an enzyme acts.

sweat gland: A gland composed of a tiny coiled tube that opens to the surface of the skin and secretes perspiration.

symbiotic relationship: A relationship in which two different types of organisms live in a close association that benefits at least one of them.

synapse: The region where nerve impulses pass from one neuron to another.

synapsis: In meiosis, the joining of homologous chromosome pairs at their centromeres, forming a tetrad.

synthesis: A process in which simple substances are combined chemically to form more complex substances.

systemic circulation: The circulatory pathways that carry blood from the heart to all parts of the body except the lungs.

systole: The period of contraction during the heartbeat cycle.

taiga: A biome in which the climax vegetation is evergreen forest, characterized by cold winters and warmer, moist summers.

Tay-Sachs disease: A genetic disease in which an enzyme necessary for the breakdown of lipids in the brain is missing.

telophase: The stage of mitosis during which the chromatin reappears, the spindle and asters disappear, and the nuclear membrane reforms.

temperate deciduous forest: A biome in which the climax vegetation is deciduous trees, and characterized by hot, humid summers and cold winters.

tendon: A strong band of connective tissue that attaches skeletal muscle to bone.

terrestrial biome: A land biome.

test cross: A genetic cross in which a test organism showing the dominant trait is crossed with one showing the recessive trait; used to determine whether the test organism is homozygous dominant or heterozygous.

testis (pl. **testes**): The male gonad, which produces sperm and secretes male sex hormones.

testosterone: A male sex hormone secreted by the testes that stimulates development of the male reproductive system and promotes male secondary sex characteristics.

tetrad: A pair of double-stranded, homologous chromosomes joined at their centromeres during meiosis.

thymine: A nitrogenous base found in DNA.

thyroid: The endocrine gland located in front of the trachea that secretes thyroxine and calcitonin.

thyroid-stimulating hormone (TSH): A hormone secreted by the anterior pituitary that stimulates the production of thyroxin by the thyroid gland.

thyroxin: An iodine-containing hormone secreted by the thyroid that regulates the rate of metabolism in the body.

trachea: The tube through which air passes from the pharynx to the lungs.

transfer RNA (tRNA): The type of RNA that carries a particular amino acid to mRNA at the ribosome in protein synthesis.

translocation: The movement of dissolved materials through a plant; in genetics, the transfer of a chromosome segment to a nonhomologous chromosome.

transpiration: The loss of water vapor from a plant through the stomates of the leaves.

transpiration pull: The chief process by which water rises through the xylem of a plant.

transport: All the processes by which substances pass into or out of cells and circulate within the organism.

tropical rain forest: A biome found around the equator in which there is a constant supply of rainfall and the temperature remains constant at about 25°C throughout the year.

tropism: A growth response in a plant caused by an environmental stimulus that comes primarily from one direction.

TSH: See **thyroid-stimulating hormone.**

tube nucleus: The nucleus that travels down the pollen tube but does not enter the ovule.

tuber: An enlarged portion of an underground stem that can grow into a new plant by vegetative reproduction.

tundra: A biome characterized by a low average temperature, permafrost, and a very short growing season.

ultracentrifuge: A high-speed centrifuge that can be used to separate the various parts of a cell from one another.

umbilical cord: In mammals, the connection between the fetus and the placenta.

uracil: A nitrogenous base that is found in RNA in place of thymine.

urea: A nitrogenous waste formed from ammonia and carbon dioxide.

ureter: A tube that carries urine from the kidney to the bladder.

urethra: The tube that carries urine from the bladder to the outside of the body.

uric acid: A dry, nitrogenous waste product excreted by birds, reptiles, and insects.

urinary bladder. See **bladder.**

urine: A liquid nitrogenous waste composed of water, urea, and salts.

uterus: The thick, muscular organ in the female mammal in which the embryo develops.

vacuole: A fluid-filled organelle enclosed by a membrane.

vagina: The structure leading from the uterus to the outside of the body in females; the birth canal.

valve: A structure that permits the flow of a liquid in one direction only.

variable: In an experiment, any factor or condition that is under the control of and is changed by the experimenter.

variation: A characteristic in an individual that is different from that of other individuals of the same species.

vascular bundle: A plant structure containing the xylem and phloem vessels; some also contain cambium.

vascular tissue: See **conducting tissue.**

vegetative reproduction: The process in which undifferentiated plant cells divide mitotically and then differentiate to form an independent plant; vegetative propagation.

vein: In leaves, a structure that contains the vascular tissues; in animals, a blood vessel that carries blood from the body tissues to the heart.

ventral: The lower or belly side of a bilaterally symmetrical animal.

ventral nerve cord: In some invertebrates, such as the earthworm and grasshopper, a large nerve running along the lower portion of the body.

ventricle: One of the lower, thick-walled chambers of the heart from which blood is pumped out to the arteries.

venule: The smallest type of vein.

vestigial structure: A nonfunctional structure in a modern organism that is a remnant of a structure that was functional in some ancestral form.

villus (pl., **villi**): A small, fingerlike projection of the lining of the small intestine.

virus: An extremely small particle consisting of DNA or RNA surrounded by a protein coat and capable of reproducing itself inside a living cell.

vitamin: An organic nutrient needed in very small amounts for certain body functions.

voluntary muscle: Muscle under conscious control; skeletal muscle.

water cycle: The cycling of water between the surface of the earth and the atmosphere.

white blood cell: A nucleated blood cell that serves as part of the body's defense against disease; leukocyte.

xylem: The tissue that conducts water and minerals from the roots upward through the plant, and helps to support the plant.

yolk: Stored food in an animal egg.

yolk sac: In shelled eggs, the extraembryonic membrane that surrounds the yolk, containing blood vessels that transport food to the embryo; in mammals, an extraembryonic membrane that forms part of the umbilical cord.

zygote: The diploid cell resulting from fertilization.

THE COLLEGE BOARD BIOLOGY ACHIEVEMENT TEST

The College Board publishes an official guide to the Achievement Tests that describes all the tests offered. A supply of the booklet is shipped at the beginning of each school year to every secondary school. Whenever you plan to take an Achievement Test, you should be able to obtain a free copy of the guide from your school office or guidance department. You may also obtain a copy by writing to the College Board ATP, P.O. Box 6200, Princeton, NJ 08541-6200.

From the booklet you will learn that the Biology Achievement Test takes one hour and consists of 95 multiple-choice questions, each with 5 answer choices. You will also find a tabulation of the topics covered, with approximate percentages of the questions devoted to each topic, and several sample questions.

The Achievement Test in Biology is divided into three parts. Part A usually contains about half the questions on the test. These are the familiar type, similar to those on the Regents Examination, in which you simply choose the best of the suggested answers or completions. Some of these questions may be based upon a graph or other illustration, as in question 9 and questions 54–59 of the following practice test. These questions also include a question format that may be unfamiliar to you, illustrated by question 3 of the practice test. Here, you have to decide which items in a list satisfy a stated condition, and choose your answer accordingly.

Part B consists of what the College Board calls classification questions. There is a series of questions preceded by a list of five choices. You choose one item from the list to answer each question in the series. Any item in the list may be used more than once or not at all in answering the questions.

Part C consists of sets of questions that require you to understand and draw inferences from a given description of a biological investigation or experimental situation. Many of the questions on laboratory skills on pages 188 to 198 of this book are of this type, as well as many in Parts II and III of the Regents Examination.

It is important to know that you receive one point for each correct answer and zero for a question you do not answer, but you lose one-fourth of a point for each wrong answer. It is therefore usually better to skip a question rather than make a random guess. However, you should answer a question whenever you can narrow the choice by eliminating answers you are sure are incorrect. Be sure to budget your time so that you get through the whole test before the hour is up. Do not spend a lot of time struggling with a question you find difficult. Your object should be to answer as many questions as you can the first time through, and then go back to the harder ones if you have time. You will find a number of other test-taking tips in the College Board guide mentioned earlier.

PREPARING FOR THE BIOLOGY ACHIEVEMENT TEST

The College Board Achievement Test in Biology includes questions on a number of topics that are not required by the Regents Syllabus and therefore not reviewed in the body of this book. The following sections summarize the basic facts and understandings of those additional topics.

CLASSIFICATION OF ORGANISMS
Principles of Classification

A highly condensed summary of the principles of classification and the five-kingdom system is given on pages 2–3 and in the table on page 4. The following additional information will be helpful in answering Achievement Test questions on this topic.

CLASSIFICATION LEVELS.   Just as each kingdom is divided into phyla, each phylum is divided into *classes;* each class, into *orders;* each order, into *families;* and each family, into *genera* (singular, *genus*). As explained on page 3, the final division is into *species* within each genus. (In the classification of plants, the term *Division* is sometimes used in place of *Phylum.*) Example: The classification of the dog is: kingdom: Animals; phylum: Chordates (subphylum: Vertebrates); class: Mammals; order: Carnivores; family: Canidae; genus: *Canis;* species: *Canis familiaris.* Other species in this genus include the wolf *(Canis lupus)* and the jackal *(Canis aureus).* The fox is in the same family, but another genus *(Vulpes).*

Some Details of Modern Classification

MONERANS (Kingdom Monera).   Organisms consisting of a single cell (or chains or colonies of cells) with no nuclear membrane or other organelles with membranes. Also called prokaryotes.
  1. Bacteria (Phylum Schizomycetes).   Smallest organisms. Some occur in pairs or chains of cells. Have cell walls. Classified by shape:
    a. Cocci.   Spherical cells.
    b. Bacilli.   Rodlike cells. (*Escherichia coli* is a bacillus.)
    c. Spirilla.   Spiral-shaped.
  2. Blue-green algae (Phylum Cyanophyta).   Larger than bacteria. Contain chlorophyll (but no chloroplasts) and are photosynthetic. Examples: *Oscillatoria, Nostoc, Gloeocapsa.*

PROTISTS (Kingdom Protista).   Unicellular or very simple multicellular organisms, with cells that have a nucleus enclosed in a membrane and other membrane-bounded organelles.
  1. Algae: Plantlike protists (photosynthetic cells with cell walls). Some authorities classify some of the algae as plants. The most common phyla include the green algae (examples: *Spirogyra, Volvox, Protococcus*) and the brown algae (seaweeds and kelps).
  2. Protozoa: Animal-like protists (nonphotosynthetic cells with no cell wall). Classified by type of locomotion.
    a. Sarcodina.   Move by pseudopods. Example: *Ameba.*
    b. Zooflagellates.   Move by flagella.
    c. Ciliates.   Move by numerous cilia. Most complex of the Protozoa, with oral groove for taking food, and protective covering (pellicle). Examples: *Paramecium, Vorticella, Stentor.*
    d. Sporozoa.   Nonmotile. Reproduce by spores. Example: *Plasmodium.*
  3. Euglenoids.   Photosynthetic cells with no cell wall. Have a light-sensitive eyespot and a single flagellum. Example: *Euglena.*
  4. Slime molds.   Have an ameboid stage with many nuclei and a funguslike stage that produces spores.

FUNGI (Kingdom Fungi).   Plantlike, nonphotosynthetic organisms. Some are unicellular, most are multicellular. Most are saprophytes, some are parasitic. Examples: bread mold, yeasts, mushrooms.

PLANTS (Kingdom Plantae)
  1. Bryophytes.   Small land plants without vascular tissue (xylem and phloem). Examples: mosses, liverworts.
  2. Tracheophytes.   Plants with vascular tissue and true roots, stems, and leaves. Major groups include:
    a. Ferns.   Large leaves (called fronds) grow from underground stems. Spores are produced on underside of fronds.
    b. Gymnosperms.   Seed plants without flowers. Naked seeds are produced in cones. The conifers are the most common gymnosperms; they have needlelike leaves and are usually evergreen.
    c. Angiosperms.   The flowering plants. Seeds are produced by flowers and are enclosed in fruits. There are two groups: monocots (seeds with one cotyledon) and dicots (seeds with two cotyledons).

ANIMALS (Kingdom Animalia).   The animal phyla with which you should be familiar are:

1. **Sponges (Phylum Porifera).** Asymmetrical bodies with a variety of cell types, but no organs. Body is pierced by numerous pores leading to a central cavity.

2. **Coelenterates (Phylum Coelenterata).** Body is a two-layered sac with a digestive cavity and a single opening usually surrounded by tentacles with stinging cells. Examples: hydra, jellyfish, sea anemone, coral.

3. **Flatworms (Phylum Platyhelminthes).** Body with three cell layers and bilateral symmetry. Most are parasitic. Digestive system has only one opening. Examples: planaria, tapeworm, flukes.

4. **Roundworms (Phylum Nematoda).** Long, tubelike, unsegmented bodies. Most are parasitic. Digestive system has mouth and anus. Examples: hookworm, trichina, *Ascaris*.

5. **Annelids (Phylum Annelida).** Segmented worms. Body consists of many similar segments. Complete digestive system, closed circulatory system, excretory organs (nephridia) in each segment, ventral nerve cord with ganglia, and true coelom (fluid-filled cavity between digestive system and body wall). Examples: earthworm, leech.

6. **Mollusks (Phylum Mollusca).** Soft-bodied, with a mantle that produces a protective limy shell. Three main classes:

   a. **Bivalves.** Body enclosed in two-part, hinged shell. Examples: oyster, clam, mussel.

   b. **Gastropods.** Most have single, coiled shell and muscular foot. Examples: snail, whelk, slug.

   c. **Cephalopods.** Large head, with mouth surrounded by tentacles. Some have no shell; others, internal cartilaginous skeleton. Examples: octopus, squid.

7. **Echinoderms (Phylum Echinodermata).** Internal skeleton with spiny projections on skin; radial symmetry; a water-vascular system for locomotion. Examples: starfish, sea urchin, sand dollar.

8. **Arthropods (Phylum Arthropoda).** Segmented bodies with exoskeleton made of chitin and jointed appendages. Five main classes:

   a. **Crustaceans.** Have gills, two pairs of antennae, five pairs of legs. Examples: lobster, shrimp, crab, crayfish.

   b. **Arachnids.** Book lungs, no antennae, two body segments, four pairs of legs. Examples: spider, scorpion, daddy longlegs.

   c. **Insects.** Tracheae, one pair of antennae, three body segments, three pairs of legs. Examples: fly, bee, butterfly. moth, grasshopper.

   d. **Centipedes.** Many body segments with one pair of legs each.

   e. **Millipedes.** Many body segments with two pairs of legs each.

   Note: All the animal groups above are called invertebrates.

9. **Chordates (Phylum Chordata).** Have notochord, gill slits, and dorsal hollow nerve cord at some stage of development.

10. **Vertebrates (Subphylum Vertebrata).** Vertebral column enclosing nerve cord replaces notochord during development. Main classes are:

   a. **Jawless fishes.** Examples: lamprey, hagfish.

   b. **Cartilaginous fishes.** Examples: shark, ray, skate.

   c. **Bony fishes.** Gills, scales, two-chambered heart, coldblooded.

   d. **Amphibians.** Undergo metamorphosis. Have gills in early life, lungs as adults. No scales, moist skin, four limbs, three-chambered heart, coldblooded. Examples: frog, salamander.

   e. **Reptiles.** Lungs, scales, four limbs (except snakes), three-chambered heart, coldblooded. Examples: crocodile, turtle, snake.

   f. **Birds.** Lungs, feathers, front pair of limbs modified to wings, four-chambered heart, warmblooded.

   g. **Mammals.** Lungs, hair, four-chambered heart, warmblooded; females have milk glands for feeding young. Monotremes are egg-laying mammals (example: duckbill platypus); marsupials are nonplacental pouched mammals (example: kangaroo); all others are placental mammals (examples: humans, whales, furred animals).

Sample Questions

1. In the classification of *Paramecium,* which of the following characteristics would NOT be significant? (A) consists of a single cell (B) lives in fresh water

(C) has a membrane-bounded nucleus (D) has cilia (E) does not carry on photosynthesis

2. A pine tree and an oak tree are classified differently because they do NOT share the following characteristic. (A) have leaves (B) have vascular tissue (C) produce seeds (D) produce fruits (E) have true roots

3. A spider and a fly differ in all the following characteristics EXCEPT (A) presence of chitinous exoskeleton (B) number of legs (C) number of antennae (D) number of body segments (E) respiratory structures

STRUCTURE OF STEMS

The nature of xylem and phloem tissue and the functions of stems are described on pages 38–39, Sections D-1 and D-2.

PHLOEM TISSUE. Phloem cells are of two types:

1. Sieve cells have end walls with openings that connect with adjacent cells. When mature, they have no nucleus.

2. Companion cells are believed to regulate the transport of materials through the sieve cells.

FIBROVASCULAR BUNDLES. Xylem and phloem tissue extends longitudinally through stems in groupings called fibrovascular bundles. In the stems of flowering plants, the arrangement of the fibrovascular bundles depends on whether the plant is a monocot or dicot (see page 116).

1. Monocot stems. In the cross section of a monocot stem, the fibrovascular bundles are arranged at random throughout the stem. The surrounding tissue of the stem is called pith. See Figure 1A.

2. Herbaceous dicot stems. The fibrovascular bundles are arranged in a ring. The outer portion of each bundle is phloem; the inner portion, xylem. There is a layer of cambium between the xylem and phloem. The central tissue of the stem is pith. See Figure 1B.

3. Woody dicot stems. There is a continuous ring of cambium, with phloem outside and xylem inside the ring. Differentiation of the growing cambium cells continuously produces new phloem tissue on the outside and new xylem inside. Each year's growth forms a new annual ring of xylem. The accumulated rings of xylem make up the wood in a woody dicot stem. See Figure 1C.

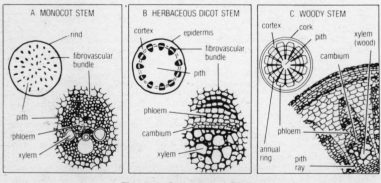

Figure 1. Structure of Stems.

Sample Questions

Questions 1–4: Which of the following lettered choices best fits each statement with respect to a woody dicot stem? (A) Annual ring (B) Cambium (C) Phloem (D) Xylem (E) Wood

1. Undifferentiated growth tissue

2. Represents one year's growth

3. Develops on the outside of the growth tissue
4. Nonliving cells in which transport occurs

ENERGY TRANSFER IN AEROBIC RESPIRATION

Basic information about aerobic respiration is given on pages 44–46.

THE KREBS CYCLE.   After a pyruvic acid molecule from the anaerobic phase of respiration enters the mitochondrion, it is broken down by enzymes in a series of chemical reactions called the Krebs cycle. In these reactions, carbon dioxide is released as a waste product and pairs of hydrogen atoms are transferred to hydrogen acceptors. The main hydrogen acceptor in the Krebs cycle is called NAD (an abbreviation of its chemical name). When NAD accepts a pair of hydrogen atoms, it is reduced to $NADH_2$ and acquires chemical energy.

THE ELECTRON TRANSPORT CHAIN.   When $NADH_2$ releases its hydrogen, the electrons from the hydrogen atoms are transferred to electron acceptors, most of which are called cytochromes. The hydrogen ions that remain go into solution temporarily. The electrons are passed along from one acceptor to another in a series of oxidation-reduction reactions called the electron transport chain. At three places in the chain, some of the chemical energy carried by the electrons is used to synthesize ATP. Most of the ATP obtained from aerobic respiration is produced in the electron transport chain. When as much energy as possible has been extracted from the electrons, oxygen becomes the final acceptor of the electrons and the hydrogen ions, forming molecules of water.

Sample Questions
1. The most significant outcome of the Krebs cycle is (A) the breakdown of glucose into pyruvic acid (B) the acceptance of hydrogen by oxygen to form water (C) the transfer of hydrogen atoms to hydrogen acceptors (D) the transfer of electrons to cytochromes (E) the synthesis of most of the ATP produced by aerobic respiration
2. Electron transfer is best described as (A) catalysis (B) an aerobic reaction (C) hydrogenation (D) decarboxylation (E) oxidation-reduction

HUMAN NUTRITION

Facts about nutrients in the human diet are given on pages 62–63. The following additional information may be helpful.

VITAMINS.   Vitamins are organic compounds needed in very small quantities for certain metabolic functions. Most vitamins are coenzymes or parts of coenzymes. Lack of a vitamin causes a vitamin-deficiency disease or condition. Some of the vitamins necessary for human nutrition and their deficiency symptoms are:

Vitamin	Deficiency Disease or Symptoms
A	xerophthalmia and night blindness
B_1 (thiamine)	beriberi (nervous and muscular disorders)
B_2 (riboflavin)	disturbed vision; sores on lips and tongue
C (ascorbic acid)	scurvy
D	rickets (soft bones)
nicotinic acid	pellagra

MINERALS.   In addition to the three main types of organic nutrients (carbohydrates, lipids, and proteins), the human diet must contain relatively small amounts of certain chemical elements, usually referred to as minerals. These elements are needed for the synthesis of substances used to build and repair tissues and regulate metabolism. Among these mineral elements are:

1. **Calcium.**   Needed for bones and teeth; blood clotting; muscle function.
2. **Phosphorus.**   Needed for bones; used in synthesis of ADP and ATP.

3. Iron. Needed for hemoglobin and the cytochromes in respiration.

4. Sodium and potassium. Needed for nerve and muscle function.

5. Iodine. Needed for hormones of the thyroid gland.

Sample Questions

1. The group of nutrients in the human diet that often function as coenzymes are the (A) carbohydrates (B) vitamins (C) lipids (D) proteins (E) minerals

Questions 2–4: Choose the letter of the nutrient in the human diet which, when lacking, is most closely associated with each condition. (A) Vitamin A (B) Vitamin C (C) Iron (D) Iodine (E) Calcium

2. A vision defect

3. Weak bones

4. Anemia

ANIMAL BEHAVIOR
Inborn and Learned Behavior

The basic ideas of inborn and acquired behavior, reflex actions, habits, and conditioned behavior are summarized on page 85.

AUTOMATIC RESPONSES TO STIMULI. Simple animals and animal-like protists may move toward or away from a stimulus. For example, a planarian moves toward the light. A paramecium moves into a region of a particular pH level. These responses are similar to plant tropisms.

HABITUATION. This type of behavior should not be confused with habit formation. In habituation, an animal gradually learns to ignore a stimulus that is of no importance to it. For example, a dog may at first respond to an unfamiliar sound, such as a bell. If nothing either favorable or unfavorable is associated with the bell, the dog eventually ignores it. In contrast, if the dog is always fed when the bell rings, the dog's salivary reflex to food becomes transferred to the bell. Ringing the bell causes the dog to salivate. This learned or acquired response is a conditioned response.

TRIAL-AND-ERROR LEARNING. Trial-and-error learning is similar to conditioned behavior. In trial-and-error learning, an animal at first does something at random. If a rewarding result follows, the animal learns to repeat the action to get the same reward or reinforcement. If the result of the action is unpleasant, the animal learns to avoid the action.

IMPRINTING. For a brief period during the earliest phase of an animal's life, it may form a strong association with the first moving object it sees. For example, a newly hatched bird normally forms a strong attachment to its mother—the first moving object it sees. This attachment is called imprinting. Under experimental conditions, the young bird (or other animal) may be imprinted on any other moving object presented to it. The bird will then follow that object as though it were its mother.

Animal Communication

COMMUNICATION BY SOUND. Many kinds of animals communicate with others of the same species by producing sounds. The communication may serve to bring individuals together for mating, to give warning of predators, or to establish an exclusive territory. Insects, frogs, birds, and many mammals use sound for these purposes.

COMMUNICATION BY CHEMICALS. Many animals release chemicals that affect the behavior of other members of the same species. Such chemical secretions are called pheromones. Many insects secrete pheromones to attract mates. Ants leave a trail of substances when returning to the nest from a food source. Other members of the colony can then follow the trail back to the food.

COMMUNICATION BY DISPLAY. Actions that deliver a message to another member of a species are called displays. Many animals use displays in courtship and mating. The spreading of the peacock's tail is a well-known example. Honey-bees communicate the location of a food source to other bees in the hive by means of a complex dance.

Biological Clocks

The behavior of many organisms (both plants and animals) is periodic and main-tains an accurate time sequence without cues from the environment. These be-havioral rhythms often have a 24-hour cycle, which is called a circadian rhythm. Organisms kept in a constant environment may maintain a circadian rhythm of activity for weeks or months. It is therefore assumed that the organisms have a built-in timing mechanism called a biological clock. How these clocks work is not yet known.

Sample Questions

Questions 1–2: A rat was admitted to a maze. When the rat reached a certain point in the maze, it received a pellet of food. The experiment was performed once a day, and the time for the rat to reach the food was recorded for each run.

1. Which of the following graphs is most likely to represent the results of the experiment?

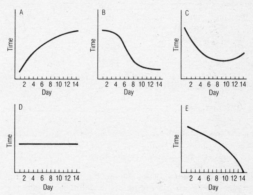

2. The results of the experiment illustrate (A) animal reasoning (B) imprinting (C) automatic response (D) conditioned response (E) trial-and-error learning

3. The secretion of pheromones by many animal species has the effect of (A) bringing individuals together for mating (B) attracting prey (C) discouraging predators (D) establishing territories (E) delaying maturation

REPRODUCTION AND DEVELOPMENT

Basic facts and concepts of cell division, reproduction, and development are on pages 94–107. The following additional information may be required.

SPORULATION IN BREAD MOLD. Bread mold is a fungus. It consists of a mass of threadlike structures called hyphae, which grow over the surface of food material (such as moist bread) and penetrate the material to digest and absorb nutrients. Certain hyphae grow upward and a spore case, or sporangium, forms at the tip of each. Spores develop in the sporangium and are scattered when the sporangium breaks open. See Figure 2 on page 224.

CONJUGATION. Sexual reproduction involves the fusion of nuclear material from cells of two individuals. Conjugation is a type of sexual reproduction that occurs in protists. The cells that take part in conjugation are similar in form (unlike the male and female gametes in fertilization), but are of opposite mating types (+ and –).

1. Conjugation in *Spirogyra*. Two strands of cells of opposite mating type come together. Projections grow out toward each other from cells in each strand and

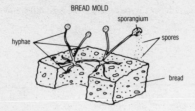

Figure 2. Sporulation in bread mold.

join to form a conjugation tube. Material from each cell of one strand flows through the tube and merges with the contents of the adjacent cell, forming a zygospore. Zygospores later develop into new *Spirogyra* strands.

2. Conjugation in *Paramecium*.   Paramecia and other ciliates have two types of nucleus: a large macronucleus and a small micronucleus. In conjugation, two individuals of opposite mating type come together. The macronuclei disappear and each micronucleus divides by meiosis into two monoploid nuclei. One of these nuclei in each cell then moves into the cytoplasm of the other cell and fuses with its remaining nucleus, forming a new diploid micronucleus. The individuals separate, and their micronuclei divide mitotically, forming new macronuclei.

ALTERNATION OF GENERATIONS.   The reproduction of mosses and ferns involves two alternating stages: a diploid sporophyte that produces monoploid spores by meiotic division, and a monoploid gametophyte that produces male and female gametes. In mosses, the leafy form generally observed is the gametophyte. In ferns, the gametophyte is a small, inconspicuous structure; the large, leafy plant is the sporophyte.

METAMORPHOSIS.   In the life cycle of some groups of animals, the developing organism passes through an immature stage that differs structurally from the adult form. This type of development is called metamorphosis.

1. Metamorphosis in insects

    a. Incomplete metamorphosis.   In incomplete metamorphosis, the young insect that hatches from the egg resembles the adult in form, but does not have certain structures of the adult, such as wings or reproductive organs. As the insect grows, it molts—sheds its exoskeleton and forms a new, larger one—several times. After the final molt, the insect develops the missing structures and is an adult capable of reproduction. In this type of metamorphosis, the immature insect is called a nymph. The grasshopper is an example of an insect in which incomplete metamorphosis occurs.

    b. Complete metamorphosis.   In complete metamorphosis, the insect that emerges from the egg is a segmented, wormlike form called a larva. A caterpillar is a common example of an insect larva. The larva eats and grows continuously, molting several times. Eventually, it enters a resting stage and is called a pupa. The pupa surrounds itself by a protective covering and its tissues and organs change into those of the adult form. When this process is complete, the adult emerges. Complete metamorphosis occurs in many kinds of insects, including butterflies, moths, bees, and flies.

2. Metamorphosis in the frog.   The young organism that hatches from a frog's egg is called a tadpole. A tadpole has gills, lives in water, and absorbs dissolved oxygen like a fish. It has a long tail and no legs. Its heart has only two chambers, again like that of a fish. After a period of life in this stage, the tadpole gradually develops into an adult frog. The gills are replaced by lungs, the tail is absorbed, legs develop, and the heart acquires a third chamber.

Sample Questions

1.   In which groups of organisms does reproduction by spores occur?
      I. Fungi   II. Ferns   III. Gymnosperms

(A) I only (B) II only (C) I and II only (D) II and III only (E) I, II, and III

Questions 2–4: Each of the following statements refers to the diagram of bread mold.

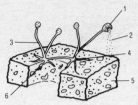

2. Most absorption of nutrients occurs in (A) 1 (B) 3 (C) 4 (D) 5 (E) 6
3. A source of nutrients is (A) 1 (B) 2 (C) 4 (D) 5 (E) 6
4. The structure that may develop into a new organism is (A) 1 (B) 2 (C) 3 (D) 4 (E) 6
5. In an insect that undergoes complete metamorphosis, the stage in which reproduction may occur is the (A) egg (B) nymph (C) adult (D) pupa (E) larva

CHROMOSOME MAPPING

See the material on gene linkage and crossing-over on page 124.

EFFECT OF CROSSING-OVER ON GENE LINKAGE.   Linked genes are usually transmitted together to offspring. However, as a result of crossing-over, different alleles of linked genes may be inherited by the offspring. If the linked genes are far apart on the chromosome, they are more likely to be switched by crossing-over than if they are close together. By studying the frequencies with which various linked alleles become separated, their sequence along the chromosome can be inferred. This analysis is called chromosome mapping. It can be applied to organisms, such as insects, that have a short reproductive cycle and produce numerous offspring in each generation. Chromosome mapping has been carried out most extensively in the fruit fly, *Drosophila*.

Sample Question
1. In genetic studies with fruit flies, it was found that gene 1 has two alleles, A and a, and gene 2 has two alleles, B and b. A and B are dominant. In a series of dihybrid crosses it was found that offspring that inherited allele A also inherited allele B 92% of the time. A reasonable inference from this observation is that (A) gene 1 and gene 2 are on different chromosomes 92% of the time (B) gene 1 and gene 2 are on the same chromosome 92% of the time (C) gene 2 has a mutation rate of 8% (D) gene 1 and gene 2 are fairly close together on the same chromosome (E) gene 1 and gene 2 are at nearly opposite ends of the same chromosome

PRACTICE TEST FOR THE COLLEGE BOARD BIOLOGY ACHIEVEMENT TEST

PART A

Directions: For each of the following, select the best response.

1. All of the following processes require the use of energy by the cell EXCEPT (A) pinocytosis (B) phagocytosis (C) glycolysis (D) osmosis (E) active transport
2. A person will not contract polio after receiving the polio vaccine. This is an example of (A) active immunity (B) passive immunity (C) interferon deactivation (D) tolerance (E) rejection
3. Which of the following nutrients are a source of energy for the body?

    I. Minerals   II. Proteins   III. Carbohydrates

(A) I only (B) II only (C) III only (D) II and III only (E) I, II, and III

4. A primary function of the large intestine is (A) reabsorption of water (B) destruction of bacteria (C) emulsification of fats (D) mechanical digestion (E) absorption of nutrients

5. In modern taxonomy, blue-green algae are grouped most closely with which of the following organisms? (A) yellow-green algae (B) green algae (C) bacteria (D) bryophytes (E) fungi

6. All the children in a family are heterozygous for type A blood. Which of the following are possible genotypes of the parents?

I. $I^A I^A$, ii   II. $I^A i$, ii   III. $I^A I^A$, $I^A i$

(A) I only (B) II only (C) III only (D) I and II only (E) I, II, and III

7. Choose the correct sequence of organelles involved in the production and secretion of an enzyme by a cell.

(A) ribosome > endoplasmic reticulum > Golgi complex > cell membrane
(B) ribosome > mitochondrion > Golgi complex > cell membrane
(C) mitochondrion > ribosome > endoplasmic reticulum > cell membrane
(D) mitochondrion > Golgi complex > cell membrane
(E) nucleus > mitochondrion > cell membrane

8. According to the heterotroph hypothesis,

(A) autotrophic nutrition developed before heterotrophic nutrition
(B) anaerobic respiration developed before aerobic respiration
(C) the primitive earth's atmosphere was rich in oxygen
(D) aerobic respiration made photosynthesis possible
(E) fermentation was originally more efficient than aerobic respiration

9. The graph shows the migration of *Daphnia* vertically in a pond during the course of a day. A student wishes to collect *Daphnia* for a laboratory experiment. During which hours would straining of the surface water be most productive? (A) Between 8 A.M. and noon. (B) Between 4 P.M. and 8 P.M. (C) Between 4 A.M. and 8 A.M. (D) Between midnight and 4 A.M. (E) Between 8 P.M. and midnight

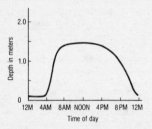

10. Which of the following is NOT a part of the human male reproductive system? (A) seminal vesicles (B) oviducts (C) seminiferous tubules (D) vas deferens (E) prostate gland

11. The cellular organelle in which the Krebs cycle operates is the (A) nucleus (B) mitochondrion (C) cell membrane (D) chloroplast (E) Golgi body

12. A three-chambered heart is characteristic of (A) humans (B) insects (C) amphibians (D) fishes (E) birds

13. Which of the following problems is common to freshwater organisms but NOT to saltwater organisms? (A) predation (B) lack of water (C) water balance (D) salt balance (E) mineral deficiency

14. The step immediately following the pollination of a flower is (A) formation of a pollen tube (B) development of the endosperm nucleus (C) transfer of pollen from anther to stigma (D) degeneration of the tube cells (E) closing of the micropyle

15. Which of the following is NOT part of any amino acid?

(A) COOH (B) PO_4 (C) NH_2 (D) H (E) CH_3

16. The rabbit population in a certain forest has recently increased. This could be the result of (A) the killing of grasses by pesticide use (B) intraspecific competition (C) the increased hunting of hawks (D) interspecific competition with field mice (E) the cutting down of deciduous trees

17. The enzyme that catalyzes the hydrolysis of ATP is called ATPase. According to the graph below, (A) in the presence of sodium ions, the greater the concentration of potassium ions, the greater the ATPase activity (B) both sodium and potassium ions are required for maximum ATPase activity (C) ATPase activity depends only on the concentration of sodium ions (D) the presence of sodium ions has little effect on the activity of ATPase (E) the activity of ATPase increases at first, then gradually decreases

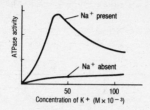

18. The scientist whose theory of evolution centered around the idea that evolutionary changes in animals were due to inheritance of acquired traits was (A) August Weismann (B) Charles Darwin (C) Jean Baptiste de Lamarck (D) Alfred Russel Wallace (E) Thomas Malthus

19. A symbiotic relationship in which one organism benefits and the other is neither harmed nor benefited is called (A) mutualism (B) parasitism (C) commensalism (D) consumerism (E) saprophytism

20. The plant structure most closely associated with gas and water exchange with the atmosphere is the (A) terminal bud (B) root hair (C) stem (D) vein (E) stomate

21. Which of the following is a type of neuron that carries impulses between neurons? (A) motor (B) associative (interneurons) (C) dendrite (D) sensory (E) efferent

22. Choose the correct statement about enzymes X and Y according to the graph. (A) Y is denatured at basic pH. (B) The active site of X changes at approximately pH 3. (C) Y requires a higher temperature than X to function most effectively. (D) X is effective at the pH found in the human stomach. (E) Y is effective at the pH found in the human stomach.

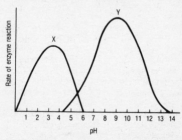

23. The process in which pyruvic acid formed from glucose is converted to an end product without further production of energy is (A) photolysis (B) glycolysis (C) fermentation (D) aerobic respiration (E) oxidation-reduction

24. Which of the following processes is regeneration LEAST similar to? (A) sporulation (B) budding (C) conjugation (D) fission (E) grafting

25. *Felis leo* (lion), *Lynx rufus* (bobcat), *Cynaelurus jubatus* (cheetah), and *Felis tigris* (tiger) all belong to the Felidae family. The two cats that belong to the same genus are the (A) lion and bobcat (B) cheetah and tiger (C) tiger and bobcat (D) lion and tiger (E) cheetah and bobcat

26. The presence of nuclear membranes, photosynthetic capability, and a multicellular form can be characteristics of organisms in which kingdom(s)?

    I. Monera   II. Protista   III. Plantae

(A) I only (B) II only (C) III only (D) II and III only (E) I and III only

27. Activities such as coughing, heartbeat, and breathing are controlled by the (A) cerebrum (B) medulla (C) gray matter (D) cerebellum (E) thalamus

28. In a DNA molecule,
(A) the amount of adenine equals the amount of uracil
(B) the amount of cytosine equals the amount of uracil
(C) the amount of deoxyribose equals the amount of thymine
(D) the amount of thymine equals the amount of adenine
(E) the amount of cytosine equals the amount of adenine

29. Most of the ATP produced during aerobic respiration come from (A) the electron transport chain (B) glycolysis (C) the Krebs cycle (D) photolysis (E) PGAL formation

30. Which of the following is NOT used in determining the members of a species? (A) similarity in structure (B) similarity in evolutionary history (C) similarity in habitat (D) similarity in biochemical composition (E) similarity in embryonic development

31. Carbon dioxide enters the photosynthetic process during (A) photolysis (B) the light reactions (C) the Krebs cycle (D) the formation of $NADH_2$ from NAD (E) the dark reactions

32. T. H. Morgan's experimental results showing that certain traits were inherited together formed the basis for the concept of (A) sex-linked traits (B) the chromosome theory (C) multiple-gene inheritance (D) crossing-over (E) gene linkage

33. Vascular bundles are scattered throughout the pith in (A) woody monocot stems (B) woody dicot stems (C) herbaceous monocot stems (D) woody monocot roots (E) herbaceous dicot stems

34. Which of the following is NOT a characteristic of the circulatory system of the earthworm? (A) Hemoglobin increases the oxygen-carrying capacity of the blood. (B) Exchange of materials between blood and body cells occurs in the sinuses. (C) Aortic arches pump blood through the blood vessels. (D) The blood is always contained within blood vessels. (E) All body cells are near a capillary.

35. The organs of excretion in humans do NOT include the (A) skin (B) liver (C) kidneys (D) lungs (E) large intestine

36. The frog and the rabbit are both members of the subphylum Vertebrata. Which characteristics do they have in common? (A) three-chambered heart, warm-bloodedness, dorsal nerve cord (B) cold-bloodedness, three-chambered heart, coelom (C) dorsal nerve cord, vertebral column, gill slits in development (D) vertebral column, internal fertilization, four-chambered heart (E) dorsal nerve cord, coelom, cold-bloodedness

37. The annual rings in a woody dicot stem are produced by (A) a year's growth of xylem cells (B) a year's growth of bark cells (C) a year's growth of cambium (D) a year's growth of phloem cells (E) a year's growth of epidermis

38. All of the following statements are reasons why the bryophytes are not considered to be completely adapted to life on land EXCEPT: (A) They carry on photosynthesis. (B) They lack xylem and phloem. (C) Water is needed for reproduction. (D) The absence of supporting tissues limits growth. (E) They require a moist environment.

39. Human skin color varies over a wide range from dark to light. This is an example of (A) environment over heredity (B) multiple-gene inheritance (C) crossing-over (D) sex linkage (E) nondisjunction

40. Which of the following animals does NOT show a dorsal nerve cord, a notochord, and gill slits at some time during its development? (A) tunicate (B) stingray (C) tortoise (D) grasshopper (E) vampire bat

41. Nitrogenous wastes are excreted in the form of uric acid in all of the following animals EXCEPT (A) earthworms (B) grasshoppers (C) owls (D) turtles (E) crocodiles

42. The human umbilical cord connects (A) the fetus to the placenta (B) the fetal blood vessels to the maternal blood vessels (C) the fetus to the corpus luteum (D) the oviduct to the uterus (E) the fetus to the amnion

43. An adaptation that assists absorption of water by roots is the (A) root hairs (B) xylem (C) cortex (D) meristem (E) pith

44. Both asexual and sexual reproduction can occur in which of the following?

I. Spirogyra   II. Paramecium   III. Hydra

(A) I only (B) II only (C) I and II only (D) II and III only (E) I, II, and III

45. An F_1 generation with a phenotype different from that of both parents and an F_2 generation with a phenotypic ratio of 1:2:1 are characteristic of (A) incomplete dominance (B) multiple alleles (C) the Hardy-Weinberg law (D) a dihybrid cross (E) hybrids

46. The embryonic germ layer from which the nervous system and skin epidermis derive is the (A) ectoderm (B) archenteron (C) mesoderm (D) endoderm (E) endometrium

47. 2,3-diphosphoglycerate (DPG) is a substance that binds to hemoglobin. The graph shows the effect of DPG on the activity of hemoglobin. Which of the following statements can be inferred from the graph?
(A) DPG increases the oxygen-binding activity of hemoglobin.
(B) DPG decreases the oxygen-binding activity of hemoglobin.
(C) The effect of DPG is greatest at high concentrations of oxygen.
(D) DPG increases the concentration of oxygen in the blood.
(E) DPG decreases the concentration of oxygen in the blood.

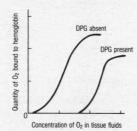

48. The stages of metamorphosis in a moth are (A) egg, pupa, adult (B) egg, larva, nymph, adult (C) egg, nymph, adult (D) egg, larva, pupa, adult (E) egg, larva, adult

49. A newly hatched chick begins to follow its mother around the barn. This is an example of (A) habituation (B) imprinting (C) trial-and-error learning (D) pheromone activation (E) conditioning

50. The many similar yet distinct species of finches on the Galapagos Islands observed by Darwin form an example of (A) polyploidy (B) the law of use and disuse (C) convergent evolution (D) the Hardy-Weinberg law (E) adaptive radiation

51. Choose the correct statement about the process of meiosis.
(A) Meiosis occurs only in body cells.
(B) Crossing-over may occur between homologous chromosomes during prophase of the first division.
(C) Each daughter cell produced has the same number of chromosomes, $2n$, as the parent cell.
(D) Replication of chromosomes takes place between the first and second division.
(E) Four daughter cells are produced by the first division during meiosis.

52. You are asked to test for the contents of an unknown liquid substance. You divide your sample into three test tubes. To the first you add Benedict's solution; then you heat the tube to boiling. The blue color of the solution does not change. To the second tube you add Lugol's solution. No changes in color are observed. To the third tube you add biuret solution. You observe that the liquid in the tube changes color to pink-purple. The substance given you was (A) positive for the presence of protein (B) positive for the presence of sugar (C) negative for the presence of carbon dioxide (D) positive for the presence of protein and starch (E) negative for the presence of hydrogen ions and carbon dioxide

53. A high level of decay, constant supply of rainfall, and little organic matter stored in the soil are characteristics of which biome? (A) tundra (B) taiga (C) grassland (D) tropical rain forest (E) deciduous forest

Questions 54–59 refer to the following diagram.

The human digestive system

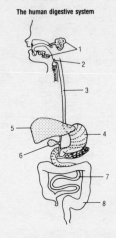

54. Food first encounters peristalsis in (A) 3 (B) 4 (C) 5 (D) 7 (E) 8
55. Bile is stored in (A) 1 (B) 2 (C) 4 (D) 5 (E) 6
56. Pancreatic juice is secreted into (A) 3 (B) 4 (C) 5 (D) 6 (E) 7
57. Food and liquid are prevented from entering the larynx by (A) 1 (B) 2 (C) 3 (D) 4 (E) 5
58. Sugars, amino acids, vitamins, and minerals are absorbed in (A) 3 (B) 4 (C) 6 (D) 7 (E) 8
59. Villi cover the lining of (A) 2 (B) 3 (C) 4 (D) 7 (E) 8

PART B

Directions: For each group of questions below, there is a set of lettered choices. Select one lettered choice in response to each question. You may use a choice once, more than once, or not at all.

Questions 60–63

(A) insulin
(B) testosterone
(C) adrenalin
(D) thyroxin
(E) luteinizing hormone

60. A hormone that increases the glucose level in the blood and is secreted in large amounts during emergencies.
61. Secreted by the pituitary; causes old follicle to form corpus luteum.
62. Secreted by the pancreas; regulates glucose metabolism.
63. Lack of this hormone results in goiter.

Questions 64–67

(A) hilum
(B) cotyledon
(C) epicotyl
(D) hypocotyl
(E) endosperm

64. Gives rise to the leaves and upper part of the stem of a young plant.
65. The point of attachment between an ovule and an ovary.
66. Stores food in the bean seed.
67. Stores food in the corn seed.

Questions 68-71

(A) nitrates
(B) nitrites
(C) nitrogen
(D) proteins
(E) ammonia

68. Synthesized by plants.
69. Characterized by the NO_3 group.
70. Produced by bacteria of decay.
71. Can be used directly by plants.

Questions 72-75

(A) vitamin A
(B) vitamin C
(C) nicotinic acid
(D) vitamin D
(E) vitamin B_1

72. Lack of this vitamin causes beriberi.
73. Lack of this vitamin results in rickets.
74. Night blindness is a result of a deficiency of this vitamin.
75. Found in citrus fruits, this vitamin prevents scurvy.

Questions 76-79

(A) population
(B) ecosystem
(C) community
(D) habitat
(E) biosphere

76. The part of the earth where living things are present.
77. All the living things in a grassland.
78. All the prairie dogs in a grassland.
79. All the living and nonliving things in a grassland.

Questions 80-82

(A) interphase
(B) prophase
(C) metaphase
(D) anaphase
(E) telophase

80. The mitotic stage in which the spindle appears.
81. The mitotic stage in which chromosomes replicate.
82. The mitotic stage in which chromosomes are in central plane of cell.

Questions 83-85

(A) geographic isolation
(B) reproductive isolation
(C) polyploidy
(D) adaptive radiation
(E) convergent evolution

83. The formation of new species as a result of abnormal cell division.
84. The formation of new species as a result of some natural land barrier.
85. Illustrated by the resemblance between the marsupial koala and the placental bear.

PART C

Directions: For each group of questions below, study the description of the laboratory or experimental situation and then choose the one best answer to each question.

Questions 86 to 89 refer to the three graphs below. In searching for a pesticide to be effective against the tobacco leafworm, an insect that damages tobacco crops, a chemical manufacturing company produced Chemical A. Chemical A was tested by three applications to a field of experimental plants at one-month intervals. The effects on the leafworm (graph 1), on leafworm predators (graph 2), and on the tobacco plants (graph 3) were investigated. The control plants received no treatment.

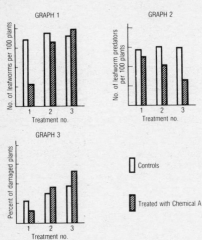

86. The treatment(s) that seemed to be most effective was (were) (A) treatment 1 only (B) treatment 2 only (C) treatment 3 only (D) treatments 1 and 2, but not 3 (E) treatments 2 and 3, but not 1

87. During the investigation it was observed that (A) the population of leafworms on the treated plants steadily decreased (B) the population of leafworm predators on the treated plants steadily decreased (C) there was very little effect of the treatment on either the leafworms or their predators (D) each treatment actually increased the amount of leafworm damage to be expected (E) the treatment increased the damage to the control plants

88. From the information given in graphs 1 and 2, one can infer that (A) chemical A is more effective against leafworm predators than against leafworms (B) chemical A is more effective against leafworms than against leafworm predators (C) chemical A enhances tobacco plant growth (D) leafworm populations and leafworm predator populations are normally inversely proportional (E) leafworm populations and leafworm predator populations are normally directly proportional

89. The best conclusion to draw from the information presented in graphs 1 to 3 is (A) By harming leafworm predators more than leafworms themselves, chemical A decreased the damage done to the crops. (B) Because of its negligible effect on leafworms and their predators, chemical A had no real effect on the damage done to the crops. (C) By harming leafworm predators more than leafworms themselves, chemical A helped to increase the leafworm population, thus increasing damage to the crops. (D) By harming leafworms more than leafworm predators, chemical A helped to increase the leafworm predator population, thus increasing damage to the crops. (E) There is insufficient data to determine the effectiveness of chemical A in reducing leafworm damage.

Questions 90 to 94 refer to the food web diagrammed below.

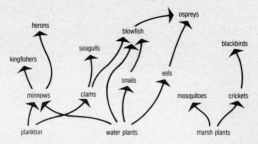

90. This food web consists of organisms living in a (A) grassland ecosystem (B) tropical rain forest ecosystem (C) river ecosystem (D) desert ecosystem (E) taiga ecosystem

91. An increase in the number of marsh plants one summer would lead most directly to (A) a decrease in the number of insects (B) an increased number of water plants (C) a drop in the blackbird population (D) an increased number of crickets and mosquitoes (E) an increased blackbird population

92. The food-web level that contains the most energy consists of (A) minnows, clams, mosquitoes, crickets (B) minnows, clams, snails, eels (C) kingfishers, herons, seagulls, ospreys (D) plankton, clams, blowfish, ospreys (E) plankton, water plants, marsh plants

93. First-level consumers in this food web include all of the following EXCEPT (A) clams (B) crickets (C) seagulls (D) eels (E) minnows

94. An omnivore that is both a herbivorous first-level consumer and a carnivorous second-level consumer is the (A) eel (B) blowfish (C) seagull (D) osprey (E) cricket

Questions 95 to 97 refer to the graph below. The graph shows the change in the eggshell thickness of two types of fish-eating birds over a period of years. This period includes the years 1945–1947, when DDT, a pesticide employed for insect control, was introduced into general use.

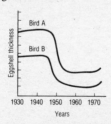

95. The most correct statement about the change in the eggshell thickness of birds A and B is (A) It increased slightly between 1950 and 1960. (B) It sharply decreased between 1930 and 1940. (C) It sharply increased between 1945 and 1950. (D) It sharply decreased between 1960 and 1970. (E) It decreased much more in bird A than in bird B.

96. According to the graph, DDT appears to have (A) had a negative effect on eggshell thickness (B) had no effect on eggshell thickness (C) reduced the populations of fish eaten by these birds (D) had little effect after about 1955 (E) been discontinued after about 1955

97. DDT was sprayed over the land to control insects. It is believed to interfere with birds' ability to metabolize calcium. The best explanation for how this pesticide came to affect the eggshells of birds A and B is: (A) DDT, washed into bodies of water, was passed through a food chain consisting of plankton, fish, and birds A and B. (B) Birds A and B were sprayed with DDT. (C) Insects sprayed

with DDT infested the nests of birds A and B. (D) Fish eaten by birds A and B were accidentally sprayed with DDT. (E) When eggs are sprayed with DDT, the calcium in the shells is destroyed.

Questions 98 to 100 refer to the graph below, which shows how populations of three freshwater organisms respond to changes in water temperature. Assume that waste water from a factory is discharged into a lake containing these organisms, causing the water temperature to increase.

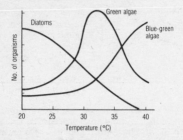

98.   An increase in water temperature to about 30°C will probably result in (A) a decrease in diatoms and an increase in green algae (B) a decrease in diatoms and a decrease in green algae (C) a sharp increase in both types of algae (D) a sharp increase, followed by a gradual decrease, in green algae (E) the disappearance of diatoms

99.   *Daphnia* feed primarily on diatoms. If the temperature increases to 35°C, (A) the number of fish that eat *Daphnia* will probably increase (B) *Daphnia* will become photosynthetic (C) the number of *Daphnia* will probably increase (D) the number of *Daphnia* will probably decrease (E) *Daphnia* will begin to eat blue-green algae

100.   If the discharge of waste water is discontinued, and the water temperature gradually drops to about 32°C, (A) the number of diatoms will be increasing and the number of blue-green algae will be decreasing (B) the number of diatoms will be decreasing and the number of blue-green algae will be increasing (C) the number of green algae will be changing rapidly (D) both types of algae will be decreasing (E) both types of algae will be increasing

INDEX

BODY STRUCTURES OF

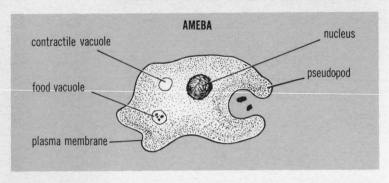

AMEBA

contractile vacuole

nucleus

food vacuole

pseudopod

plasma membrane

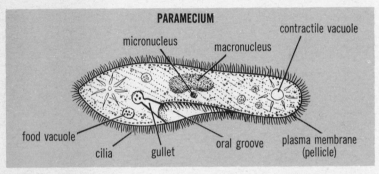

PARAMECIUM

micronucleus

macronucleus

contractile vacuole

food vacuole

cilia

gullet

oral groove

plasma membrane
(pellicle)

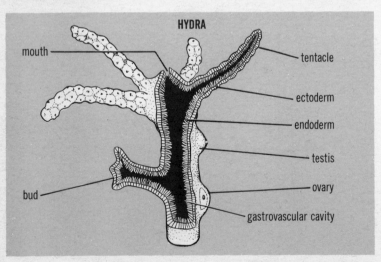

HYDRA

mouth

tentacle

ectoderm

endoderm

testis

ovary

bud

gastrovascular cavity

REPRESENTATIVE ORGANISMS

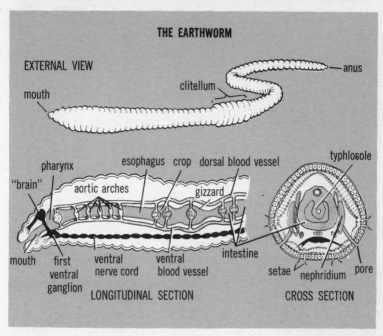

THE EARTHWORM

EXTERNAL VIEW

anus

clitellum

mouth

pharynx   esophagus crop   dorsal blood vessel   typhlosole

"brain"   aortic arches   gizzard

mouth   first ventral ganglion   ventral nerve cord   ventral blood vessel   intestine

setae   nephridium   pore

LONGITUDINAL SECTION   CROSS SECTION

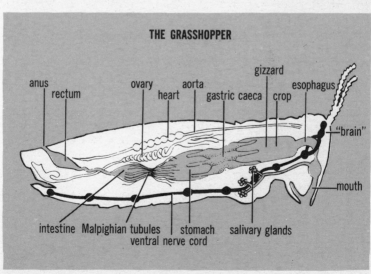

THE GRASSHOPPER

anus   ovary   aorta   gizzard   esophagus

rectum   heart   gastric caeca   crop   "brain"

mouth

intestine   Malpighian tubules   stomach   salivary glands
ventral nerve cord

BIOLOGY REGENTS QUESTIONS CLASSIFIED BY TOPICS

Parts I and II

	Examination and Question Numbers				
Topics	1991	1992	1993	1994	1995
1995					
I:1–2	1–3	1–3	1, 2	1, 2, 9	1, 2
I:3	4, 5	4, 5, 126	3–5, 129	3, 6, 133, 134	3, 4
I:4–5	6, 7, 132	6, 7	6, 7	4, 7, 18	5, 6, 9
II:1–3	8, 110	8, 12, 127	8	13	7
II:4	9–10, 121	9, 23	9, 10	10, 11, 20	8, 12
II:5	11–12	10, 11, 13	11–14	5, 9, 12	10, 11, 13, 14, 19
II:6–7	13–15, 111	14, 16, 18	15, 16	8, 16, 17, 112, 118	17, 21
II:8–9	16, 18	15, 17	17, 18	14, 21, 27	15
II:10–13	17, 19, 20	19–21, 29	19–21	15, 19, 23	16, 18, 20, 23, 28
II:14	21, 22	22	22	24	22
III:1	(Extended Area—Human Physiology. No questions in Part I.)				
III:2	23	23	25	125	24, 25
III:3	24	24	23	22	26
III:4	25, 26	28	23, 28	25, 26	27
III:5	28	25, 27	21	27	29
III:6	27	—	26	29	28
III:7	(Extended Area—Human Physiology. No questions in Part I.)				
III:8	29	30	24, 27	15, 30	30
IV:1–2	30, 33	26, 31, 33	29	28, 31, 32, 130–132	31, 32
IV:3–4	31, 32, 34	32, 34, 35	30, 32, 35–37	33–35	33–35, 37
IV:5	35–37, 118	36, 37	33, 34	34, 38, 39	36, 40
V:1–2	38, 39, 43	38, 40–43	38–42	36, 40–42, 44	38, 39, 41–43
V:3	41, 45	44	43	37–47	44
V:4–6	40, 42, 44	39	44	—	—
V:7	—	45	45	45	45
VI:1	46–50	46–48, 50–52	46–50, 52	43, 46, 48–50, 57	46–49, 51, 52
VI:2	51, 52	49	51	54	50
VII:1–3	53–56	53–57	53–56, 58	51–53, 55, 56, 58, 59	53–58
VII:4	(Extended Area—Ecology. No questions in Part I.)				
VII:5	57, 58	58, 59	57	—	59

Part III Questions Classified by Laboratory Skills

	Examination and Question Numbers				
Skills	1991	1992	1993	1994	1995
1–3	112–118	114, 118, 129	130, 134	120, 122, 124, 126	118, 125, 127, 133
4–5	115–117, 119	121, 122, 124	120–124	133, 134	110–112, 114
6–7	114, 118, 122	120, 123	129, 134	121, 130–132	113
8	110, 111, 123	130, 133	126, 131	127	130
9	—	131, 134	133	—	111, 134
10	118, 120, 121	132	127, 128, 134	123	126, 131
11	134	—	132	128	—
12–15	110–113, 125–133	110–113, 115–117, 119, 125, 128	110–114, 125, 126	110–117, 119, 125, 129	115–118, 120– 124, 128, 129, 132

REGENTS EXAMINATIONS

BIOLOGY

June 19, 1991

PART I

Answer all 59 questions in this part. [65]

Directions (1–59): For *each* statement or question, select the word or expression that, of those given, best completes the statement or answers the question.

1. The life function of transport in an organism directly involves those activities used to
   (1) absorb and distribute materials
   (2) obtain and hydrolyze materials
   (3) release energy from food
   (4) produce cellular waste products

2. Which term includes all the activities required to keep an organism alive?
   (1) growth
   (2) excretion
   (3) metabolism
   (4) nutrition

3. The diagram below represents part of a filament composed of a number of organisms.

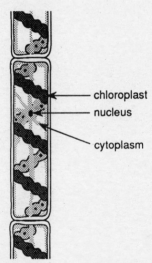

   In which kingdom would these organisms most likely be classified?
   (1) Fungi
   (2) Animalia
   (3) Protista
   (4) Monera

4. The structure of a cell nucleus would be seen in the greatest detail by use of
   (1) a compound light microscope
   (2) an ultracentrifuge
   (3) a dissecting microscope
   (4) an electron microscope

5. Microscopic examination of an animal cell reveals the presence of a plasma membrane but no cell wall. Which additional structures would normally be present within this cell?
   (1) starch grains
   (2) centrioles
   (3) chloroplasts
   (4) large vacuoles

6. Some vitamins are essential to an organism because they function as
   (1) coenzymes
   (2) auxins
   (3) hormones
   (4) neurotransmitters

7. What is the ratio of hydrogen atoms to oxygen atoms in a molecule of glucose?
   (1) 1:1
   (2) 2:1
   (3) 3:1
   (4) 1:2

8. An inorganic molecule required by green plants for the process of photosynthesis is
   (1) oxygen
   (2) starch
   (3) carbon dioxide
   (4) glucose

9. Why is the organism in the diagram at the right considered a heterotroph rather than an autotroph?
   (1) It manufactures its own food.
   (2) It divides by mitosis.
   (3) It transforms light energy into chemical energy.
   (4) It absorbs preformed organic molecules.

10. The digestive systems of humans, grasshoppers, and earthworms are similar in that all three
    (1) contain a tubelike system with two openings
    (2) contain a long, coiled intestine
    (3) mechanically break down food in a mouth cavity
    (4) chemically digest food in Malpighian tubules

11. Movement of organelles within the cytoplasm of plant and animal cells is due most directly to
    (1) osmosis
    (2) cyclosis
    (3) hydrolysis
    (4) photosynthesis

12. Which organism has a circulatory system that consists of a pulsating vessel that pumps the blood into sinuses?
    (1) earthworm
    (2) hydra
    (3) grasshopper
    (4) ameba

13. Which process produces the greatest quantity of ATP per molecule of glucose oxidized?
    (1) aerobic respiration
    (2) lactic acid production
    (3) photosynthesis
    (4) fermentation

14. The transport of oxygen by hemoglobin occurs in the
    (1) hydra and earthworm
    (2) earthworm and grasshopper
    (3) hydra and human
    (4) earthworm and human

15. Painting the woody stems of plants may interfere with
    (1) gas exchange through lenticels
    (2) water intake through lenticels
    (3) gas exchange through stomates
    (4) water intake through stomates

16. Which organism has specialized organs for the excretion of metabolic wastes?
    (1) yeast
    (2) ameba
    (3) earthworm
    (4) hydra

17. Ventral nerve cords and peripheral nerves are characteristic of
    (1) hydras
    (2) earthworms
    (3) protozoans
    (4) mammals

18. Which pair of organisms in the diagrams below remove the waste products carbon dioxide and ammonia by diffusion through their cell membranes directly into the environment?

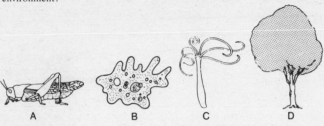

A   B   C   D

    (1) *A* and *B*
    (2) *B* and *C*
    (3) *C* and *D*
    (4) *A* and *D*

19. The diagram below shows the tips of two oat seedlings exposed to a fixed light source. In seedling *A*, metal foil was inserted partially through the seedling just below the tip, blocking the flow of any chemicals down the side of the stem facing the source of light.

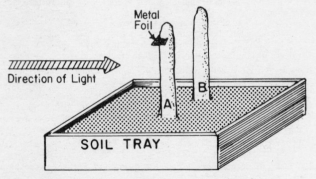

    What was most likely observed after 3 days of exposure to the light?
    (1) Seedling *A* grew away from the light source and seedling *B* grew toward the light source.
    (2) Seedling *A* grew toward the light source and seedling *B* grew away from the light source.
    (3) Both seedlings grew away from the light source.
    (4) Both seedlings grew toward the light source.

20. A change in the external or internal environment of an organism is known as
    (1) a response
    (2) an impulse
    (3) a synapse
    (4) a stimulus

21. Flagella, cilia, and pseudopods increase the chances of survival of unicellular organisms by
    (1) increasing opportunities to obtain food
    (2) increasing the rate of mitotic cell division
    (3) decreasing production of metabolic wastes
    (4) decreasing the requirements for oxygen

22. In which organism is locomotion accomplished by the interaction of muscles and chitinous appendages?
    (1) grasshopper
    (2) paramecium
    (3) hydra
    (4) human

23. Which process in humans would be most directly affected if peristalsis were to stop?
    (1) the transmission of nerve impulses throughout the body
    (2) the movement of food through the gastrointestinal tract
    (3) the flow of blood through the lungs
    (4) the removal of excess amino acids from the blood

24. The space marked X in the diagram at the right would normally contain
    (1) hemoglobin
    (2) neurotransmitters
    (3) intercellular fluid
    (4) hydrolytic enzymes

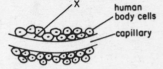

25. Humans breathe more rapidly during exercise than before it because during exercise the blood contains
    (1) an increased level of oxygen
    (2) a decreased number of red blood cells
    (3) an increased level of carbon dioxide
    (4) a decreased amount of hemoglobin

26. Smoking may damage the respiratory system because deposits from the smoke can
    (1) interfere with ciliary action in the trachea
    (2) trigger the release of antigens by the alveoli
    (3) block the transmission of impulses that regulate breathing
    (4) lower blood pressure in the mucous membranes of the bronchioles

27. Which portion of the central nervous system coordinates motor activities and aids in maintaining balance?
    (1) cerebrum
    (2) cerebellum
    (3) medulla
    (4) spinal cord

28. The graph below shows the effect of environmental temperature on a girl's skin temperature and on her internal body temperature.

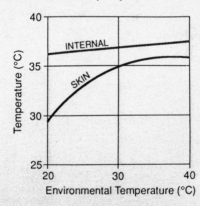

Which statement best describes what happens as environmental temperature increases from 20°C to 30°C?
    (1) Both the internal and the skin temperatures reach 40°C.
    (2) Both the internal and the skin temperatures increase by about 7°C.
    (3) The skin temperature decreases to about 30°C.
    (4) The internal temperature increases by about 1°C.

29. Which letter in the diagram below indicates a ligament?

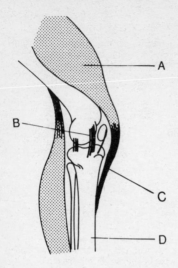

A

B

C

D

   (1) *A*   (3) *C*
   (2) *B*   (4) *D*

30. Asexual reproduction of diploid organisms normally results in new organisms that contain cells with
   (1) more chromosomes than are found in the cells of the parent
   (2) the *n* number of chromosomes
   (3) the 2*n* number of chromosomes
   (4) fewer chromosomes than are found in the cells of the parent

31. Random separation and distribution of homologous chromosomes occurs during
   (1) cleavage
   (2) mitotic cell division
   (3) fertilization
   (4) meiotic cell division

32. Each body cell of a chimpanzee contains 48 chromosomes. How many chromosomes would normally be present in a gamete produced by this chimpanzee?
   (1) 24   (3) 48
   (2) 36   (4) 96

33. In certain plants, roots will develop from a stem cutting. This type of reproduction is known as
   (1) vegetative propagation
   (2) binary fission
   (3) unicellular budding
   (4) spore formation

34. Which reproductive adaptation is characteristic of most fish and amphibians?
   (1) Their gametes always fuse in the moist reproductive tract of the female.
   (2) They only produce nonmotile gametes.
   (3) They produce small numbers of eggs.
   (4) Their zygotes are formed in the external environment.

35. Many fruits contain specialized structures that are adaptations for
   (1) synthesizing minerals
   (2) aiding in seed dispersal
   (3) attracting pollinating insects
   (4) promoting germination of pollen grains

36. Which letter indicates the structure within which fertilization takes place?

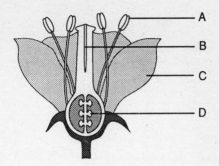

      — A

      — B

      — C

      — D

    (1) *A*   (3) *C*
    (2) *B*   (4) *D*

37. In which part of a pine tree stem is meristematic tissue located?
    (1) phloem   (3) cambium
    (2) xylem   (4) epidermis

38. Some basic principles of heredity were established when Gregor Mendel crossed large numbers of pea plants and then
    (1) mapped the loci of various genes
    (2) analyzed the mathematical ratios of certain traits in the offspring
    (3) microdissected the chromosomes of the offspring
    (4) determined how many genes had mutated

39. In chickens, rose comb (*R*) is dominant over single comb (*r*). When a heterozygous rose-combed rooster is mated with several single-combed hens, what is the expected phenotypic ratio of the offspring?
    (1) 100% rose-combed
    (2) 100% single-combed
    (3) 75% rose-combed and 25% single-combed
    (4) 50% rose-combed and 50% single-combed

40. The best method for determining if a woman may be a carrier of the trait for color blindness is to
    (1) give her an eye examination
    (2) analyze a sample of her red blood cells
    (3) analyze a sample of her urine
    (4) check her family pedigree for the trait

41. In certain plants, each cell contains double the normal chromosome number. These 4*n* cells are an example of the condition known as
    (1) replication   (3) polyploidy
    (2) diploidy   (4) disjunction

42. Which is a true statement about people with the genotype $I^A I^B$ for blood type?
    (1) They have two alleles that are codominant.
    (2) They exhibit a type O phenotype.
    (3) They are homozygous for blood type A.
    (4) They can have only type O children.

43. Genes for two different traits that are located next to each other on the same chromosome would most likely be
    (1) inherited separately
    (2) codominant
    (3) recombined
    (4) inherited together

44. A common practice used by breeders to maintain a desired trait in dogs is
    (1) artificial selection
    (2) regeneration
    (3) vegetative propagation
    (4) sporulation

45. Strontium-90, a radioactive isotope found in nuclear fallout, is incorporated and used by the human body in much the same manner as calcium. Because of its radioactive nature, strontium-90 would probably
    (1) cause disjunction of chromosomes
    (2) take the place of phosphorus in chromosomes
    (3) act as a mutagenic agent within bone cells
    (4) inhibit the development of mutations

46. The sequence of amino acids in the cytochrome *c* molecule, an enzyme found in mitochondria, is identical in humans and chimpanzees. This fact best supports the concept that
    (1) simpler organisms synthesized cytochrome *c*
    (2) humans and chimpanzees have similar nutritional requirements
    (3) simpler organisms evolved into more complex organisms
    (4) humans and chimpanzees have a common ancestor

47. In the diagram below of undisturbed sedimentary rock strata, in which rock layer are the fossils of more complex animals generally found?

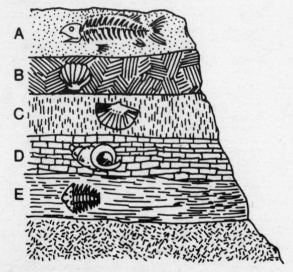

    (1) *A*   (3) *E*
    (2) *B*   (4) *D*

48. Evolution refers to change over a long period of time in
    (1) a fossil   (3) a rock
    (2) a population   (4) an embryo

49. Which evolutionary concept is best illustrated by the cartoon below?

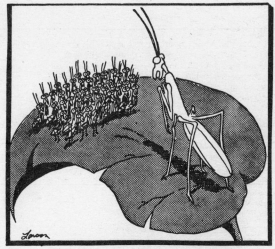

"Of course, long before you mature, most of you will be eaten."

(1) production of mutations
(2) use and disuse
(3) survival of the fittest
(4) speciation

50. Which theory of evolutionary change suggests that species have long periods of stability interrupted by geologically brief periods of significant change during which new species are formed?
(1) gradualism
(2) geographic isolation
(3) punctuated equilibrium
(4) reproductive isolation

51. According to the heterotroph hypothesis, in addition to water, the raw materials used to produce the most primitive life forms on Earth were probably
(1) nitrogen, carbon dioxide, and oxygen
(2) hydrogen, methane, and ammonia
(3) carbon monoxide, ammonia, and oxygen
(4) hydrogen, oxygen, and nitrogen

52. A weakness in Darwin's original theory of evolution was that
(1) the genetic basis for variation was not explained
(2) overproduction never occurs in nature
(3) competition occurs in animals but not in plants
(4) natural selection does not occur in domestic animals

53. The study of the interactions between organisms and their interrelationships with the physical environment is known as
(1) ecology
(2) cytology
(3) embryology
(4) physiology

54. An abiotic factor affecting the behavior and survival of such organisms as robins and violets is the
    (1) population of rabbits
    (2) length of daylight
    (3) presence of harmful bacteria
    (4) number of herbivores

55. An overpopulation of deer in a certain area will most likely lead to
    (1) a decrease in the number of predators of the deer
    (2) an increase in the number of autotrophs available for food
    (3) a decrease in the incidence of disease
    (4) an increase in competition between the deer

56. In an abandoned field, the gradual replacement of grasses by shrubs and then by trees is known as
    (1) predation
    (2) saprophytism
    (3) ecological succession
    (4) transfer of energy

57. Which activity has had the most negative effect on the environment?
    (1) recycling of aluminum cans
    (2) biological control of insect pests
    (3) importation of the gypsy moth
    (4) control of air pollution

58. Which activities most directly control erosion?
    (1) use of reforestation and covercropping
    (2) establishment of game laws and fisheries
    (3) use of phosphates and hydrocarbons
    (4) establishment of wildlife refuges and national parks

59. Which term best describes the interactions between the physical and living factors shown in the diagram below?

    (1) a biosphere   (3) a community
    (2) an ecosystem   (4) a biome

PART II

This part consists of five groups, each containing ten questions. Choose two of these five groups. Be sure that you answer all ten questions in each group chosen. [20]

Group 1—Biochemistry

If you choose this group, be sure to answer questions 60–69.

Base your answers to questions 60 through 62 on the chart below which gives incomplete information about certain biochemical reactions and on your knowledge of biology.

Reactants	Products	Enzyme Involved
maltose, water	A	maltase
B	amino acids	protease
lipids, water	fatty acids, glycerol	C

60. The products represented by letter A are
    (1) glucose molecules
    (2) ATP molecules
    (3) alcohol molecules
    (4) polypeptide molecules

61. The reactants represented by letter B are
    (1) glucose and water
    (2) ATP and water
    (3) dipeptides and water
    (4) alcohol and water

62. The enzyme represented by letter C is known as
    (1) ATPase   (3) sucrase
    (2) lipase   (4) amylase

Base your answers to questions 63 and 64 on the information and diagram below and on your knowledge of biology.

A student conducted an investigation on fermentation. Yeast, molasses, and water were combined in a fermentation tube and left for several hours at room temperature. The results are shown below.

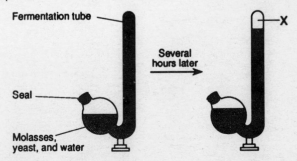

63. Which substance would most likely be found in the greatest amount in area X?
    (1) O_2
    (3) H_2O
    (2) $C_6H_{12}O_6$
    (4) CO_2

64. If the fermentation tube had been maintained at 60°C instead of at room temperature, the substance in area X would not have been produced. Which statement is the best explanation for this?
    (1) ADP molecules are destroyed at 60°C.
    (2) High temperatures denature enzymes.
    (3) Molasses turns to starch at 60°C.
    (4) Gases cannot form at high temperatures.

65. If the leaves of a geranium plant receive an adequate supply of raw materials, which graph shows how the rate of photosynthesis is related to increasing light intensity received by the plant?

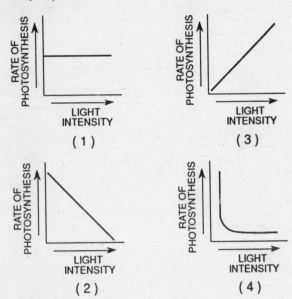

66. Which reactions are involved in the process of photosynthesis?
    (1) photochemical reactions, only
    (2) carbon-fixation reactions, only
    (3) both photochemical and carbon-fixation reactions
    (4) neither photochemical nor carbon-fixation reactions

67. Which equation represents a process that results from a lack of oxygen in human muscle cells?
    (1) glucose $\xrightarrow{\text{enzymes}}$ lactic acid + ATP
    (2) glucose $\xrightarrow{\text{enzymes}}$ carbon dioxide + alcohol + ATP
    (3) sucrose $\xrightarrow{\text{enzymes}}$ simple sugars
    (4) polypeptide $\xrightarrow{\text{enzymes}}$ dipeptides

68. Fatty acids and amino acids both contain
    (1) alcohol
    (3) simple sugars
    (2) glycerol
    (4) carboxyl groups

69. Gastric protease operates most efficiently in the presence of hydrochloric acid. Which pH range would be optimal for gastric protease?
    (1) 1 to 3
    (3) 10 to 11
    (2) 8 to 9
    (4) 12 to 14

Group 2—Human Physiology

If you choose this group, be sure to answer questions 70–79.

Base your answers to questions 70 through 73 on the diagrams below of organ systems and on your knowledge of biology.

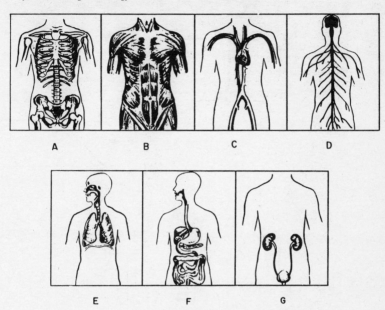

A   B   C   D

E   F   G

70. Which disorder would most directly involve an organ in system *F*?
    (1) anemia
    (2) constipation
    (3) bronchitis
    (4) meningitis

71. Polio is a disease caused by a virus that directly destroys cells in system
    (1) *A*
    (2) *B*
    (3) *C*
    (4) *D*

72. Cardiovascular diseases interfere most directly with the normal functioning of system
    (1) *E*
    (2) *G*
    (3) *C*
    (4) *D*

73. Tendonitis is a condition that would most directly involve which two systems?
    (1) *A* and *B*
    (2) *C* and *D*
    (3) *E* and *F*
    (4) *A* and *G*

Base your answers to questions 74 through 76 on the diagram below and on your knowledge of biology. Many of the endocrine glands found in humans are represented and labeled in the diagram.

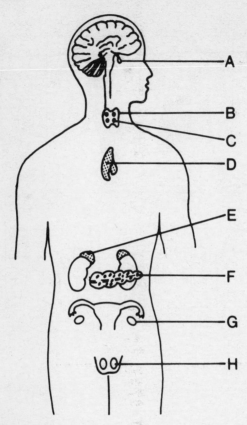

74. Estrogen is secreted by structure
    (1) *A*   (3) *G*
    (2) *F*   (4) *D*

75. A hormone that directly stimulates glands *G* and *H* is secreted by structure
    (1) *A*   (3) *C*
    (2) *B*   (4) *E*

76. Glucagon is secreted by structure
    (1) *E*   (3) *C*
    (2) *B*   (4) *F*

77. For blood to pass through the heart from the left atrium to the left ventricle, it must *first* pass through
    (1) an artery   (3) a vein
    (2) a valve   (4) a capillary

78. Bacteria and dead cells are removed from circulatory fluid in the
    (1) urinary bladder   (3) alveoli
    (2) gallbladder   (4) lymph nodes

79. In humans, gout is caused by excess production and deposition of
    (1) lactic acid
    (2) uric acid
    (3) fatty acids
    (4) amino acids

Group 3—Reproduction and Development

If you choose this group, be sure to answer questions 80–89.

Base your answers to questions 80 through 84 on the diagrams below and on your knowledge of biology.

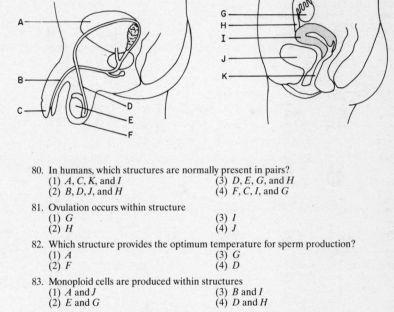

80. In humans, which structures are normally present in pairs?
    (1) $A, C, K,$ and I
    (2) $B, D, J,$ and H
    (3) $D, E, G,$ and H
    (4) $F, C, I,$ and G

81. Ovulation occurs within structure
    (1) G
    (2) H
    (3) I
    (4) J

82. Which structure provides the optimum temperature for sperm production?
    (1) A
    (2) F
    (3) G
    (4) D

83. Monoploid cells are produced within structures
    (1) A and J
    (2) E and G
    (3) B and I
    (4) D and H

84. Hormones that regulate the development of secondary sex characteristics are produced within structures
    (1) E and G
    (2) C and K
    (3) F and J
    (4) A and H

85. Which is an embryonic germ layer that gives rise to the muscular, skeletal, and circulatory systems of a human?
    (1) epidermis
    (2) endoderm
    (3) ectoderm
    (4) mesoderm

86. Thickening and vascularization of the uterine lining in the human female is initiated during which stage of the menstrual cycle?
    (1) corpus luteum
    (2) menstruation
    (3) follicle
    (4) ovulation

87. In humans, the number of sperm cells required to produce a pair of identical twins is
    (1) 1
    (2) 2
    (3) 3
    (4) 4

88. Which structure serves as a storage site for uric acid waste for a developing bird embryo?
    (1) shell
    (2) yolk
    (3) amnion
    (4) allantois

89. Which is the normal sequence of events in the development of the embryo of an animal?
    (1) gastrulation → fertilization → blastula formation → cleavage
    (2) fertilization → cleavage → gastrulation → blastula formation
    (3) cleavage → blastula formation → fertilization → gastrulation
    (4) fertilization → cleavage → blastula formation → gastrulation

Group 4—Modern Genetics

If you choose this group, be sure to answer questions 90–99.

Base your answers to questions 90 through 94 on the diagram below of the chromosomes from a human cell and on your knowledge of biology.

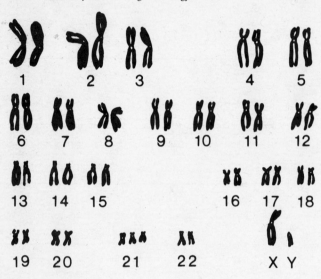

90. The diagram represents a
    (1) deletion
    (2) synapsis
    (3) karyotype
    (4) disjunction

91. The chromosomes are arranged to show
    (1) homologous pairs
    (2) tetrads
    (3) independent assortment
    (4) nucleotides

92. The individual from whom these chromosomes were taken is a
    (1) male
    (2) female
    (3) hermaphrodite
    (4) polyploid

93. This chromosomal arrangement indicates that the individual has
    (1) phenylketonuria
    (2) Down's syndrome
    (3) sickle-cell anemia
    (4) Tay-Sachs disease

94. Which procedure can be performed during fetal development to detect the chromosomal disorder illustrated by the diagram?
    (1) genetic counseling
    (2) amniocentesis
    (3) urine analysis
    (4) cloning

Base your answers to questions 95 through 97 on the diagram below of a biochemical process that occurs within cells and on your knowledge of biology.

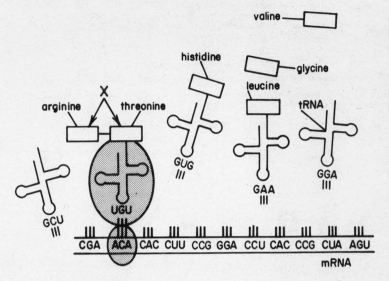

95. Structure X represents a
    (1) dipeptide
    (2) disaccharide
    (3) fat
    (4) polysaccharide

96. The process represented in the diagram occurs on the cell organelle known as a
    (1) vacuole
    (2) ribosome
    (3) chloroplast
    (4) mitochondrion

97. The process represented in the diagram is
    (1) lipid digestion
    (2) cell respiration
    (3) protein synthesis
    (4) protein hydrolysis

98. According to the table below, which animo acid sequence would most likely be determined by a section of a DNA molecule with the base sequence A-A-G-G-A-T-C-C-G?

Messenger RNA Codon	Amino Acid
A-G-A	arginine
C-U-A	leucine
G-G-C	glycine
U-U-C	phenylalanine

    (1) phenylalanine-arginine-glycine
    (2) glycine-arginine-leucine
    (3) glycine-leucine-arginine
    (4) phenylalanine-leucine-glycine

99. Which statement concerning the evolution of a population of coyotes is true if the gene frequencies of the population remain constant over several generations?
    (1) The rate of evolution will decrease, only.
    (2) The rate of evolution will increase, only.
    (3) The rate of evolution will increase slowly, then decrease rapidly.
    (4) Evolution will not occur at any rate.

Group 5—Ecology

If you choose this group, be sure to answer questions 100–109.

Base your answers to questions 100 through 104 on the diagram below and on your knowledge of biology.

AN ENERGY PYRAMID FOR A POND

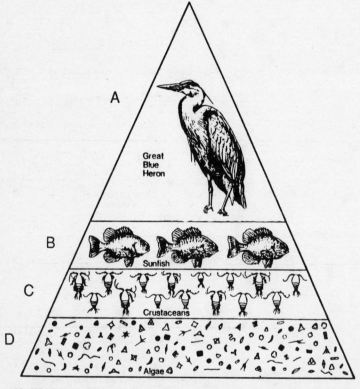

100. Which level of consumers contains the largest percentage of total stored energy?
    (1) *A*   (3) *C*
    (2) *B*   (4) *D*

101. Which level of the pyramid contains autotrophic organisms?
    (1) *A*   (3) *C*
    (2) *B*   (4) *D*

102. Which organism is a primary consumer?
    (1) alga   (3) sunfish
    (2) crustacean   (4) great blue heron

103. Which is a possible food chain sequence derived from this energy pyramid?
    (1) sunfish → algae → great blue heron → crustaceans
    (2) great blue heron → crustaceans → sunfish → algae
    (3) algae → crustaceans → sunfish → great blue heron
    (4) crustaceans → great blue heron → algae → sunfish

104. Which level of the pyramid contains the greatest biomass?
    (1) *A*   (3) *C*
    (2) *B*   (4) *D*

Directions (105–108): For *each* statement in questions 105 through 108 select the biome, *chosen from the list below*, that is best described by that statement.

         Biomes

    (1) Tundra
    (2) Desert
    (3) Tropical forest
    (4) Taiga
    (5) Temperate deciduous forest

105. Plants that grow here, such as mesquite and saguaro cactus, develop extensive root systems for absorbing water and have water storage cells in their stems and roots.

106. The subsoil is permanently frozen, and lichens and mosses are the dominant plant species.

107. A coniferous forest growing just below the tree line on mountains is densely populated by climax communities of spruce and fir trees.

108. Forests of maple, beech, oak, and hickory make up the dominant vegetation.

109. Nitrogen-fixing bacteria live on the roots of leguminous plants in swellings called nodules. The bacteria synthesize nitrogen compounds that are used by the plants, and the plants provide moisture and nutrients for the bacteria. The interaction between the nitrogen-fixing bacteria and the leguminous plants is known as
    (1) parasitism   (3) saprophytism
    (2) mutualism   (4) commensalism

PART III

This part consists of five groups. Choose three of these five groups.   [15]

Group 1

If you choose this group, be sure to answer questions 110–114.

Base your answers to questions 110 through 112 on the information and diagrams below and on your knowledge of biology.

In an investigation of the cycling of environmental gases, a student placed water and bromthymol blue in each of four test tubes as shown in the diagrams below. No additional items were placed in tube 1, a snail was placed in tube 2, an aquatic plant (elodea) was placed in tube 3, and both a snail and an elodea were placed in tube 4. The tubes were then stoppered and placed in bright light for 24 hours.

Tube 1   Tube 2   Tube 3   Tube 4

110. How would the solution in tube 3 change after 24 hours?
    (1) It would contain more oxygen.
    (2) It would change from yellow to blue.
    (3) It would change from blue to brick red.
    (4) It would contain less nitrogen.

111. The most probable explanation for a color change in tube 2 is that
    (1) water was released by the snail.
    (2) oxygen was removed from the water
    (3) carbon dioxide was added to the water
    (4) the snail's body temperature increased

112. The function of tube 1 in this investigation is to
    (1) detect the presence of glucose
    (2) determine the amount of gases in the water
    (3) demonstrate the transparency of the solution
    (4) serve as a control

113. In one of his experiments with pea plants, Mendel noted that 75% of the offspring of a certain cross had green pea pods. This statement would be considered
    (1) an observation   (3) a hypothesis
    (2) an inference   (4) a conclusion

114. Using one or more complete sentences, describe how to place a coverslip on a wet mount so that the slide preparation has as few air bubbles as possible.

Group 2

If you choose this group, be sure to answer questions 115–119.

Base your answers to questions 115 through 117 on the diagram below of a microscope and on your knowledge of biology.

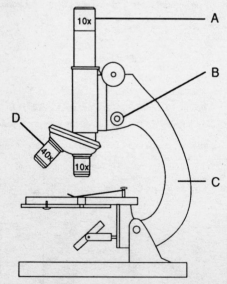

115. While viewing a specimen under high power, a student noticed that the specimen was out of focus. Which part of the microscope should the student use to obtain a clearer image?
    (1) A   (3) C
    (2) B   (4) D

116. The highest possible magnification that can be obtained when using this microscope is
(1) 40×
(2) 100×
(3) 400×
(4) 4,000×

117. The diagram at the right represents a strand of algae viewed under the low-power objective of this microscope. Under the high-power objective, how would this same slide appear?

(1) (2) (3) (4)

118. Which procedure should be used to prepare a wet mount of pollen grains? [Use the diagram of a flower below for reference.]

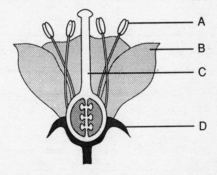

(1) Scrape the surface of structure *A* into a drop of water on a slide and cover with a coverslip.
(2) Remove the contents of structure *C* with a pipette. Then place the contents in a drop of water on a slide and cover with a coverslip.
(3) Crush structure *D* on a slide and cover with a coverslip.
(4) Place a piece of structure *B* in a drop of water on a slide and cover with a coverslip.

119. A student determined that exactly 10 pollen grains could fit along the diameter of the field of view of a microscope. If each pollen grain has a diameter of 200 micrometers, what is the diameter in millimeters of this microscope's field of view?
(1) 2,000 mm
(2) 2 mm
(3) 5 mm
(4) 500 mm

Group 3

If you choose this group, be sure to answer questions 120–124.

Base your answers to questions 120 and 121 on the diagram below of a dissected grasshopper and on your knowledge of biology.

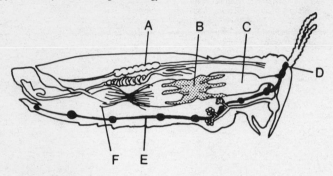

120. The position of structure *B* could best be described as
    (1) dorsal to *A*
    (2) ventral to *E*
    (3) anterior to *D*
    (4) posterior to *C*

121. Which structures are part of the grasshopper's digestive system?
    (1) *A* and *B*
    (2) *B* and *C*
    (3) *D* and *E*
    (4) *B* and *F*

122. A student would most likely place cotton fibers in a drop of paramecia culture placed on a slide in order to
    (1) interfere with the functioning of the contractile vacuoles
    (2) cover the eyespots to interfere with responses to light
    (3) stop the formation of pseudopods to prevent ingestion
    (4) slow down the movement of the paramecia

123. The seed coat was removed from a bean and the bean was separated into halves and soaked in Lugol's iodine. According to the results shown in the diagram below, which conclusion can be drawn about the seed?

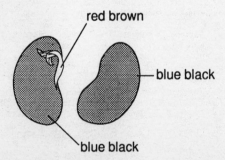

    (1) The red-brown area is the cotyledon.
    (2) Starch is present in the hypocotyl.
    (3) The blue-black area contains starch.
    (4) Glucose is present in the epicotyl.

124. Name an indicator that could be used to determine if a solution is an acid or a base.

Group 4

If you choose this group, be sure to answer questions 125–129.

Base your answers to questions 125 through 129 on the reading passage below and on your knowledge of biology.

Indigestion as a Basis of Plant Defense

Scientists used to think of plants as generally defenseless against herbivores. Research now shows that plants use a complex variety of chemical defenses. When a tomato, potato, or alfalfa leaf is wounded by a chewing insect or by other mechanical means, a chemical message travels rapidly throughout the plant. In response to this message, the plant produces and accumulates substances that inhibit digestion in the alimentary canal of the animal that eats the leaf. These wound-induced molecules function as inhibitors of trypsin, one type of enzyme involved in protein digestion.

In laboratory experiments, these wound-induced inhibitors had serious effects on animals. Because they could not break down ingested protein, chicks fed the inhibitors died, and rats and mice became malnourished. The growth period of insect larvae was prolonged, allowing diseases and predators to kill a greater number of the larvae.

Trypsin inhibitors had previously been detected only in the seeds of legumes, making up about 5 percent of the protein in such seeds. These substances were once thought to be storage proteins, minerals broken down for food as the seed germinated and grew into a plant. Scientists now believe that these trypsin inhibitors may act as protective agents.

Alfalfa, potatoes, and tomatoes have similar wound-stimulated defense systems, each producing its own distinct inhibitors. Scientists are analyzing the genes that produce each inhibitor to determine whether the defense systems share a common ancestry. Many plant families may contain similar gene-regulated mechanisms that produce a variety of defense substances.

In the future, genetic engineering may be used to increase the amount of inhibitor produced and thus provide greater protection for the plant. Human consumers of cooked foods would not be harmed since the wound-induced inhibitors are broken down by heat.

125. In legume seeds, trypsin inhibitor probably functions as
    (1) an inhibitor of premature germination
    (2) an inhibitor of predation by animals
    (3) an energy source during seed dormancy
    (4) a regulator of seed development

126. Trypsin inhibitors in tomato, potato, and alfalfa plants are best described as factors that
    (1) stimulate growth
    (2) promote species survival
    (3) alter gene regulation
    (4) promote protein storage in seeds

127. To produce trypsin inhibitors, plants must synthesize these proteins from
    (1) amino acids
    (2) fatty acids
    (3) carbohydrates
    (4) alcohols

128. In the future, genetic engineering in this field of study could be of value by resulting in
    (1) greater destruction of crops by bacteria
    (2) more efficient digestion of food by insect pests
    (3) an increase in the life expectancy of insect pests
    (4) an increase in the available food supply for humans

129. The most likely result of ingestion of trypsin inhibitor by the larva of an insect would be
    (1) the insect's immediate death
    (2) the destruction of the insect's gene-regulating system
    (3) a delay in completion of the insect's metamorphosis
    (4) an increase in the insect's metabolic rate

Group 5

If you choose this group, be sure to answer questions 130–134.

Base your answers to questions 130 through 134 on the investigation described below and on your knowledge of biology.

An investigation was performed to determine the effect of temperature on the activity of the enzyme catalase, which breaks down hydrogen peroxide, releasing oxygen. Six test tubes, each containing water and equal concentrations of hydrogen peroxide and catalase, were maintained at different temperatures. Observations made during the investigation were used to construct the data table below.

Data Table

Test Tube	Temperature (°C)	Bubbles of Oxygen per Minute
1	0	3
2	10	22
3	20	40
4	30	58
5	40	71
6	50	2

Directions (130–131): Using the information in the data table, construct a line graph on the grid provided, following the directions below.

130. Mark an appropriate scale on each of the labeled axes.

131. Plot the data on the graph. Surround each point with a small circle and connect the points.

Example:

THE EFFECT OF TEMPERATURE ON THE ENZYME CATALASE

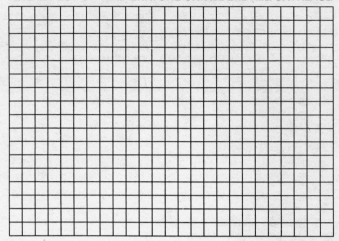

NUMBER OF BUBBLES PER MINUTE

TEMPERATURE (°C)

132. An increase in the rate of bubbling in each of tubes 1 through 5 would most likely be noticed after
    (1) increasing the temperature of each tube to 80°C
    (2) decreasing the temperature of each tube to −10°C
    (3) increasing the light intensity on each tube, but not the temperature
    (4) adding more enzyme molecules to each tube

Directions (133–134): Your answers must be written in complete sentences.

133. State the effect of an increase in temperature from 0°C to 40°C on the rate of the activity of catalase.

134. Describe one safety procedure that should be used when the investigation is performed.

BIOLOGY

June 19, 1992

PART I

Answer all 59 questions in this part. [65]

Directions (1–59): For *each* statement or question, select the word or expression that, of those given, best completes the statement or answers the question.

1. Which process most directly enables sperm cells to move from place to place and enables root hair cells to absorb minerals by active transport?
   (1) digestion
   (2) respiration
   (3) reproduction
   (4) excretion

2. Which type of organism is an exception to the cell theory?
   (1) virus
   (2) bacterium
   (3) plant
   (4) protozoan

3. The wildlife naturalist M. T. Thompson classified an African antelope as *Gazella thompsonii*. The common name "gazelle" is derived from which part of the scientific name?
   (1) kingdom
   (2) phylum
   (3) genus
   (4) species

4. Which cell structures are most directly involved in protein synthesis?
   (1) chloroplast and centriole
   (2) endoplasmic reticulum and cell wall
   (3) nucleus and ribosome
   (4) cell membrane and lysosome

5. Which instrument could best be used to transfer a chloroplast from an elodea cell into a root cell of a bean plant?
   (1) ultracentrifuge
   (2) microdissection apparatus
   (3) electron microscope
   (4) scalpel

6. Which environmental condition would most likely have the *least* effect on the rate of an enzyme-controlled hydrolytic reaction in humans?
   (1) the pH of the solution
   (2) the temperature of the solution
   (3) the amount of enzyme present
   (4) the amount of light present

7. When a plant extract containing enzymes was used to hydrolyze meat for several hours, the meat became soft, but the fat it contained did not change. This difference is most likely due to the fact that the plant extract *lacked*
   (1) lipases
   (2) amylase
   (3) maltase
   (4) proteases

8. Heterotrophic organisms are characterized by their
   (1) ability to convert light energy into chemical energy
   (2) dependence on the chemical activities of chloroplasts in their cells
   (3) ability to convert simple inorganic compounds into organic compounds
   (4) dependence on obtaining organic compounds from their environment for nutrition

9. In which organism is digestion accomplished by both intracellular and extracellular methods?
   (1) ameba
   (2) paramecium
   (3) geranium
   (4) hydra

10. Many end-products of digestion leave the digestive system and enter the circulatory system by the process of
    (1) diffusion
    (2) cyclosis
    (3) osmosis
    (4) locomotion

11. Which animal has an open circulatory system and an infolded digestive tube?
    (1) human   (3) grasshopper
    (2) earthworm   (4) hydra

12. Organic molecules are constructed from inorganic raw materials as a result of
    (1) regulation   (3) digestion
    (2) photosynthesis   (4) hydrolysis

13. Sugar is transported from leaves to other plant structures by
    (1) xylem cells   (3) palisade cells
    (2) guard cells   (4) phloem cells

14. Carbon dioxide and water are wastes produced by the process of
    (1) dehydration synthesis   (3) emulsification
    (2) photosynthesis   (4) aerobic respiration

15. Which structures are used most directly by all protists for the process of excretion?
    (1) cell walls   (3) mitochondria
    (2) cell membranes   (4) cilia

16. Respiratory gases are exchanged between a hydra and its environment primarily by the process of
    (1) pinocytosis
    (2) active transport
    (3) diffusion
    (4) dehydration synthesis

17. Which life function prevents the accumulation of metabolic wastes in a bald eagle?
    (1) ingestion   (3) excretion
    (2) locomotion   (4) digestion

18. A chemical that clogs spiracles and tracheal tubes would directly interfere with respiration in
    (1) a grasshopper   (3) an earthworm
    (2) a hydra   (4) a human

19. What do the human adrenal gland and the masseter muscle in the human jaw have in common?
    (1) They function as receptors.
    (2) They function as effectors.
    (3) They are located in the same part of the body.
    (4) They are components of the transport system.

20. Which statement concerning hormones is true?
    (1) Hormones are produced by every cell of an organism.
    (2) Hormones are produced only by the pituitary gland.
    (3) Hormones produced by endocrine glands travel through ducts to various organs.
    (4) Hormones produced in one part of the body may affect the action of another part of the body.

21. A live geranium plant was tipped so that its stem and roots were both horizontal. New growth in the root tip was in a downward direction. This change in the direction of growth is known as
    (1) a tropism   (3) an auxin
    (2) a stimulus   (4) a neurotransmitter

22. The organelles indicated by *A* and *B* in the diagram below are found in many protozoans.

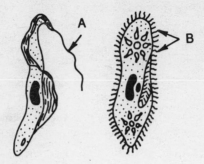

The main function of these organelles is to aid in
(1) secreting hormones and mating
(2) obtaining food and avoiding predators
(3) seeking shelter and excreting wastes
(4) controlling metamorphosis and moving

23. In humans, most of the building blocks necessary for the synthesis of organic compounds come from the
(1) end-products of digestion
(2) products of cellular respiration
(3) products of excretion
(4) breakdown of white blood cells.

24. The diagrams below represent different types of cells found in the human body. Which type of cell is a component of blood tissue?

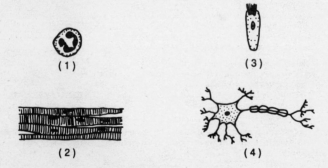

25. A kidney stone was produced and passed into the urinary bladder. To leave the body, the kidney stone will have to pass through the
(1) ureter   (3) glomerulus
(2) urethra   (4) Bowman's capsule

26. The diagrams below represent two different cells undergoing mitotic cell division.

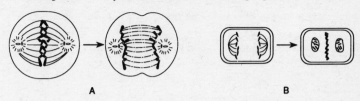

A   B

Which statement about these divisions is true?
(1) Both divisions could occur in a human.
(2) Division *A* could occur in a grasshopper and division *B* could occur in a hydra.
(3) Division *A* could occur in a bean plant and division *B* could occur in a maple tree.
(4) Division *A* could occur in a grasshopper and division *B* could occur in a maple tree.

27. Which homeostatic adjustment does the human body make in response to an increase in environmental temperature?
(1) secretion of insulin to decrease blood glucose levels
(2) storage of fats to provide insulation
(3) increase in the production of perspiration
(4) increase in urine production

28. The apparatus shown in the diagram below represents a model of part of the human respiratory system.

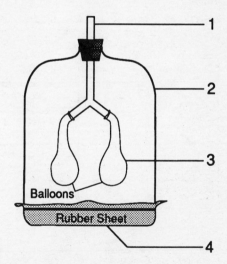

Balloons

Rubber Sheet

The movement of which part demonstrates the contraction and relaxation of the diaphragm during breathing?
(1) 1   (3) 3
(2) 2   (4) 4

29. In humans, one difference between the nervous system and the endocrine system is that
    (1) nerve responses are of longer duration than endocrine responses
    (2) nerve responses are more rapid than endocrine responses
    (3) only the endocrine system secretes chemicals
    (4) only the nervous system plays a role in homeostasis

30. Which component of the human skeletal system should be present in the regions labeled *A* in the diagram below to reduce friction and increase flexibility?

    (1) tendons   (3) cartilage
    (2) striated muscle   (4) ligaments

31. Cancer is a disease characterized by the
    (1) uncontrolled division of abnormal cells
    (2) unlimited production of abnormal gametes
    (3) uncontrolled replication and synapsis of chromosomes
    (4) limited production of normal zygotes

32. Which row in the chart below indicates the correct number of functional sex cells produced from one primary sex cell in the human female and from one primary sex cell in the human male?

Row	Number of egg cells produced from one primary sex cell	Number of sperm cells produced from one primary sex cell
A	1	1
B	1	4
C	2	1
D	3	4

    (1) *A*   (3) *C*
    (2) *B*   (4) *D*

33. The process known as budding is characterized by
    (1) the formation of a cell plate
    (2) an unequal distribution of cytoplasm
    (3) a decrease in chromosome number
    (4) a large number of nuclei

34. During which process is a diploid cell produced by the fusion of two monoploid cells?
    (1) sporulation
    (2) synapsis
    (3) sexual reproduction
    (4) gametogenesis

35. Normally, each cell of a specific organism contains 64 chromosomes. However, some cells in that organism may each contain only 32 chromosomes as a result of
    (1) crossing-over
    (2) mitotic cell division
    (3) regeneration
    (4) meiotic cell division

36. In flowering plants, nectar and brightly colored petals attract insects. Which process is most directly aided by these adaptations?
    (1) pollination
    (2) fertilization
    (3) differentiation
    (4) germination

37. In the diagram below of a green plant, which letters indicate the locations of apical meristems?

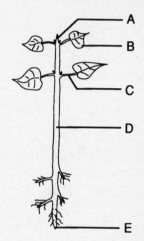

    (1) *A* and *B*
    (2) *B* and *E*
    (3) *C* and *D*
    (4) *A* and *E*

38. The genotype for coat color of roan cattle is represented as $C^R C^W$. The offspring produced by crosses of these cattle typically exhibit a 1:2:1 genotypic ratio. What is the phenotypic ratio of these same offspring?
    (1) 1:2:1
    (2) 3:1
    (3) 1:1
    (4) 2:1

39. The color pattern of a normal Himalayan rabbit that is homozygous for coat color is shown in diagram *A*. Diagram *B* shows this rabbit with the fur shaved from an area on its back and an ice pack applied to this area. Diagram *C* shows the same rabbit after new fur grew in the shaved area.

A   B   C

The best explanation for this change in color pattern is that
(1) the genes are linked
(2) the genotype of a rabbit is dependent on temperature
(3) the environment affects gene expression
(4) low temperature produces recessive genes

40. When hybrids for a certain characteristic are crossed (*Aa* × *Aa*), the recessive genotype (*aa*) may appear in some of the offspring because of
(1) segregation and recombination
(2) crossing-over
(3) dominance
(4) mutation and gene linkage

41. The sex of a human baby is initially determined by the
(1) DNA in the sperm
(2) DNA in the egg
(3) RNA in the sperm
(4) DNA and RNA in both the sperm and the egg

42. In a certain species of army ant, the gene for long mandibles (*M*) is dominant over the gene for short mandibles (*m*). If a biologist wants to produce ants with long mandibles only, which ants should be crossed?
(1) heterozygous long-mandibled ants with heterozygous long-mandibled ants
(2) heterozygous long-mandibled ants with homozygous short-mandibled ants
(3) homozygous long-mandibled ants with heterozygous long-mandibled ants
(4) homozygous short-mandibled ants with homozygous short-mandibled ants

43. The gene-chromosome theory includes the concept that
(1) genes are made up of specific polysaccharides
(2) hereditary factors exist on chromosomes
(3) external characteristics are not inherited
(4) mutagenic agents rarely produce changes in genes

44. A change in the chemical structure of a DNA molecule results in the formation of
(1) a gene mutation   (3) sterile polyploids
(2) a mutagenic agent   (4) a tetrad

45. Which molecule is composed of two complementary chains of nucleotides?
(1) ADP   (3) RNA
(2) DNA   (4) ATP

46. The use of x-ray analysis of the skeletal structures of the woolly mammoth and the modern-day elephant to investigate evolutionary relationships would most likely occur in the field of comparative
(1) embryology   (3) biochemistry
(2) cytology   (4) anatomy

47. The diagrams below show two cliffs that are located several kilometers apart. Both cliffs are made of undisturbed sedimentary strata with distinct layers.

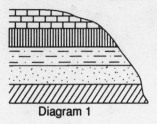 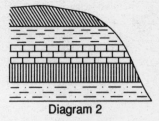

Diagram 1   Diagram 2

Which layer would contain the oldest fossils?

(1)    (3)

(2) 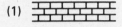   (4)

48. Lamarck's theory of evolution includes the concept that new organs in any species appear as a result of
    (1) an accumulation of small mutations
    (2) the specific needs of the organisms
    (3) an unchanging local environment
    (4) the natural variations within the population of organisms

49. The earliest life forms on Earth could not synthesize organic compounds, but obtained them directly from the environment. This explanation is part of the
    (1) cell theory
    (2) concept of use and disuse
    (3) heterotroph hypothesis
    (4) lock-and-key model

50. Geologically brief periods of significant change during which species evolve are separated by much longer periods during which the species do not change substantially. This statement best describes the concept of
    (1) natural selection
    (2) gradualism
    (3) use and disuse
    (4) punctuated equilibrium

51. According to the modern theory of evolution, variations within a species can best be explained by
    (1) mutations and gene recombinations
    (2) changing needs and sexual reproduction
    (3) gene linkage and vegetative propagation
    (4) adaptation and asexual reproduction

52. One possible reason many plant and animal species have become extinct is that they could *not*
    (1) reproduce sexually
    (2) carry on aerobic respiration
    (3) adapt to environmental changes
    (4) pass on acquired characteristics

53. Pigeons of the same species inhabiting a city park represent a
    (1) population   (3) food chain
    (2) biome   (4) food web

54. An abiotic factor that might affect the types of organisms that inhabit a pond is the
    (1) number of offspring produced by fish in the water
    (2) production of food by green algae in the water
    (3) introduction of goldfish into the pond
    (4) amount of oxygen available in the pond

55. The characteristics of some organisms are listed below.

    > Trout—carnivorous fish
    > Minnow—herbivorous fish
    > Algae—producers
    > Osprey—large carnivorous birds
    > Bacteria—decomposers

    Based on the information given above, which food chain is most probable?
    (1) trout → osprey → algae → minnow → bacteria
    (2) bacteria → algae → trout → minnow → osprey
    (3) minnow → algae → trout → bacteria → osprey
    (4) algae → minnow → trout → osprey → bacteria

56. The change of an ecosystem over time until a stable stage is reached is known as
    (1) competition   (3) succession
    (2) transpiration   (4) homeostasis

57. In the system represented by the diagram below, which processes are involved in the water cycle?

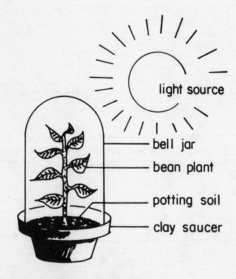

    (1) precipitation, respiration, and runoff
    (2) transpiration, evaporation, and condensation
    (3) decomposition, locomotion, and synthesis
    (4) digestion, excretion, and transport

58. In order to prevent the erosion of soil by running water, farmers may
    (1) keep the soil saturated at all times
    (2) dredge rivers and lakes
    (3) cover the soil with new plantings
    (4) allow livestock to overgraze fields

59. Which human activity resulting in a negative impact upon an ecosystem is best represented in the drawing below?

(1) importation of organisms to areas where their natural enemies are absent
(2) exploitation of fauna for products used by humans
(3) technological oversights leading to widespread pollution
(4) use of biocides for the control of pest species

PART II

This part consists of five groups, each containing ten questions. Choose two of these five groups. Be sure that you answer all ten questions in each group chosen. [20]

Group 1—Biochemistry

If you choose this group, be sure to answer questions 60-69.

Base your answers to questions 60 through 62 on the diagram of enzyme activity below and on your knowledge of biology.

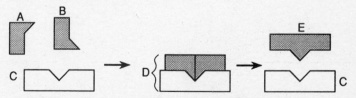

60. If structure E contains a peptide bond, structures A and B must represent
(1) amino acids   (3) fatty acids
(2) nucleotides   (4) simple sugars

61. An organic catalyst is indicated by letter
(1) A   (3) C
(2) B   (4) E

62. Letter D represents
    (1) the formation of ATP bonds
    (2) the formation of RNA
    (3) a digestive end-product
    (4) an enzyme-substrate complex

Directions (63–65): For *each* phrase in questions 63 through 65 select the type of molecule, *chosen from the list below*, that is best described by that phrase.

Types of Molecules

(1) Lipid
(2) Nucleic acid
(3) Protein
(4) Carbohydrate

63. Usually contains hydrogen and oxygen atoms in the ratio 2:1

64. May be formed by the dehydration synthesis of fatty acid molecules and glycerol molecules

65. May replicate and controls, either directly or indirectly, the manufacture of the other molecules in the list

66. Which compound is a three-carbon sugar and a product of the dark reactions of photosynthesis?
    (1) PGAL   (3) DNA
    (2) ADP   (4) ATP

67. The complete hydrolysis of a polysaccharide results in the production of
    (1) fatty acids   (3) inorganic acids
    (2) nucleic acids   (4) simple sugars

Base your answers to questions 68 and 69 on the structural formulas below and on your knowledge of biology.

A

B

C

D

E

68. Which molecule represents a monosaccharide?
    (1) A (3) C
    (2) B (4) D

69. Which two molecules are components of molecule A?
    (1) B and C (3) C and D
    (2) B and E (4) D and E

Group 2—Human Physiology

If you choose this group, be sure to answer questions 70–79.

Base your answers to questions 70 through 74 on the diagram below and on your knowledge of biology.

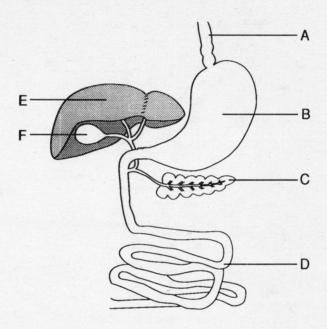

70. One digestive function of the secretion stored in structure *F* is the
    (1) hydrolysis of proteins
    (2) excretion of cellulose
    (3) emulsification of lipids
    (4) synthesis of hydrolytic enzymes

71. An accumulation of hardened cholesterol deposits within structure *F* may result in
    (1) gallstones   (3) constipation
    (2) a stroke   (4) diabetes

72. Small lymph vessels known as lacteals are found within organ
    (1) *F*   (3) *C*
    (2) *B*   (4) *D*

73. Which structure destroys wornout red blood cells as one of its excretory functions?
    (1) *A*   (3) *C*
    (2) *B*   (4) *E*

74. Ulcers are erosions of the surfaces of which two structures?
    (1) *B* and *C*   (3) *C* and *D*
    (2) *B* and *D*   (4) *A* and *E*

Base your answers to questions 75 and 76 on the diagram of the human heart below and on your knowledge of biology.

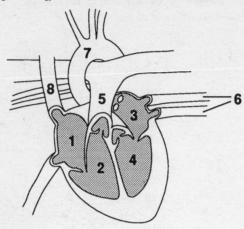

75. The blood vessel indicated by number 8 transports
    (1) deoxygenated blood from the heart to the body
    (2) deoxygenated blood from the body to the heart
    (3) oxygenated blood from the heart to the body
    (4) oxygenated blood from the body to the heart

76. The movement of blood between structures 5 and 6 is known as
    (1) coronary circulation
    (2) lymphatic circulation
    (3) pulmonary circulation
    (4) systemic circulation

77. The long bones of a child with dwarfism do not elongate as much as those of other children. This condition results from a malfunction of the
    (1) pituitary gland
    (2) gonads
    (3) kidneys
    (4) islets of Langerhans

78. Which hormone stimulates the conversion of glycogen to glucose within the cells of the liver?
    (1) insulin   (3) parathormone
    (2) glucagon   (4) testosterone

79. Painful and inflamed joints are symptoms of both
    (1) diabetes and cerebral palsy
    (2) tendinitis and meningitis
    (3) asthma and emphysema
    (4) arthritis and gout

Group 3—Reproduction and Development

If you choose this group, be sure to answer questions 80–89.

Base your answers to questions 80 through 83 on diagrams *A* and *B* below and on your knowledge of biology.

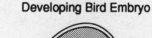

Diagram A
Fertilized Amphibian
(Frog) Egg

Diagram B
Developing Bird Embryo

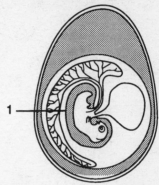

80. In diagram *B*, structure 1 encloses a fluid. The function of this fluid is to
    (1) provide nourishment to the embryo
    (2) provide the embryo with a liquid to drink
    (3) filter out the damaging radiation
    (4) protect the embryo from physical shock

81. Which statement best describes how the eggs in diagrams *A* and *B* were fertilized?
    (1) Egg *A* was fertilized internally and egg *B* was fertilized externally.
    (2) Egg *A* was fertilized externally and egg *B* was fertilized internally.
    (3) Both eggs were fertilized internally.
    (4) Both eggs were fertilized externally.

82. Which statement best describes where these eggs will continue to develop?
    (1) Both eggs will develop in water.
    (2) Both eggs will develop on land.
    (3) Egg *A* will develop in water and egg *B* will develop on land.
    (4) Egg *A* will develop on land and egg *B* will develop in water.

83. If these eggs were each compared to the egg of a placental mammal, the mammal's egg would be
    (1) much smaller than either *A* or *B*
    (2) larger than *A* but smaller than *B*
    (3) about the same size as *B*
    (4) larger than either *A* or *B*

Base your answers to questions 84 through 86 on the diagram below of the human male reproductive system and on your knowledge of biology.

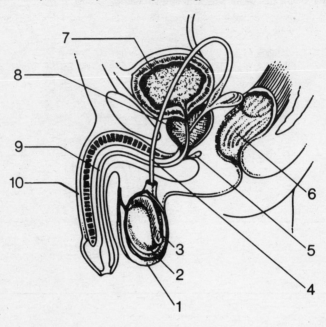

84. Male gametes and sex hormones are produced in structure
    - (1) 6
    - (2) 2
    - (3) 7
    - (4) 10

85. The function of structure 1 is to provide
    - (1) a storage site for urine until it is excreted from the body
    - (2) a storage site for progesterone until it is secreted into the blood
    - (3) an optimum temperature for sperm production
    - (4) an optimum temperature for the production of estrogen

86. Which sequence of structures correctly represents the pathway of sperm as they travel from their site of formation to the external environment?
    - (1) 2 → 3 → 4 → 9
    - (2) 1 → 4 → 5 → 7
    - (3) 1 → 2 → 3 → 4
    - (4) 2 → 5 → 6 → 8

Directions (87–88): For *each* event described in questions 87 and 88 select the stage of the menstrual cycle, *chosen from the list below*, that is most closely associated with that event.

Stages

- (1) Corpus luteum stage
- (2) Follicle stage
- (3) Menstruation
- (4) Ovulation

87. An egg is released from a follicle.

88. Estrogen is secreted, initiating the thickening of the uterine lining.

89. Which tissue of the adult human body is derived primarily from mesoderm?
    - (1) epidermal skin tissue
    - (2) digestive lining tissue
    - (3) nerve tissue
    - (4) muscle tissue

Group 4—Modern Genetics

If you choose this group, be sure to answer questions 90–99.

Base your answers to questions 90 through 94 on the diagram below of protein synthesis and on your knowledge of biology.

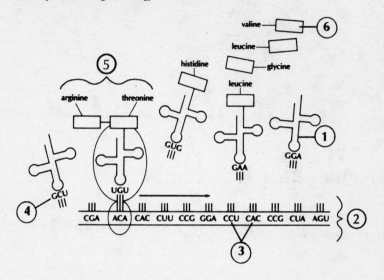

90. In the diagram, A, C, G, and U represent
    - (1) fatty acids
    - (2) nitrogenous bases
    - (3) amino acids
    - (4) ribosomes

91. Which structures are composed of RNA?
    - (1) 1 and 2
    - (2) 3 and 5
    - (3) 4 and 5
    - (4) 5 and 6

92. The portion of DNA that carries the code for leucine is
    - (1) G-T-T
    - (2) C-U-U
    - (3) C-T-T
    - (4) G-A-A

93. A dipeptide is represented by
    - (1) 1
    - (2) 2
    - (3) 5
    - (4) 6

94. The process that results in the formation of structure 2 is
    - (1) nondisjunction
    - (2) hydrolysis
    - (3) crossing-over
    - (4) RNA synthesis

Base your answers to questions 95 and 96 on the investigation described below and on your knowledge of biology.

A researcher prepared artificial messenger RNA molecules containing only uracil nucleotides, and then added to these molecules a mixture of amino acids, ATP, ribosomes, and transfer RNA's. The polypeptide that was produced contained only one kind of amino acid, phenylalanine.

95. The ribosomes were added to the system to
    - (1) provide ATP for the chemical reaction
    - (2) provide a place for the messenger RNA to attach
    - (3) react chemically with the amino acids
    - (4) add nucleotides to the chemical solution

96. The ATP was most likely added to the solution to provide
    (1) more amino acids   (3) energy
    (2) nucleotides   (4) enzymes

97. The individuality of an organism is determined by the organism's
    (1) amino acids
    (2) transfer RNA molecules
    (3) DNA nucleotide sequence
    (4) nitrogenous bases

98. The diagram below represents a karyotype.

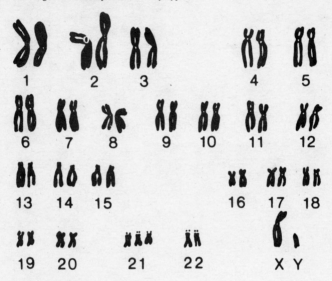

The karyotype indicates that this human is a
    (1) normal female
    (2) normal male
    (3) female with Down's syndrome
    (4) male with Down's syndrome

99. A human DNA segment was inserted into a bacterial cell and became incorporated into the bacterial DNA. This technique is an example of
    (1) genetic engineering
    (2) cloning
    (3) genetic counseling
    (4) artificial selection

Group 5—Ecology

If you choose this group, be sure to answer questions 100-109.

Base your answers to questions 100 through 103 on the diagram below which provides information about some major terrestrial biomes and on your knowledge of biology.

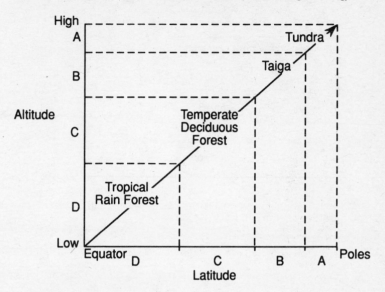

100. The diagram is based on the concept that biomes vary with
    (1) the number of mammals present
    (2) variation in soil type
    (3) changing climatic conditions
    (4) the depth of marine environments

101. The climax fauna in biome *C* includes
    (1) deer
    (2) monkeys
    (3) prairie dogs
    (4) caribou

102. The physical characteristics of biome *D* include
    (1) moderate rainfall, cold winters, and warm summers
    (2) great variation in temperature and rainfall
    (3) hot days, cold nights, and little rainfall
    (4) constant warmth and heavy rainfall

103. The climax flora in biome *B* includes
    (1) broad-leaved plants
    (2) conifers
    (3) deciduous trees
    (4) lichens

104. The diagram below represents a food pyramid.

If krill, a marine crustacean, were overharvested by commercial fishermen, which population of organisms would most likely increase?
(1) orca whales   (3) squid
(2) leopard seals   (4) plankton

105. The relationship between nitrogen-fixing bacteria and legumes is an example of a type of symbiotic relationship known as
(1) parasitism   (3) mutualism
(2) commensalism   (4) saprophytism

106. Dead plants and animal wastes are broken down by
(1) producers   (3) consumers
(2) decomposers   (4) autotrophs

107. Ammonia is converted into atmospheric nitrogen by
(1) denitrifying bacteria
(2) nitrifying bacteria
(3) bacteria of decay
(4) nitrogen-fixing bacteria

Base your answers to questions 108 and 109 on the information below and on your knowledge of biology. The ecological successions occurring in three different locations are shown below.

Location A	*Location B*	*Location C*
plowed field	bare rock	plowed field
↓	↓	↓
grasses	lichens	grasses
↓	↓	
shrubs	mosses	
↓	↓	
poplar and pine trees	grasses	
↓	↓	
oak-hickory forest	tropical shrubs	
	↓	
	palm trees	

108. What are the pioneer organisms in these locations?
    (1) oak, hickory, and palm trees
    (2) shrubs and palm trees
    (3) mosses and shrubs
    (4) grasses and lichens

Note that question 109 has only three choices.

109. The ecological succession that most often occurs in New York State is most like that of
    (1) location *A*
    (2) location *B*
    (3) location *C*

PART III

This part consists of five groups. Choose three of these five groups. [15]

Group 1

If you choose this group, be sure to answer questions 110–114.

Base your answers to questions 110 through 114 on the information and data table below and on your knowledge of biology.

An investigation was designed to determine the effect of temperature on respiration in germinating seeds. Two sets of test tubes were prepared. In each set of two tubes, one tube contained a number of germinating peas and the other tube contained an equal number of glass beads. An equal amount of a chemical was placed in each tube to absorb carbon dioxide so that the volume of oxygen consumed could be measured. One set of tubes was placed in a controlled-temperature water bath at 10°C. The other set of tubes was placed in a controlled-temperature water bath at 26°C. Total oxygen consumption was measured every 5 minutes for a period of 20 minutes. The data are summarized in the data table below.

DATA TABLE

Time (minutes)	Total Oxygen Consumption (mL)			
	10°C		26°C	
	Beads	Peas	Beads	Peas
0	0	0	0	0
5	0	0.3	0	0.5
10	0	0.6	0	1.0
15	0	0.9	0	1.5
20	0	1.2	0	2.0

Directions (110–112): Using the information in the data table, construct a line graph on the grid provided, following the directions below.

110. Mark an appropriate scale on each axis.

111. Plot the data for oxygen consumption by peas at 10°C on the grid. Surround each point with a small circle and connect the points.

    Example:

112. Plot the data for oxygen consumption by peas at 26°C on the grid. Surround each point with a small triangle and connect the points.

    Example:

    KEY
    ⊙ Peas at 10°C
    ▲ Peas at 26°C

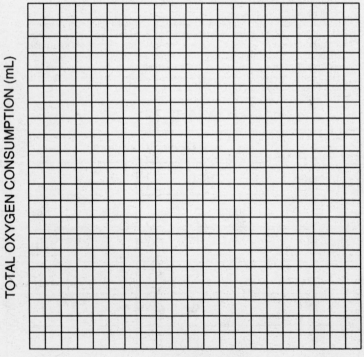

113. Using one or more complete sentences, state one conclusion that relates the rate of respiration in germinating peas to temperature.

114. Using one or more complete sentences, state one reason for including the tube containing the glass beads in each set.

Group 2

If you choose this group, be sure to answer questions 115–119.

Base your answers to questions 115 through 119 on the reading passage below and on your knowledge of biology.

Clues on Aging

Researchers appear to have found a link between the aging of human cells and a specific human chromosome. The findings may be useful not only to the understanding of aging but also to the study of cancer.

Normal human cells have a limited lifespan, after which the cells undergo a process called cellular senescence, or aging, which eventually results in a cell's death. But many animal tumor cells grow indefinitely and escape senescence. Scientists describe those cells as "immortal." Normal cells can be made "immortal" by exposure to chemical carcinogens, by the introduction of certain viruses, and by the addition of some genes found in tumors.

Researchers have developed cells that were hybrids between immortal Syrian hamster cells and normal human fetal lung cells. After a period of time, they found that most of the hybrid cells died. The few hybrid cells that became immortal shared one feature: they had lost copies of the human chromosome number 1. When a copy of human chromosome 1 was introduced into the immortal hybrid cells, they began to show signs of aging.

The linking of cellular aging to a specific chromosome suggests that aging is genetically programmed.

115. Why do normal human cells have a limited lifespan?
    (1) They grow to a large size and cannot get enough food.
    (2) They go through the process of cellular senescence.
    (3) They die when they touch other cells.
    (4) They are regulated by chemical carcinogens.

116. Based on the reading passage, a cell cannot be made immortal by
    (1) chemical carcinogens   (3) viruses
    (2) genes   (4) human chromosome number 1

117. The results of the research indicate that aging is
    (1) caused by viruses   (3) controlled by genetic material
    (2) caused by cancer   (4) absent in human cells

118. Using one or more complete sentences, describe how the researchers showed the effect of chromosome 1 on aging.

119. Using one or more complete sentences, explain why many human tumor cells are described as immortal.

Group 3

If you choose this group, be sure to answer questions 120–124.

120. A student prepared two slides. One was a wet mount of onion tissue. The other was a wet mount of the letter "f" which the student placed on the microscope stage in the position shown in the diagram below.

After viewing both slides through the compound microscope, the student drew the images observed. The student's diagrams would most closely resemble which two diagrams shown below?

A

B

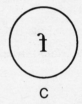
C

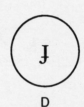
D

(1) *A* and *C*   (3) *B* and *C*
(2) *A* and *D*   (4) *B* and *D*

121. Which objective of a compound microscope would show the largest field of view?
(1) 5 ×   (3) 20 ×
(2) 10 ×   (4) 44 ×

122. If the microscope's field of view represented by the diagram at the right measures 1,400 micrometers (μm) in diameter, what is the approximate length of the microorganism within this field of view?
(1) 150 μm
(2) 250 μm
(3) 600 μm
(4) 1,000 μm

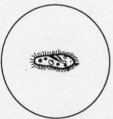

123. Which structures are visible in an ameba viewed with a compound light microscope?
(1) vacuoles, nucleus, and cytoplasm
(2) cell wall, cytoplasm, and lysosomes
(3) chloroplast, vacuoles, and nucleus
(4) ribosomes, nucleus, and nucleolus

124. When a student changes the objective lens of a compound microscope from low power to high power, the student should remember that
(1) the ocular will also have to be changed
(2) focusing with the fine-adjustment knob will no longer be necessary
(3) the field of view will be lighter under the high-power objective than under the low-power objective
(4) the field of view will be darker under the high-power objective than under the low-power objective

Group 4

If you choose this group, be sure to answer questions 125–129.

Base your answers to questions 125 through 127 on the information and diagram below and on your knowledge of biology.

Several drops of concentrated pigment extract obtained from spinach leaves were placed at the bottom of a strip of highly absorbent paper. When the extract dried, the paper was suspended in a test tube containing solvent so that only the tip of the paper was in the solvent. As the solvent was absorbed and moved up the paper, the various pigments contained within the extract became visible as shown in the diagram below.

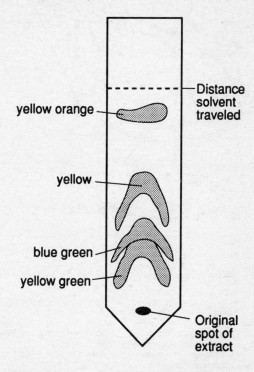

125. A valid conclusion that can be drawn from this information is that spinach leaves
    (1) use only chlorophyll during photosynthesis
    (2) contain pigments in addition to chlorophyll
    (3) contain more orange pigment than yellow pigment
    (4) are yellow orange rather than green

126. The technique used to separate the parts of the extract in the diagram is known as
    (1) staining
    (2) ultracentrifuging
    (3) chromatography
    (4) microdissection

127. In which organelle would most of the pigments be found?
    (1) centrioles
    (2) nucleus
    (3) mitochondria
    (4) chloroplast

128. The map below shows the distribution of acid rain over eastern North America. Each line connects points where the rainfall has equal acidity, represented by a specific pH value.

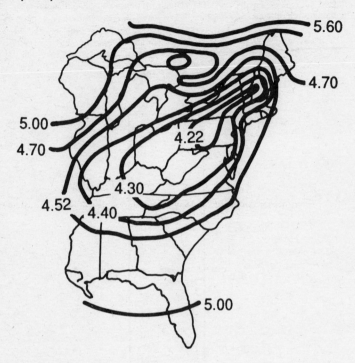

According to the map, the most acidic rainfall in New York State has a pH of
(1) 4.22   (3) 4.40
(2) 4.30   (4) 4.52

129. As part of a laboratory experiment, a thin slice of peeled raw potato weighing 100 grams is placed in an oven at 80°C. After 5 hours, the potato sample is removed from the oven and weighed again. The purpose of this experiment might be to
(1) test for the presence of starch in living tissues
(2) isolate cells in various stages of mitotic division
(3) determine the water content of potato tissue
(4) study the rate of transpiration in potatoes

Group 5

If you choose this group, be sure to answer questions 130–134.

130. Sucrose is broken down to simple sugars by placing the sucrose in a test tube, adding an acid solution, and slowly heating the mixture. Which solution, when added to the test tube, would indicate when the breakdown of sucrose occurs?
(1) salt solution   (3) bromthymol blue
(2) methylene blue   (4) Benedict's solution

131. Which group of measurements contains only metric units?
(1) 5 in, 3 lb, 40 mL   (3) 5 mm, 3 g, 40 lb
(2) 5 in, 3 kg, 40 oz   (4) 5 mm, 3 g, 40 mL

132. Which view of the frog is shown in the diagram below?

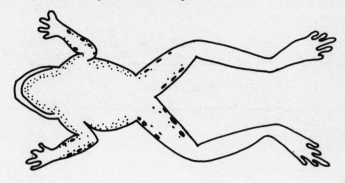

   (1) dorsal   (3) anterior
   (2) ventral   (4) posterior

133. When iodine solution is mixed with an unknown sample of food, the mixture turns blue black. This color change indicates the presence of
   (1) a carbohydrate   (3) a protein
   (2) an enzyme   (4) a lipid

134. What is the total volume of water in the graduated cylinder represented in the diagram below?

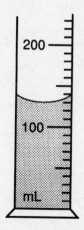

   (1) 115 mL   (3) 135 mL
   (2) 130 mL   (4) 140 mL

BIOLOGY

June 22, 1993

PART I

Answer all 59 questions in this part. [65]

Directions (1–59): For *each* statement or question, select the word or expression that, of those given, best completes the statement or answers the question.

1. In the diagram at the right, the arrows show the direction of movement of various substances. Which of the cell's life activities are represented by the arrows?

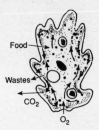

   (1) nutrition, reproduction, and regulation
   (2) excretion, transport, and respiration
   (3) growth, digestion, and locomotion
   (4) ingestion, regulation, and synthesis

2. Plants *A* and *B* are classified as members of the same species. Plants *C* and *D* are classified in the same genus as *A* and *B*, but not the same species as *A* and *B*. According to this information, which statement is correct?
   (1) Plant *A* has many characteristics in common with plant *B*.
   (2) Plant *C* cannot be the same species as plant *D*.
   (3) Plants *A* and *B* belong to a different kingdom than plants *C* and *D*.
   (4) Plants *A*, *B*, *C*, and *D* must all belong to different phyla.

3. Which statement describes an *exception* to the cell theory?
   (1) Cells arise from previously existing cells.
   (2) The cell is the basic unit of function in animals.
   (3) Mitochondria and chloroplasts can reproduce within the cell.
   (4) The cell is the basic unit of structure in plants.

4. The ultracentrifuge is an instrument that separates cellular components into distinct layers according to their relative
   (1) charges
   (2) solubilities
   (3) acidities
   (4) densities

5. Which organelles' activity contributes most directly to muscle contraction in an earthworm?
   (1) Golgi bodies
   (2) chloroplasts
   (3) mitochondria
   (4) lysosomes

6. Which of these elements is found in the *smallest* amount in living matter?
   (1) iodine
   (2) carbon
   (3) nitrogen
   (4) oxygen

7. A certain enzyme will hydrolyze egg white but not starch. Which statement best explains this observation?
   (1) Enzymes are specific in their actions.
   (2) Starch molecules are too large to be hydrolyzed.
   (3) Starch is composed of amino acids.
   (4) Egg white acts as a coenzyme for hydrolysis.

8. Which activity occurs in the process of photosynthesis?
   (1) Chemical energy from organic molecules is converted into light energy.
   (2) Organic molecules are obtained from the environment.
   (3) Organic molecules are converted into inorganic food molecules.
   (4) Light energy is converted into the chemical energy of organic molecules.

9. Which process is illustrated in the diagram below?

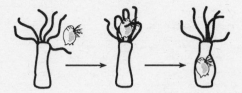

   (1) egestion   (3) synthesis
   (2) ingestion   (4) respiration

10. In the earthworm, the mixture of soil and food moving through the digestive tract is temporarily stored in the
   (1) mouth   (3) ganglia
   (2) crop   (4) setae

11. The process of osmosis would explain the net movement of water into a cell if the percentage of
   (1) water was 90% inside the cell and 95% outside the cell
   (2) protein was 30% inside the cell and 35% outside the cell
   (3) water was 95% inside the cell and 90% outside the cell
   (4) water and protein was equal inside and outside the cell

12. Vascular tissue in plants consists of
   (1) stomates and lenticels   (3) spongy cells and xylem
   (2) xylem and phloem   (4) lenticels and phloem

13. The diagram below represents a cross section of an earthworm.

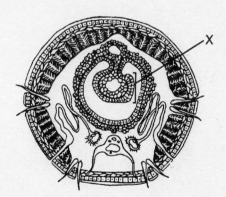

The function of structure X is to provide a greater surface area for
   (1) transport of deoxygenated blood   (3) carbon dioxide absorption
   (2) transmission of nerve impulses   (4) nutrient absorption

14. In which organism is the transport of oxygen aided by hemoglobin?
   (1) grasshopper   (3) earthworm
   (2) hydra   (4) ameba

15. The products produced by yeast cells as a result of anaerobic respiration include ATP and
   (1) alcohol and oxygen   (3) water and oxygen
   (2) alcohol and carbon dioxide   (4) water and carbon dioxide

16. Which statement best describes one of the events taking place in the chemical reaction represented below?

$$H_2O + ATP \xrightarrow{\text{ATPase}} ADP + P + energy$$

    (1) Energy is being stored as a result of aerobic respiration.
    (2) Fermentation is taking place, resulting in the synthesis of ATP.
    (3) Energy is being released for metabolic activities.
    (4) Photosynthesis is taking place, resulting in the storage of energy.

17. The production of nitrogenous waste from excess amino acids is most directly associated with the process of
    (1) dehydration synthesis   (3) excretion
    (2) glycogen storage   (4) reproduction

18. Which organism eliminates water, urea, and mineral salts by means of nephridia?
    (1) human   (3) grasshopper
    (2) hydra   (4) earthworm

19. The diagram below represents a neuron.

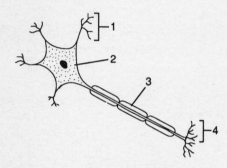

    Which number indicates an area where a stimulus is detected and an electrochemical impulse is conducted to the cyton?
    (1) 1   (3) 3
    (2) 2   (4) 4

20. The diagrams below show two sequences of events.

    Both sequences of events most likely result from
    (1) impulse transmission   (3) artificial selection
    (2) neurotransmitter secretion   (4) hormonal control

21. The tympana and antennae of grasshoppers function primarily as
    (1) effectors for locomotion   (3) producers of hormones
    (2) glands for regulation   (4) receptors of stimuli

22. The diagrams below represent four different organisms.

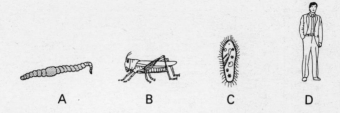

A   B   C   D

The interactions of muscles and jointed appendages is responsible for movement in
(1) *B*, only   (3) *D*, only
(2) *B* and *D*, only   (4) *A* and *C*, only

23. Which body structures have walls one cell thick?
(1) veins and arteries   (3) capillaries and alveoli
(2) trachea and bronchi   (4) lymph vessels and stomach

24. Producing blood cells and providing anchorage sites for muscles are two functions of
(1) skin   (3) cartilage
(2) bones   (4) ligaments

25. The diagram below represents a portion of the esophagus.

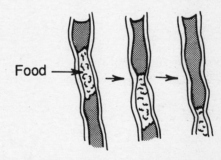

Food →

Which is a correct statement about the process shown in the diagram?
(1) It transports nutrients within the digestive tract.
(2) It must occur prior to mechanical digestion of food in the oral cavity.
(3) It emulsifies fats for hydrolysis in the small intestine.
(4) It increases water absorption by the esophagus.

26. Increased perspiration, a higher body temperature, and a rapidly beating heart are all possible responses to a stressful situation. These body responses are most likely a direct result of the interaction of the
(1) digestive and endocrine systems
(2) digestive and respiratory systems
(3) nervous and endocrine systems
(4) nervous and reproductive systems

27. The graph below shows the number of push-ups a student completed in each of four 2-minute trials (*A–D*) during a 15-minute exercise period.

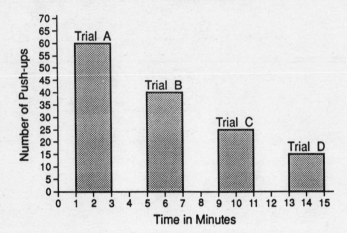

The concentration of lactic acid in the student's muscle tissue was most likely greatest during trial

(1) *A* (3) *C*
(2) *B* (4) *D*

28. Which statement best describes the human respiratory system?
    (1) It is composed of a network of moist passageways that permit air to flow from the external environment to the lungs.
    (2) Each cell of the human body is in direct contact with the external environment, and gas exchange occurs by diffusion.
    (3) The external body surface is kept moist to allow for gas exchange.
    (4) Gases diffuse across membranes on both the external and internal surfaces of the body.

29. The members of a certain species of grass in a lawn are genetically identical. The best explanation for this observation is that the species most probably reproduces
    (1) by an asexual method
    (2) after pollination by the wind
    (3) after pollination by a particular species of bee
    (4) by identical sperm fertilizing the eggs

30. In humans, which cell is produced most directly by mitotic cell division?
    (1) a sperm cell
    (2) a skin cell
    (3) an egg cell
    (4) a zygote

31. What is a major function of the blood vessel represented in the diagram below?

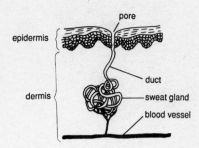

(1) releasing carbon dioxide into the sweat gland
(2) transporting oxygen away from the sweat gland
(3) transporting wastes to the sweat gland
(4) filtering starch out of the sweat gland

32. During meiotic cell division, the process in which homologous pairs of chromosomes separate and move apart is known as
(1) internal fertilization   (3) binary fission
(2) regeneration   (4) disjunction

33. In which region of the flower represented below do diploid cells change to monoploid male gametes?

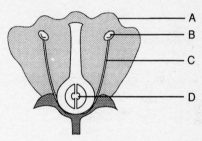

(1) A   (3) C
(2) B   (4) D

34. In the diagram of a dissected seed below, which letter indicates the epicotyl?

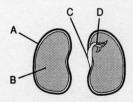

(1) A   (3) C
(2) B   (4) D

35. Which process is represented by the diagram below?

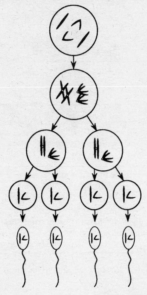

(1) fertilization
(2) gametogenesis
(3) binary fission
(4) vegetative propagation

36. An adaptation for reproduction in most terrestrial vertebrates is
(1) internal fertilization
(2) regeneration
(3) mitosis
(4) vegetative propagation

37. Which is a true statement about the process illustrated below?

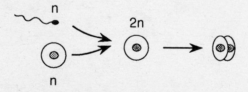

(1) It is the beginning of embryonic development and occurs only in a freshwater environment.
(2) It is the beginning of regeneration and occurs only within the female.
(3) It is the beginning of embryonic development and occurs within the female or in water.
(4) It is the beginning of ovule formation and occurs on the stigma of flowers.

38. The principles of dominance, segregation, and independent assortment resulted from studies by Mendel of the inheritance of traits in
(1) four-o'clock flowers
(2) roan cattle
(3) fruit flies
(4) pea plants

39. In the diagram below of two homologous chromosomes, what do *r* and *R* represent?

(1) two different alleles
(2) two gametes that can form a zygote
(3) two identical alleles
(4) two chromosomes in a hybrid pea plant

40. In certain rats, black fur is dominant over white fur. If two rats, both heterozygous for fur color, are mated, their offspring would be expected to have
(1) four different genotypes and two different colors
(2) two different genotypes and three different colors
(3) three different genotypes and two different colors
(4) three different genotypes and three different colors

41. Which pair of gametes can unite to produce a zygote that will develop into a normal human male embryo?

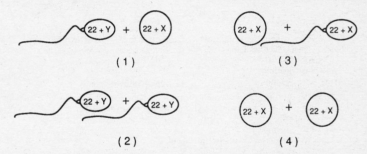

42. The diagrams below represent paired double-stranded chromosomes that contain genes indicated by letters.

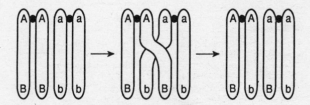

When does the process illustrated by the diagrams occur?
(1) in meiosis, after disjunction of homologous chromosomes
(2) in mitosis, after replication of chromosomes
(3) in meiosis, during synapsis of homologous chromosomes
(4) in mitosis, while chromosomes are attaching to spindle fibers

43. Mutagenic agents are substances that
    (1) increase the rate of gene mutations
    (2) decrease the rate of gene mutations
    (3) have no effect upon the rate of gene mutations
    (4) cause gene mutations but not other chromosomal changes

44. Which breeding method results in the production of offspring with the same gen-
    otype as the parents?
    (1) cross-pollination   (3) inbreeding
    (2) vegetative propagation   (4) hybridization

45. In the diagram of a polymer at the right, the
    repeating subunits are known as
    (1) amino acids
    (2) polysaccharides
    (3) nucleotides
    (4) fatty acids

46. Which area of biology compares and attempts to explain the structural changes that
    have taken place in living things over millions of years, as well as those changes
    occurring today?
    (1) classification   (3) physiology
    (2) reproduction   (4) evolution

47. In the early stages of development, both chicken and pig embryos have gill slits,
    two-chambered hearts, and tails. This similarity suggests that chickens and pigs
    most probably
    (1) have a common ancestry
    (2) carry on anaerobic respiration as adults
    (3) use gills for breathing during embryonic development
    (4) have inadequate circulation

48. The concept that, due to a need, organisms acquired the ability to move from an
    aquatic environment onto the land is most closely associated with a theory proposed
    by
    (1) Weismann   (3) Miller
    (2) Lamarck   (4) Mendel

49. Charles Darwin proposed that organisms produce many more offspring than can
    possibly survive on the limited amount of resources available to them. According to
    Darwin, the offspring most likely to survive are those that
    (1) are born first and grow fastest
    (2) are largest and most aggressive
    (3) are best adapted to the environment
    (4) have no natural predators

50. The graph below shows the results of an investigation related to evolution.

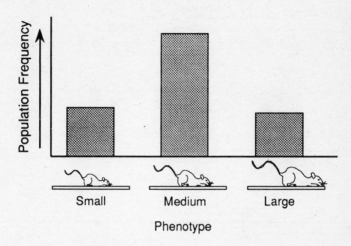

This graph was most likely developed from data involving a study of the
(1) transmission of acquired characteristics
(2) concept of punctuated equilibrium
(3) concept of gradualism
(4) variation within a species

51. According to the heterotroph hypothesis, which change contributed most directly to the evolution of aerobic organisms?
(1) the appearance of organisms able to carry on photosynthesis
(2) an increase in fermentation by organisms in the soil
(3) a decrease in the intensity of light from the Sun
(4) an increase in the concentration of hydrogen gas in the atmosphere

Base your answer to question 52 on the information and statement below.

Information

The Galapagos Islands in the Pacific were probably never connected to South America. However, in the various habitats on the islands, there are about 14 species of finchlike birds that appear to be related to the finches on the South American mainland. Although the Galapagos finches vary in beak structure, there is a close resemblance between these species in plumage, calls, nests, and eggs. These species do not interbreed and do not compete for food.

Statement

Isolation from the South American mainland and different habitats on the Galapagos Islands are important factors in the production of new species.

52. What is the relationship between the statement and the information given?
(1) The statement is supported by the information given.
(2) The statement is not supported by the information given.
(3) The statement is contradicted by the information given.
(4) No relevant information is given regarding the statement.

53. In the four diagrammatic statements below, the arrows should be read as "influ-ences." For example, **A** 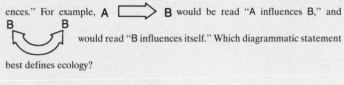 **B** would be read "A influences B," and **B** would read "B influences itself." Which diagrammatic statement best defines ecology?

(1) organisms ⟹ environment

(2) organisms ⟹ environment

(3) organisms ⟸ environment

(4) organisms ⟺ environment

54. Which statement is best supported by the diagram below of the carbon-oxygen cycle?

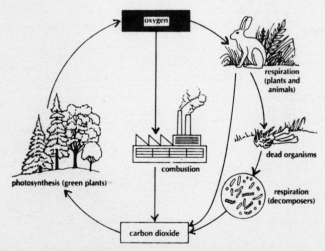

(1) Decomposers add oxygen to the atmosphere and remove carbon dioxide.
(2) Combustion adds oxygen to the atmosphere and removes carbon dioxide.
(3) Producers generate oxygen and utilize carbon dioxide.
(4) Consumers generate oxygen and utilize carbon dioxide.

55. An owl cannot entirely digest the animals it preys upon. Therefore, each day it expels from its mouth a pellet composed of fur, bones, and sometimes cartilage. By examining owl pellets, ecologists would be able to determine the
(1) consumers that owls prefer
(2) autotrophs that owls prefer
(3) organisms that feed on owls
(4) saprophytes that affect owls

56. If birds eat insects that feed on corn, which pyramid level would birds occupy?

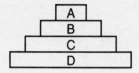

(1) *A*   (3) *C*
(2) *B*   (4) *D*

57. In an attempt to prevent certain species from becoming extinct, humans have
    (1) placed all endangered species in zoos
    (2) increased the trapping of predators
    (3) increased wildlife management and habitat protection
    (4) attempted to mate organisms from different species to create new and stronger organisms

58. All the interacting populations in a given area represent an ecological unit known as a
    (1) biosphere   (3) world biome
    (2) community   (4) saprophytic relationship

59. Which is an abiotic factor that functions as a limiting factor for the autotrophs in the ecosystem below?

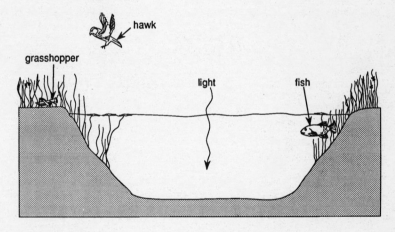

(1) grasshopper   (3) fish
(2) light   (4) hawk

PART II

This part consists of five groups, each containing ten questions. Choose two of these five groups. Be sure that you answer all ten questions in each group chosen.   [20]

Group 1—Biochemistry

If you choose this group, be sure to answer questions 60–69.

Base your answers to questions 60 through 62 on the model of a biochemical reaction below and on your knowledge of biology.

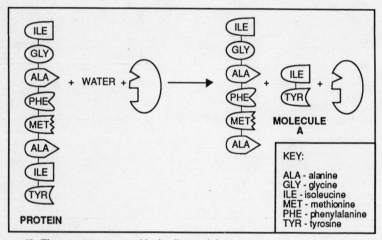

60. The process represented in the diagram is known as
    (1) dehydration synthesis   (3) photolysis
    (2) carbon fixation   (4) hydrolysis

61. Molecule A can best be described as a
    (1) dipeptide   (3) starch
    (2) disaccharide   (4) fat

62. The bond that exists between alanine and phenylalanine is known as
    (1) an ionic bond   (3) a hydrogen bond
    (2) a peptide bond   (4) a phosphate bond

63. According to the graph below, at what temperature will the denaturation of lipase begin?

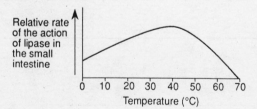

    (1) below 0°C   (3) at 40°C
    (2) between 0°C and 38°C   (4) at 68°C

64. Which compound has the structural formula shown below?

(1) starch (3) ATP
(2) PGAL (4) glucose

Base your answers to questions 65 and 66 on the structural formulas of molecules below and on your knowledge of biology.

Molecule A

Molecule B

65. The portion of molecule A represented in box X is known as
    (1) a nitrogenous base (3) a hydrocarbon chain
    (2) an amino group (4) a carboxyl group

66. How many molecules of A normally combine with one molecule of B to form a single fat molecule?
    (1) 5 (3) 3
    (2) 6 (4) 4

Directions (67–68): For *each* statement in questions 67 and 68 select the metabolic process, *chosen from the list below*, that is most closely associated with that statement. Then record its *number* on the separate answer paper.

Metabolic Processes

(1) $2ATP + C_6H_{12}O_6 \xrightarrow{\text{enzymes}} 4ATP + 2 \text{ lactic acid}$

(2) $6CO_2 + 12H_2O \xrightarrow[\text{chlorophyll}]{\text{light, enzymes}} C_6H_{12}O_6 + 6O_2 + 6H_2O$

(3) $C_{12}H_{22}O_{11} + H_2O \xrightarrow{\text{enzymes}} C_6H_{12}O_6 + C_6H_{12}O_6$

67. This process occurs in humans only when certain cells do not receive an adequate supply of oxygen.

68. Part of this process takes place in structures known as grana.

69. What is the net gain in ATP following the completion of aerobic cellular respiration of one molecule of glucose in a brain cell?
    (1) 30   (3) 36
    (2) 2   (4) 4

Group 2—Human Physiology

If you choose this group, be sure to answer questions 70–79.

Directions (70–72): For *each* phrase in questions 70 through 72 select the transport pathway, *chosen from the list below*, that is most closely related to that phrase. Then record its *number* on your answer paper.

Transport Pathways

    (1) Coronary circulation
    (2) Systemic circulation
    (3) Lymphatic circulation
    (4) Pulmonary circulation

70. Carries blood from the heart to the lungs and from the lungs to the heart

71. Contains nodes that filter foreign substances such as bacteria from transport fluid

72. Carries blood from the heart to the digestive and reproductive structures of the body

73. The nerves that directly control the muscles used in writing are
    (1) part of the autonomic nervous system
    (2) regulated by the hypothalamus
    (3) part of the somatic nervous system
    (4) regulated by the medulla

74. Structures 1, 2, and 3 in the diagram at the right are connected to striated muscles by connective tissue. An inflammation of this connective tissue is known as
    (1) tendinitis
    (2) gout
    (3) polio
    (4) angina pectoris

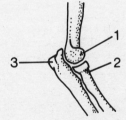

Directions (75–78): For *each* statement in questions 75 through 78 select the organ, *indicated in the diagram below*, that is most closely associated with that statement. Then record its *number* on the separate answer paper. [A number may be used more than once or not at all.]

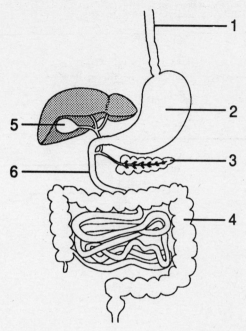

75. This organ stores bile.

76. Gastric juice is produced in this organ.

77. The chemical digestion of protein begins within this organ.

78. Materials to be egested are stored in this organ.

79. An example of the maintenance of homeostasis in humans is the action of glucagon and insulin in regulating the
    (1) temperature of the body
    (2) concentration of blood sugar
    (3) excretion of urine from the bladder
    (4) secretion of thyroxin

Group 3—Reproduction and Development

If you choose this group, be sure to answer questions 80–89.

Base your answers to questions 80 through 82 on the diagram below of the male reproductive system and on your knowledge of biology.

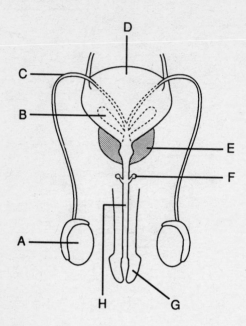

80. Which structures are glands that secrete a liquid for the transport of sperm?
    (1) *A* and *D*   (3) *C* and *H*
    (2) *B* and *E*   (4) *F* and *G*

81. A male sex hormone is produced within structure
    (1) *A*   (3) *E*
    (2) *B*   (4) *F*

82. Male gametes are produced within structure
    (1) *A*   (3) *F*
    (2) *B*   (4) *D*

Directions (83–85): For *each* statement in questions 83 through 85 select the part of the human female reproductive system, *indicated in the diagram below*, that is most closely associated with that statement. Then record its *number* on your answer paper. [A number may be used more than once or not at all.]

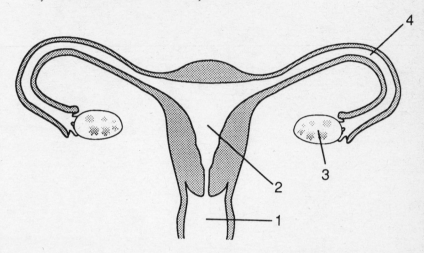

83. The wall of this structure breaks down during one of the stages of the menstrual cycle.

84. This structure produces chemicals that regulate the development of secondary sex characteristics such as the mammary glands.

85. The process of embryo implantation normally occurs within this structure.

86. Which is the correct sequence of stages in a normal menstrual cycle?
    (1) corpus luteum stage → menstruation → ovulation → follicle stage
    (2) ovulation → follicle stage → menstruation → corpus luteum stage
    (3) follicle stage → ovulation → corpus luteum stage → menstruation
    (4) menstruation → corpus luteum stage → ovulation → follicle stage

87. Different embryonic layers of tissue form during the process of
    (1) fertilization   (3) cleavage
    (2) birth   (4) gastrulation

88. Which adaptation for successful development is characteristic of all embryos?
    (1) a shell for protection from predators
    (2) a parent for protection from predators
    (3) a sac for storage of wastes
    (4) a mechanism for absorbing oxygen

89. Eggs that develop externally on land contain a membrane that collects and stores nitrogenous wastes until the egg hatches. This membrane is known as the
    (1) amnion   (3) allantois
    (2) yolk sac   (4) chorion

Group 4—Modern Genetics

If you choose this group, be sure to answer questions 90–99.

90. The diagram below shows some steps involved in preparing tissue cultures of a plant.

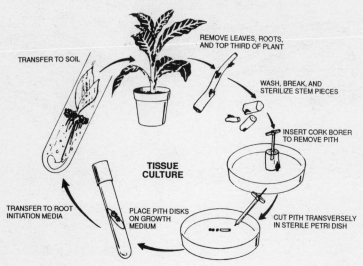

Which technique is represented in the diagram?
(1) hybridization   (3) cloning
(2) amniocentesis   (4) karyotyping

Base your answers to questions 91 through 93 on the information below and on your knowledge of biology.

Two alleles for coloration, black and silver, exist in small minnows that inhabit a particular lake. Largemouth bass also live in this lake, and the minnows are a major portion of their diet. Bass recognize their prey to some extent by the degree to which the prey contrast with their background.

91. According to the Hardy-Weinberg principle, which factor will contribute to the maintenance of a stable gene pool in the minnow population?
(1) mutations   (3) minnow migration
(2) random mating   (4) increased predation

92. The percentage of each allele for coloration in minnows is known as the
(1) gene frequency   (3) mutation rate
(2) genetic code   (4) abiotic factor

93. In areas of aquatic vegetation, black minnows outnumber silver minnows, but in areas of open water, silver minnows outnumber black minnows. In time, the aquatic vegetation will increase and cover the entire lake. What change will most likely occur in the frequency of the minnows' alleles for color?
(1) The frequency of the black allele will decrease.
(2) The frequency of both alleles will change randomly.
(3) The frequency of the black allele will increase.
(4) The frequency of both alleles will remain the same.

Base your answers to questions 94 and 95 on the pedigree chart below and on your knowledge of biology. The pedigree chart represents the inheritance of color blindness through three generations.

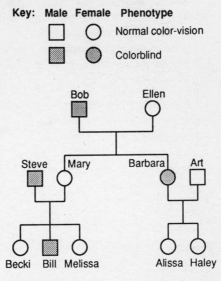

Key: Male Female Phenotype

□ ○ Normal color-vision

▨ ▨ Colorblind

94. Mary and Steve are expecting another child. What is the probability that the new baby will be colorblind?
    (1) 0%   (3) 50%
    (2) 25%   (4) 100%

95. Which is a true statement about the genotype of Alissa and Haley regarding color blindness?
    (1) Both carry one recessive allele.
    (2) Alissa is a carrier, and Haley is homozygous dominant.
    (3) Both are homozygous recessive.
    (4) Alissa is homozygous dominant, and Haley is a carrier.

96. Genetic engineering has been utilized for the production of
    (1) salivary amylase   (3) hydrochloric acid
    (2) human growth hormone (4) uric acid crystals

97. Which nitrogenous base is normally present in RNA molecules but *not* in DNA molecules?
    (1) adenine   (3) thymine
    (2) cytosine   (4) uracil

Base your answers to questions 98 and 99 on the "help-wanted advertisements" below and on your knowledge of biology.

Job A	**Accuracy and Speed** vital for this job in the field of translation. Applicants must demonstrate skills in transporting and positioning amino acids. Salary commensurate with experience.
Job B	**Executive Position** available. Must be able both to maintain genetic continuity through replication and to control cellular activity by regulation of enzyme production. Limited number of openings. All benefits.

98. Which "applicant" would qualify for job *A*?
    (1) DNA
    (2) messenger RNA
    (3) recombinant DNA
    (4) transfer RNA

99. Which "applicant" would qualify for job *B*?
    (1) DNA
    (2) messenger RNA
    (3) transfer RNA
    (4) ADP

Group 5—Ecology

If you choose this group, be sure to answer questions 100–109.

Base your answers to questions 100 through 102 on the chart below and on your knowledge of biology.

Symbiotic Relationships

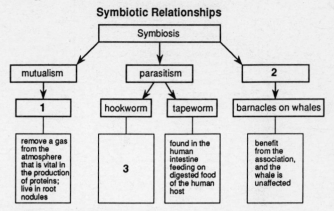

100. Which organisms are represented by box 1?
    (1) nitrifying bacteria
    (2) nitrogen-fixing bacteria
    (3) saprophytic bacteria
    (4) denitrifying bacteria

101. Which term belongs in box 2?
    (1) tropism
    (2) gradualism
    (3) saprophytism
    (4) commensalism

102. Which description belongs in box 3?
    (1) derives nourishment from human body fluids
    (2) feeds on dead animals, assisting in the recycling of nutrients
    (3) stalks, kills, and eats fish in deep ocean environments
    (4) carries on autotrophic nutrition in the tropical forest biome

103. Which group in the food web represented below would most likely have the greatest biomass?

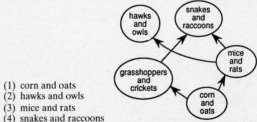

    (1) corn and oats
    (2) hawks and owls
    (3) mice and rats
    (4) snakes and raccoons

104. When animals excrete nitrogenous wastes into the soil, certain soil bacteria convert these wastes into nitrates, which are absorbed by plants. These soil bacteria function as
    (1) autotrophs
    (2) secondary consumers
    (3) decomposers
    (4) abiotic factors

105. Which organisms would most likely be the pioneer organisms on a newly formed volcanic island?
    (1) conifers
    (2) lichens
    (3) deciduous trees
    (4) tall grasses

Base your answers to questions 106 and 107 on the information in the chart below and on your knowledge of biology.

Biome	Characteristics
A	Moisture is a limiting factor Extreme daily temperature variations Climax flora includes many succulent plants
B	Heavy annual rainfall Constant warm temperature Climax flora includes many species of broad-leaved plants
C	Areas vary greatly in concentration of dissolved particles and velocity of currents Seasonal dieback of vegetation Concentration of dissolved gases is a limiting factor
D	Provides the most stable aquatic environment Provides a large amount of the world's food production Contains a relatively constant supply of nutrient materials and dissolved salts

106. Which letter most likely indicates a marine biome?
 (1) A (3) C
 (2) B (4) D

107. Which letter most likely indicates a tropical forest biome?
 (1) A (3) C
 (2) B (4) D

Base your answers to questions 108 and 109 on the diagram below and on your knowledge of biology.

Desert Community

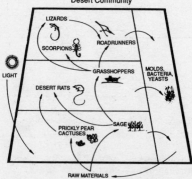

108. Which is an example of the nutritional pattern of a primary consumer?
 (1) grasshoppers → lizards (3) prickly pear cactuses → desert rats
 (2) scorpions → bacteria (4) lizards → roadrunners

109. A carnivore in this desert community is represented by the
 (1) lizard (3) yeast
 (2) sage (4) desert rat

PART III

This part consists of five groups. Choose three of these five groups. [15]

Group 1

If you choose this group, be sure to answer questions 110–114.

Base your answers to questions 110 through 114 on the information and data table below and on your knowledge of biology.

When a culture of cells is exposed to gamma rays, chromosome damage results. This damage is very evident when the cells are stained and observed with a compound light microscope. The chromosome damage is primarily in the form of breaks and gaps, which are commonly referred to as chromosome aberrations. Investigations have shown that when the amino acid cysteine is added to the cell culture prior to gamma-ray exposure, the number of aberrations is reduced. The results of one investigation are shown in the data table below. In this investigation, each cell culture received the same amount of gamma-ray exposure.

Data Table

Cell Culture Tube Number	Amount of Cysteine Added (g)	Average Number of Chromosome Aberrations per Cell After Gamma-Ray Exposure
1	0.0	1.20
2	0.7	0.65
3	1.0	0.58
4	2.6	0.40
5	5.3	0.33
6	10.5	0.25
7	15.8	0.18

Directions (110–111): Using the information in the data table, construct a line graph on the grid provided, following the directions below.

110. Mark an appropriate scale on each labeled axis.

111. Plot the data and connect the points. Surround each point with a circle.

Example: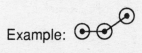

Amount of Cysteine Added (g)

112. A culture tube in which the average number of chromosome aberrations per cell is 0.30 would most likely contain approximately how many grams of added cysteine?
    (1) 7.0
    (2) 1.15
    (3) 0.3
    (4) 0.4

113. Chromosome aberrations that result from gamma-ray exposure would most likely cause
    (1) the condition known as polyploidy
    (2) mutations in cells
    (3) an increase in the lifespan of cells
    (4) a reduction in cysteine synthesis

114. Culture tube 1 was exposed to the same amount of gamma rays as the other six tubes, but no cysteine was added to this tube. Using one or more complete sentences, explain the role of culture tube 1 as a control in this investigation.

Group 2

If you choose this group, be sure to answer questions 115–119.

Base your answers to questions 115 through 119 on the reading passage below and on your knowledge of biology.

Carnivorous Plants

Carnivorous plants make carbohydrates by the process of photosynthesis, as do other green plants. However, few nitrogenous minerals are available in the acid bog environment, and the roots of carnivorous plants are not efficient at absorbing them. In order to survive, these plants have evolved modified leaves that trap insects to supplement their nutrition. The modified leaves contain nectar glands which give off substances that attract and aid in the capture of insects. Once an insect is trapped, the leaves begin to produce digestive enzymes. Nutrients from the digested insects are then absorbed by the leaves.

Carnivorous plants have several types of traps. The Venus flytrap is an example of an active trap. It has colorful red-lined leaves that are hinged in the middle. When an insect lands and touches the sensitive hairs on the inner surface of the leaf, the leaf folds. Spines along the leaf's edges interlock, keeping the insect from escaping. Glands secrete enzymes that digest the insect's soft parts. When digestion is complete, the leaf reopens, allowing the undigested parts to blow away.

The largest of the carnivorous plants are the pitcher plants, which have pitfall traps. The leaves of these plants form a slender tube with a hood that prevents rain from entering. Nectar glands on the lip of the tube attract insects. The insects land on a slick area of the tube and fall into a pool of digestive juices at the bottom. Hairs inside the plant prevent the insect from crawling out.

The sundew is a flypaper trap. The attractive leaves of this plant are covered with hairs that secrete sticky droplets. The odor produced by this liquid lures insects to the plant. The insect then becomes entangled in the hairs on the leaf, where enzymes digest the soft parts of the insect.

These and other varieties of carnivorous plants grow in the marshes, swamps, and bogs of the eastern United States. These plants are becoming endangered or threatened species as wetlands are drained for commercial or residential development.

115. Which is a characteristic of some varieties of carnivorous plants?
    (1) They carry on autotrophic nutrition similar to the fungi.
    (2) They have modified leaves that trap insects.
    (3) They have roots that absorb nutrients from dead insects.
    (4) They trap all species of insects.

116. Carnivorous plants are similar to other green plants because they have the ability to
    (1) secrete enzymes from leaf surfaces
    (2) absorb digestive end products through the leaves
    (3) produce carbohydrates from inorganic materials
    (4) carry on heterotrophic nutrition

117. Nitrogen-containing minerals are inefficiently absorbed by which structures of carnivorous plants?
    (1) roots   (3) flowers
    (2) leaves   (4) stems

118. Which carnivorous plant is correctly paired with its adaptation for the capture of insects?
    (1) sundew—spines on leaf edges
    (2) pitcher plant—sensitive hairs
    (3) pitcher plant—hairs with sticky droplets
    (4) Venus flytrap—hinged leaves

119. Which statement is true of many carnivorous plant species of the United States?
    (1) They are used in the chemical control of insects.
    (2) They are becoming endangered species.
    (3) They are poisonous to various species of mammals.
    (4) They are adapted to habitats with a high pH.

Group 3

If you choose this group, be sure to answer questions 120–124.

Base your answers to questions 120 and 121 on the diagram below of a single-celled organism observed by a student using the low-power objective of a microscope.

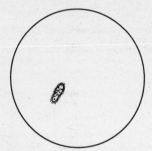

120. How should the student move the slide on the stage to center the single-celled organism in the field?
    (1) away from herself and to her right
    (2) away from herself and to her left
    (3) toward herself and to her right
    (4) toward herself and to her left

121. As the student observes the organism under the high-power objective, the organism swims out of focus. To bring it back into focus, the student should
    (1) open the diaphragm
    (2) turn the fine adjustment
    (3) turn the ocular
    (4) adjust the light source

122. The diagram below shows a portion of a compound microscope.

A student observes 12 onion epidermal cells along the diameter of the low-power field. How many of these cells would the student observe along the diameter of the high-power field?
    (1) 48   (3) 3
    (2) 40   (4) 24

123. To locate a specimen on a prepared slide with a compound microscope, a student should begin with the low-power objective rather than the high-power objective because the
    (1) field of vision is smaller under low power than under high power
    (2) field of vision is larger under low power than under high power
    (3) specimen does not need to be stained for observation under low power but must be stained for observation under high power
    (4) amount of the specimen that can be observed under low power is less than the amount that can be observed under high power

124. Using one or more complete sentences, explain how the light intensity in the high-power field of view of a compound microscope may be increased.

Group 4

If you choose this group, be sure to answer questions 125–129.

125. Two groups of 100 corn seeds were planted in two separate containers of soil and watered regularly. Group I was grown in light for 4 weeks and group II was grown in the dark for 2 weeks and then in the light for 2 weeks. The color of the seedlings was recorded after each 2-week period. Light was the only variable in the experiment. The results are summarized in the data table below.

	Group I		Group II	
	After 2 Weeks (in light)	After 2 More Weeks (in light)	After 2 Weeks (in darkness)	After 2 More Weeks (in light)
Number of Green Seedlings	75	75	0	80
Number of White Seedlings	25	25	100	20

This experiment demonstrates that
(1) the environment interacts with genes in the expression of an inherited trait
(2) water and fertilizer are important for seed germination
(3) heat should have been provided along with carbon dioxide for proper growth
(4) the principles of genetics apply only to plants and not to animals.

126. To test for the presence of glucose, a student added the same amount of Benedict's solution to three test tubes, two of which contained unknown solutions. The third test tube contained water. The chart below shows the color results obtained after the solutions were heated in the three test tubes in a hot water bath.

Tube	Contents	Color After Heating
1	unknown solution plus Benedict's solution	Royal blue
2	unknown solution plus Benedict's solution	Red orange
3	water plus Benedict's solution	Royal blue

The student could correctly conclude that
(1) none of the tubes contained glucose
(2) tubes 1 and 2 contained glucose
(3) tube 1 did not contain glucose, but tube 2 did
(4) tube 2 did not contain glucose, but tube 1 did

Base your answers to questions 127 and 128 on the diagram below and on your knowledge of biology.

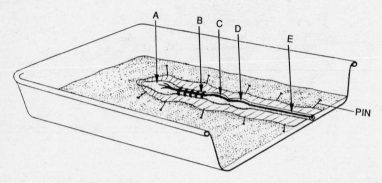

127. Select one of the lettered digestive structures from the diagram. Record the letter of this structure and the name of the structure it indicates.

128. Which statement best describes the relative positions of two structures in the diagram?
    (1) A is anterior to C.
    (2) E is dorsal to B.
    (3) C is ventral to A.
    (4) D is posterior to E.

129. Select one of the lettered parts from the diagram below of a human cheek cell. Record the letter of the part chosen. Using one or more complete sentences, state the function of this part.

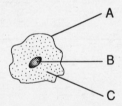

Group 5

If you choose this group, be sure to answer questions 130–134.

130. An organism was kept at a temperature of 40°C for a period of 2 weeks. At the end of that time, the investigator determined that the organism was sterile. To support the hypothesis that high temperatures cause sterility, the investigator should be able to show that the
    (1) organism was not sterile before the experimental period began
    (2) high temperature did not alter the blood pressure of the organism
    (3) pituitary gland of the organism had not degenerated
    (4) organism was homozygous for temperature sensitivity

131. A student wants to test the hypothesis that a certain aquarium plant absorbs CO_2. The student placed a sprig of the aquarium plant in a test tube with water and exhaled CO_2 into the water. Which indicator should the student add to the test tube to help him test this hypothesis?
    (1) Benedict's solution
    (2) iodine solution
    (3) salt solution
    (4) bromthymol blue solution

Base your answer to question 132 on the diagram below and on your knowledge of biology.

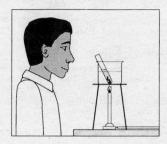

132. Which statement describes *two* unsafe laboratory practices represented in the diagram?
    (1) The flame is too high and the test tube is unstoppered.
    (2) The opening of the test tube is pointed toward the student and the student is not wearing goggles.
    (3) The test tube is unstoppered and the student is not wearing goggles.
    (4) The beaker has water in it and the flame is under the tripod.

133. What must a student do to obtain a volume of 12.5 milliliters of liquid in the graduated cylinder shown below?

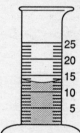

    (1) Add 0.5 mL of liquid.
    (2) Add 1.5 mL of liquid.
    (3) Remove 0.5 mL of liquid.
    (4) Remove 1.5 mL of liquid.

Base your answer to question 134 on the information below, which describes the purpose and procedure of two investigations, *A* and *B*.

Investigation A

Purpose: To observe the nucleus of an ameba

Procedure: Place a drop of water containing living amebas on the stage of a compound microscope. Add a drop of Benedict's solution and observe with the low-power objective and then with the high-power objective.

Investigation B

Purpose: To observe the nerve cord of an earthworm

Procedure: Place an earthworm dorsal side up on a slide. Cut through the skin and muscle of the dorsal surface and, using a compound microscope, observe the nerve cord on the upper surface of the intestine.

134. Choose *one* of these investigations, and using one or more complete sentences, identify *one* error in the procedure. Then describe the proper procedure to correct this error.

BIOLOGY

June 21, 1994

PART I

Answer all 59 questions in this part. [65]

Directions (1–59): For *each* statement or question, select the word or expression that, of those given, best completes the statement or answers the question.

1. Short-tailed shrews and ruby-throated hummingbirds have high metabolic rates. As a result, these animals
   (1) utilize energy rapidly
   (2) need very little food
   (3) have very few predators
   (4) hibernate in hot weather

2. Which activity would *not* be carried out by an organism in order to maintain a stable internal environment?
   (1) removal of metabolic waste products
   (2) transport of organic and inorganic compounds
   (3) production of offspring by the organism
   (4) regulation of physiological processes

3. Which statement about viruses is true?
   (1) They carry on aerobic respiration.
   (2) They can reproduce both sexually and asexually.
   (3) They are photosynthetic organisms.
   (4) They are an exception to the cell theory.

4. The structural formula below represents urea.

   This structural formula indicates that urea is
   (1) an organic compound
   (2) an inorganic compound
   (3) a carbohydrate
   (4) a nucleic acid

5. Which activity is an example of cyclosis?
   (1) the movement of water from the soil into a root hair
   (2) the movement of food vacuoles through the cytoplasm of a paramecium
   (3) blood cells moving through the capillaries in a goldfish tail
   (4) the pumping action of a contractile vacuole in an ameba

6. The diagram below represents a sample of crushed onion cells that was centrifuged. Cells and cell components were dispersed in layers as illustrated.

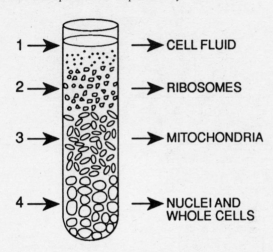

The organelles that act as the sites of protein synthesis are found in the greatest concentration within layer

(1) 1
(2) 2
(3) 3
(4) 4

7. Maltose molecules are formed from glucose by the process of
   (1) dipeptide synthesis
   (2) intracellular digestion
   (3) dehydration synthesis
   (4) biological oxidation

8. Two species of bacteria produce different respiratory end products. Species A always produces ATP, CO_2, and H_2O; species B always produces ATP, ethyl alcohol, and CO_2. Which conclusion can correctly be drawn from this information?
   (1) Only species A is aerobic.
   (2) Only species B is aerobic.
   (3) Species A and species B are both anaerobic.
   (4) Species A and species B are both aerobic.

9. Two plants were observed to have the characteristics indicated in the chart below. An X indicates that the characteristic was present.

Specimen	Multicellular	Photosynthetic	Vascular Tissue	Roots	Stems	Leaves
Plant A	X	X				
Plant B	X	X	X	X	X	X

According to the chart, which statement about these plants is correct?
(1) Plant A is a tracheophyte, and plant B is a bryophyte.
(2) Plant A has xylem and phloem, but plant B does not.
(3) Plant A could be a pine tree, and plant B could be a moss.
(4) Plant A is a bryophyte, and plant B is a tracheophyte.

10. The diagram below represents a protist.

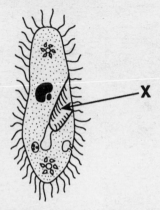

Structure *X* is most directly involved in the process of
(1) extracellular digestion   (3) ingestion
(2) enzymatic hydrolysis   (4) transpiration

11. A fungus is classified as a heterotroph rather than an autotroph because it
(1) grows by mitosis
(2) absorbs food from the environment
(3) manufactures its own food
(4) transforms light energy into chemical energy

12. The concentration of nitrates is often higher in plant roots than in the soil around them. Plants maintain this difference in concentration through
(1) active transport   (3) diffusion
(2) osmosis   (4) waste egestion

13. A wet-mount slide of photosynthetic protists was prepared and then exposed to light that had been broken up into a spectrum. When viewing this preparation through the microscope, a student would most likely observe that most of the protists had clustered in the regions of
(1) yellow and blue light   (3) green and yellow light
(2) orange and green light   (4) red and blue light

14. In an ameba, which process is best represented by the arrows shown in the diagram below?

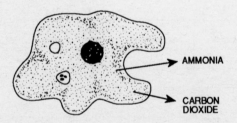

(1) absorption by active transport
(2) excretion by diffusion
(3) respiratory gas exchange
(4) egestion of digestive end products

15. Which statement describes a relationship between the human cells illustrated in the diagrams below?

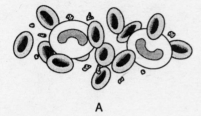

A

C

B

D

(1) *B* may cause *D* to contract. (3) *C* transports oxygen to *A*.
(2) *A* is produced by *D*. (4) *B* is used to repair *C*.

16. One way in which the intake of oxygen is similar in the hydra and the earthworm is that both organisms
    (1) absorb oxygen through a system of tubes
    (2) utilize cilia to absorb oxygen
    (3) use capillaries to transport oxygen
    (4) absorb oxygen through their external surfaces

17. The life function of transport in the grasshopper involves
    (1) an internal gas exchange surface and alveoli
    (2) an open circulatory system and tracheal tubes
    (3) moist outer skin and hemoglobin
    (4) a dry external body surface and hemoglobin

18. Which process is correctly paired with its major waste product?
    (1) respiration — oxygen (3) dehydration synthesis — water
    (2) protein synthesis — amino acids (4) hydrolysis — carbon dioxide

19. The diagram below represents a growth response in a plant.

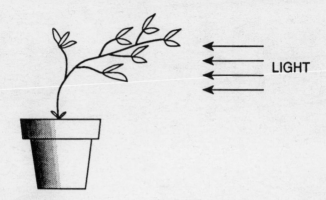

LIGHT

This growth response was most likely due to the effect of light on
(1) acetylcholine   (3) auxin distribution
(2) minerals   (4) vascular tissue

20. The diagram below represents three steps of a chemical reaction.

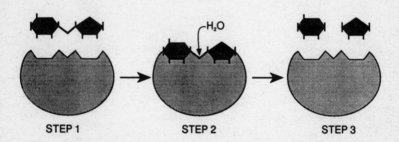

H_2O

STEP 1   STEP 2   STEP 3

This diagram best illustrates the
(1) deamination of amino acids   (3) synthesis of a polysaccharide
(2) emulsification of a fat   (4) hydrolysis of a carbohydrate

21. Which statement best describes protein metabolism in the hydra?
    (1) It produces excess carbon dioxide, which is recycled for photosynthesis.
    (2) It produces urea, which is eliminated by nephridia.
    (3) It produces ammonia, which is transported out of the animal into the environment.
    (4) It produces mineral salts, all of which are retained for other metabolic processes.

22. The diagram below shows a longitudinal section of the human heart.

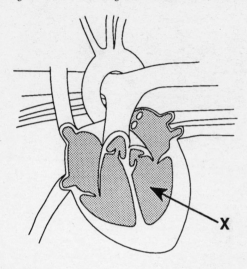

The structure labled X is known as
(1) a ventricle   (3) a valve
(2) an atrium   (4) the aorta

23. A hawk sees a field mouse, which it then captures for food. In this activity, the eyes of the hawk function as
(1) effectors   (3) stimuli
(2) receptors   (4) neurotransmitters

24. Methyl cellulose is a chemical that slows the movement of paramecia on a slide. This chemical most likely interferes with the movement of
(1) pseudopods   (3) setae
(2) flagella   (4) cilia

25. Which adaptation found within the human respiratory system filters, warms, and moistens the air before it enters the lungs?
(1) clusters of alveoli
(2) rings of cartilage
(3) involuntary smooth muscle
(4) ciliated mucous membranes

26. Food is usually kept from entering the trachea by the
(1) diaphragm   (3) villi
(2) epiglottis   (4) ribs

27. The nephrons and alveoli of humans are most similar in function to the
(1) nephridia and skin of earthworms
(2) Malpighian tubules and gastric caecae of grasshoppers
(3) nerve nets and gastrovascular cavities of hydras
(4) cilia and pseudopods of protozoa

28. The diagrams below represent stages of a cellular process.

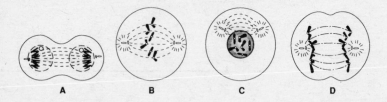

A   B   C   D

Which is the correct sequence of these stages?
(1) $A \to B \to C \to D$ (3) $C \to B \to D \to A$
(2) $B \to D \to C \to A$ (4) $D \to B \to A \to C$

29. Which part of the human central nervous system is correctly paired with its function?
(1) spinal cord — coordinates learning activities
(2) cerebellum — serves as the center for reflex actions
(3) cerebrum — serves as the center for memory and reasoning
(4) medulla — maintains muscular coordination

30. Tendons are best described as
(1) tissue that is found between bones and that protects them from damage
(2) cords that connect bone to bone and that stretch at the point of attachment
(3) striated tissue that provides a wide range of motion
(4) fibrous cords that connect muscles to bones

31. Which statement best describes the division of the cytoplasm and the nucleus in budding?
(1) Both the cytoplasm and the nucleus divide equally.
(2) The cytoplasm divides unequally, but the nucleus divides equally.
(3) The cytoplasm divides equally, but the nucleus divides unequally.
(4) Both the cytoplasm and the nucleus divide unequally.

32. *Rhizopus,* a bread mold, usually reproduces asexually by
(1) budding (3) regeneration
(2) sporulation (4) fission

33. In sexually reproducing species, doubling of the chromosome number from generation to generation is prevented by events that take place during the process of
(1) gametogenesis (3) nondisjunction
(2) cleavage (4) fertilization

34. Which statement is true about the process of fertilization in both tracheophytes and mammals?
(1) It normally results in the production of monoploid offspring.
(2) It occurs externally in a watery environment.
(3) It is followed by yolk production.
(4) It occurs within female reproductive organs.

35. The production of large numbers of eggs is necessary to insure the survival of most
(1) mammals (3) fish
(2) molds (4) yeasts

36. Mendel developed his basic principles of heredity by
(1) microscopic study of chromosomes and genes
(2) breeding experiments with drosophila
(3) mathematical analysis of the offspring of pea plants
(4) ultracentrifugation studies of cell organelles

37. The diagrams below represent the gametes and zygotes associated with two separate fertilizations in a particular species.

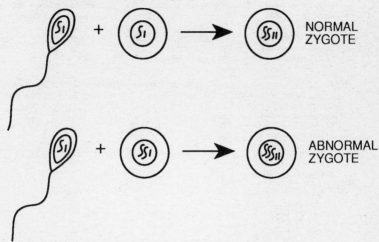

The abnormal zygote is most likely the result of
(1) polyploidy   (3) chromosome breakage
(2) nondisjunction   (4) gene linkage

Base your answers to questions 38 and 39 on the diagram below of a flower and on your knowledge of biology.

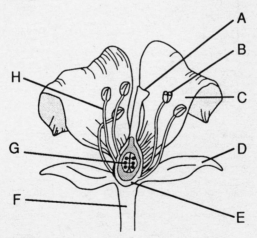

38. Which structures form the stamen?
(1) *A* and *F*   (3) *C* and *D*
(2) *B* and *H*   (4) *E* and *G*

39. During pollination, pollen is transferred from
(1) *B* to *A*   (3) *B* to *G*
(2) *C* to *D*   (4) *F* to *H*

40. Pea plants heterozygous for both height and color of seed coat (*TtYy*) were crossed with pea plants that were homozygous recessive for both traits (*ttyy*). The offspring from this cross included tall plants with green seeds, tall plants with yellow seeds, short plants with green seeds, and short plants with yellow seeds. This cross best illustrates
    (1) gene mutation
    (2) environmental influence on heredity
    (3) independent assortment of chromosomes
    (4) intermediate inheritance

41. In raccoons, a dark face mask is dominant over a bleached face mask. Several crosses were made between raccoons that were heterozygous for dark face mask and raccoons that were homozygous for bleached face mask. What percentage of the offspring would be expected to have a dark face mask?
    (1) 0%   (3) 75%
    (2) 50%   (4) 100%

42. Traits that are controlled by genes found on an *X*-chromosome are said to be
    (1) autosomal dominant   (3) codominant
    (2) autosomal recessive   (4) sex-linked

43. The diagram below represents possible lines of evolution of primates.

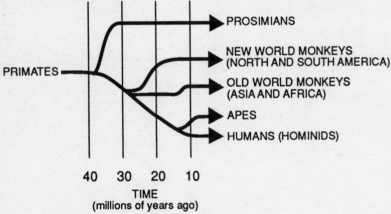

    Which inference can best be made based on the diagram?
    (1) Acquired adaptations for living in trees are inherited.
    (2) Humans and apes have a common ancestor.
    (3) The embryos of monkeys and apes are identical.
    (4) The period of maturation is similar in most primates.

44. Which situation is a result of crossing-over during meiosis?
    (1) Genes are duplicated exactly, ensuring that offspring will be identical to the parents.
    (2) Chromatids thicken and align themselves, helping to ensure genetic continuity.
    (3) Genes are rearranged, increasing the variability of offspring.
    (4) Chromatids fail to sort independently, creating abnormal chromosome numbers.

45. What is the role of DNA in controlling cellular activity?
    (1) DNA provides energy for all cell activities.
    (2) DNA determines which enzymes are produced by a cell.
    (3) DNA is used by cells for the excretion of nitrogenous wastes.
    (4) DNA provides nucleotides for the construction of plasma membranes.

46. The best scientific explanation for differences in structure, function, and behavior found between life forms is provided by the
    (1) heterotroph hypothesis
    (2) lock-and-key model
    (3) theory of use and disuse
    (4) theory of organic evolution

47. Substances that increase the chance of gene alterations are known as
    (1) mutagenic agents
    (2) genetic agents
    (3) chromosomal agents
    (4) adaptive agents

48. Fossils of two different organisms, *A* and *B*, are found in different undisturbed layers of rock. The layer containing fossil *A* is located above the layer containing fossil *B*. Which statement about these fossils is most likely true?
    (1) Fossil *B* is older than fossil *A*.
    (2) Fossils *A* and *B* represent organisms that are closely related and evolved from a common ancestor.
    (3) Fossil *A* represents an organism that evolved from fossil *B*.
    (4) Fossil *B* represents an organism that evolved from fossil *A*.

49. Since the time of Darwin, increased knowledge of heredity has resulted in
    (1) the addition of use and disuse to Lamarck's theory
    (2) the elimination of all previous evolutionary theories
    (3) increased support for the theory of natural selection
    (4) disagreement with Mendel's discoveries

50. The diagrams below represent homologous structures.

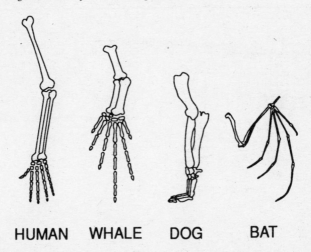

HUMAN   WHALE   DOG   BAT

The study of the evolutionary relationships between these structures is known as comparative
    (1) cytology
    (2) biochemistry
    (3) anatomy
    (4) embryology

51. Which processes are directly involved in the carbon-hydrogen-oxygen cycle?
    (1) respiration and photosynthesis
    (2) transpiration and evaporation
    (3) nutrition and ecological succession
    (4) diffusion and alcoholic fermentation

52. Which title would be most appropriate for a textbook on general ecology?
    (1) *The Interactions Between Organisms and Their Environment*
    (2) *The Cell and Its Organelles*
    (3) *The Physical and Chemical Properties of Water*
    (4) *The Hereditary Mechanisms of Drosophila*

53. Which is an example of an ecosystem?
    (1) a population of monarch butterflies
    (2) the interdependent biotic and abiotic components of a pond
    (3) all the abiotic factors found in a field
    (4) all the mammals that live in the Atlantic Ocean

54. According to the heterotroph hypothesis, which event immediately preceded the evolution of aerobes?
    (1) the production of oxygen by autotrophs
    (2) the production of ammonia by heterotrophs
    (3) the production of carbon dioxide by autotrophs
    (4) the production of carbon dioxide by heterotrophs

55. In a self-sustaining ecosystem, which component *cannot* be recycled because it is lost from food chains and becomes unavailable?
    (1) carbon   (3) water
    (2) nitrogen   (4) energy

56. Termites can be found living in dead trees partially buried under soil and stones. Within the tree trunks, the termites feed on the wood fiber, creating passageways having a high humidity. The wood fiber is digested by protozoans living within the digestive tract of the termite.

    What are the biotic factors in this habitat?
    (1) tree trunk, stones, and protozoans
    (2) soil and humidity
    (3) termites and protozoans
    (4) humidity, soil, and stones

57. One theory about the extinction of dinosaurs is that the collision of an asteroid with the Earth caused environmental changes that killed off the dinosaurs in a relatively short time, changing the course of evolution. This theory is an example of which evolutionary concept?
    (1) gradualism   (3) the heterotroph hypothesis
    (2) competition   (4) punctuated equilibrium

58. The cartoon below illustrates a type of nutrition.

"Just think . . . Here we are, the afternoon sun beating down on us, a dead, bloated rhino underfoot, and good friends flying in from all over. . . . I tell you, Frank, this is the best of times."

Frank and the other birds in this cartoon are classified as
(1) saprophytes   (3) scavengers
(2) herbivores   (4) producers

59. Which type of organism is *not* represented in the diagram below?

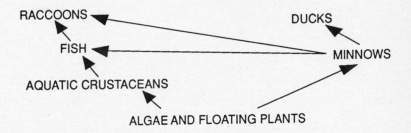

(1) secondary consumers   (3) carnivores
(2) producers   (4) decomposers

PART II

This part consists of five groups, each containing ten questions. Choose two of these five groups. Be sure that you answer all ten questions in each group chosen.   [20]

Group I — Biochemistry

If you choose this group, be sure to answer questions 60–69.

Base your answers to questions 60 through 62 on the structural formulas below and on your knowledge of biology.

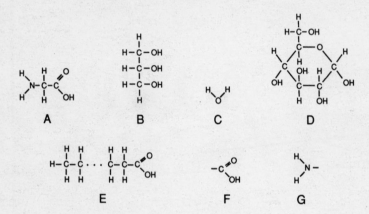

60. By which formula can molecule D be represented?
    (1) $C_6H_{12}O_6$
    (2) $C_5H_{12}O_5$
    (3) $C_3H_5(OH)_3$
    (4) C_3H_5COOH

61. Which structural formulas represent the building blocks of a lipid?
    (1) A and C
    (2) B and E
    (3) C and E
    (4) F and G

62. A single carboxyl group is represented by
    (1) F
    (2) B
    (3) C
    (4) G

63. According to the summary equations below, what is the net gain of ATP molecules from the complete oxidation of one glucose molecule?

    (A) 1 glucose + 2 ATP $\xrightarrow{\text{enzymes}}$ 2 pyruvic acid + ATP

    (B) 2 pyruvic acid + oxygen $\xrightarrow{\text{enzymes}}$ 2 carbon dioxide + water + 34 ATP

    (1) 34
    (2) 36
    (3) 38
    (4) 40

64. If an enzyme works best at a neutral pH, in which pH range is that enzyme expected to function?
    (1) 1–3
    (2) 3–5
    (3) 6–8
    (4) 10–12

65. Bread dough that contains yeast and sugar expands during alcoholic fermentation as a result of an increase in the
    (1) production of molecular oxygen
    (2) absorption of minerals
    (3) secretion of ATP
    (4) production of carbon dioxide

Base your answers to questions 66 and 67 on the diagrams below of some stages of an enzyme-controlled reaction and on your knowledge of biology.

A　　　**B**　　　**C**　　　**D**

66. An enzyme-substrate complex is represented by diagram
    (1) A   (3) C
    (2) B   (4) D

67. A nonprotein vitamin required for this reaction would function as a
    (1) product   (3) polypeptide
    (2) substrate   (4) coenzyme

Base your answers to questions 68 and 69 on the diagram below which represents some of the events that take place in a plant cell.

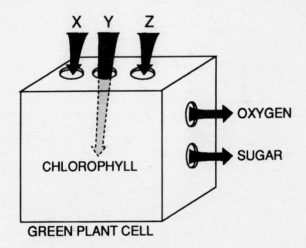

68. The oxygen and sugar leaving the cell were most likely produced by the processes of
    (1) hydrolysis and anaerobic respiration
    (2) dehydration synthesis and aerobic respiration
    (3) photolysis and carbon fixation
    (4) deamination and fermentation

69. The letters X, Y, and Z most likely represent
    (1) N_2, O_2, and H_2O
    (2) CO_2, light, and H_2O
    (3) light, ammonia, and H_2O
    (4) light, O_2, and methane

Group 2 — Human Physiology

If you choose this group, be sure to answer questions 70–79.

Base your answers to questions 70 through 72 on the diagram below and on your knowledge of biology.

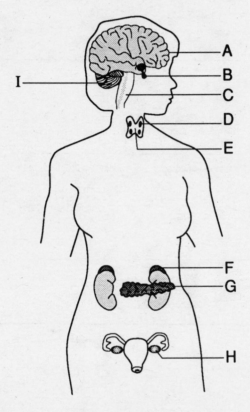

70. Which structure produces secretions that regulate E and H?
    (1) A
    (2) B
    (3) I
    (4) D

71. Which structure controls involuntary activities such as breathing and heartbeat?
    (1) A
    (2) B
    (3) C
    (4) G

72. Which two structures secrete substances that control the menstrual cycle?
    (1) A and F
    (2) B and H
    (3) C and D
    (4) E and I

73. Which letter indicates the location of nephrons in the diagram below?

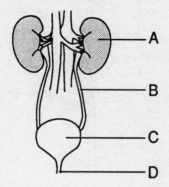

(1) *A*   (3) *C*
(2) *B*   (4) *D*

74. Which sequence represents the direction of flow of carbon dioxide as it passes out of the respiratory system into the external environment?
    (1) alveoli → trachea → bronchioles → bronchi → pharynx → nasal cavity
    (2) alveoli → bronchi → pharynx → bronchioles → trachea → nasal cavity
    (3) alveoli → pharynx → trachea → bronchioles → bronchi → nasal cavity
    (4) alveoli → bronchioles → bronchi → trachea → pharynx → nasal cavity

75. An inflammation of the region labeled *A* in the diagram at the right is known as
    (1) meningitis
    (2) arthritis
    (3) bronchitis
    (4) tendinitis

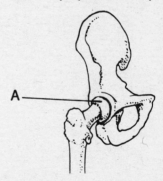

76. Which substances produced in the body are directly responsible for the rejection of a transplanted organ?
    (1) antigens   (3) antibodies
    (2) histamines   (4) excretions

Base your answers to questions 77 through 79 on the diagram below and on your knowledge of biology.

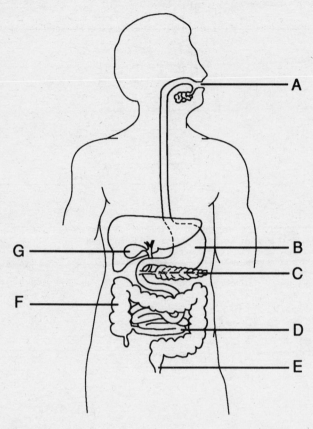

77. Which letter indicates the organ that secretes hydrochloric acid and protease?
    (1) *A*   (3) *E*
    (2) *B*   (4) *D*

78. Which letter indicates the organ that produces insulin and glucagon?
    (1) *E*   (3) *C*
    (2) *B*   (4) *F*

79. A painful condition resulting from the formation of small stone-like deposits of cholesterol may be treated by surgically removing structure
    (1) *G*   (3) *F*
    (2) *E*   (4) *D*

Group 3 — Reproduction and Development

If you choose this group, be sure to answer questions 80–89.

Base your answers to questions 80 through 83 on the diagram below and on your knowledge of biology. The diagram shows stages in the life cycle of a unicellular flagellated green alga.

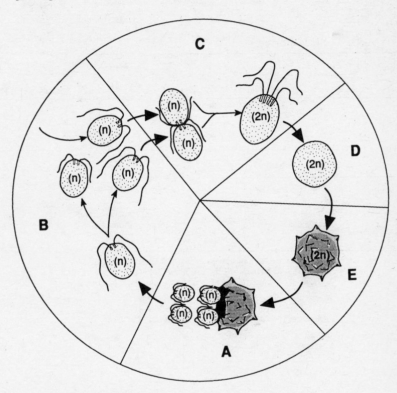

80. The process that takes place at stage *B* normally produces cells with
    (1) the same chromosome number as the parent cell
    (2) fewer chromosomes than the parent cell
    (3) pairs of homologous chromosomes
    (4) a polyploid number of chromosomes

81. Fertilization involving like gametes takes place at stage
    (1) *A*   (3) *C*
    (2) *B*   (4) *E*

82. The process that most likely takes place between stages *E* and *A* is
    (1) mitosis   (3) fertilization
    (2) meiosis   (4) cleavage

83. A specialized structure that provides protection from harsh environmental conditions is represented at stage
    (1) *E*   (3) *C*
    (2) *B*   (4) *D*

Base your answers to questions 84 through 86 on the graph below and on your knowledge of biology. The graph shows the different concentrations of female reproductive hormones during the menstrual cycle of humans.

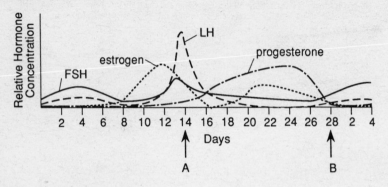

84. Which event normally occurs at *A*?
    (1) ovulation
    (2) embryo implantation
    (3) differentiation
    (4) follicle formation

85. Which process usually begins at *B*?
    (1) fertilization
    (2) embryo development
    (3) corpus luteum development
    (4) menstruation

86. Which is a correct inference about an event that occurs prior to day 14?
    (1) A high level of estrogen may stimulate the production of LH.
    (2) A high level of LH may stimulate the production of FSH.
    (3) A low level of FSH inhibits the production of estrogen.
    (4) A low level of progesterone inhibits the production of estrogen.

87. The yolk of a developing bird embryo functions as a
    (1) moist respiratory membrane
    (2) storage site for waste
    (3) food source
    (4) fluid environment

88. In humans, the fertilization of two eggs at the same time usually results in
    (1) chromosome abnormalities
    (2) gene mutations
    (3) identical twins
    (4) fraternal twins

89. In chicken eggs, the embryonic membrane known as the allantois functions in the
    (1) release of oxygen to the atmosphere
    (2) storage of nitrogenous wastes
    (3) absorption of nitrogen for use in protein synthesis
    (4) transport of carbon dioxide directly to the embryo

Group 4 — Modern Genetics

If you choose this group, be sure to answer questions 90–99.

Base your answers to questions 90 through 92 on the chart below and on your knowledge of biology. The chart represents the inheritance of Tay-Sachs disease in a family.

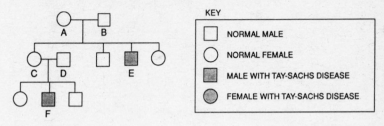

KEY

☐ NORMAL MALE

○ NORMAL FEMALE

▨ MALE WITH TAY-SACHS DISEASE

◉ FEMALE WITH TAY-SACHS DISEASE

90. What are the genotypes of individuals *A* and *B* with regard to Tay-Sachs disease?
    (1) One must be homozygous dominant and the other must be homozygous recessive.
    (2) One must be homozygous dominant and the other must be heterozygous.
    (3) Both must be homozygous.
    (4) Both must be heterozygous.

91. If individuals *C* and *D* have another child, what is the chance this child will exhibit Tay-Sachs disease?
    (1) 0%   (3) 50%
    (2) 25%   (4) 100%

92. Which statement is true about individuals *E* and *F*?
    (1) They are unable to metabolize glucose.
    (2) They are unable to metabolize phenylalanine because they lack a specific enzyme.
    (3) They have an accumulation of excess fatty material in their nerve tissue.
    (4) They have an abnormal chromosome number.

93. Which event is *not* part of the process of DNA replication?
    (1) Nitrogenous base pairs are formed.
    (2) Hydrogen bonds are broken.
    (3) A double-stranded molecule unwinds.
    (4) Ribosomes are synthesized.

94. Deoxyribonucleic acid molecules serve as a template for the synthesis of molecules of
    (1) amino acids   (3) messenger RNA
    (2) carbohydrates   (4) lipids

95. Which procedure is usually used to help determine whether a child will be born with Down's syndrome?
    (1) amniocentesis
    (2) cloning
    (3) microdissection of sperm cells and egg cells
    (4) analysis of urine samples from the mother

Base your answers to questions 96 through 99 on the information below and on your knowledge of biology.

For many generations, a particular species of snail has lived in an isolated pond. Some members of the species have light-colored shells and some have dark-colored shells. During this time, the species has been producing large numbers of offspring through random mating, and no migration has occurred.

96. Which additional condition must be present if the gene frequencies of these snails are to remain constant?
    (1) asexual reproduction
    (2) lack of mutations
    (3) genetic variation
    (4) common ancestry

97. A change in the environment of the pond caused the light-colored shells to become an important survival trait, and the number of light-colored snails increased. This situation will most likely cause
    (1) the addition of a fifth nitrogenous base to the DNA of the snails
    (2) a change in the frequency of the genes for shell color
    (3) an increase in the number of ribosomes in the cells of the snail
    (4) the extinction of this species of snail

98. The total of all the inheritable genes found in these snails is referred to as a
    (1) pedigree
    (2) karyotype
    (3) phenotypic ratio
    (4) gene pool

99. All of the snails of this species living in the pond may be classified as
    (1) a population
    (2) an ecosystem
    (3) a community
    (4) a biome

Group 5 — Ecology

If you choose this group, be sure to answer questions 100–109.

Base your answers to questions 100 and 101 on the diagram below and on your knowledge of biology.

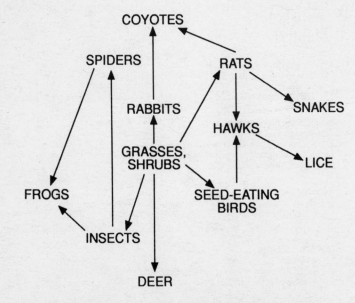

100. Which organisms would contain the greatest amount of available energy?
     (1) rabbits and deer
     (2) grasses and shrubs
     (3) lice
     (4) hawks

101. The primary consumers include
     (1) rabbits and snakes
     (2) insects and seed-eating birds
     (3) rats and frogs
     (4) spiders and coyotes

102. The diagram below represents the feeding areas during summer and fall of two populations in the same ecosystem. Both populations feed on oak trees.

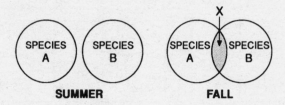

The portion of the diagram labeled *X* most likely indicates that
(1) these populations compete for food in the fall, but not in the summer
(2) the species are separated by a geographic barrier in the fall
(3) the supply of oxygen is greater in the summer than in the fall
(4) random mating occurs between these species in the summer

103. One reason a marine organism may have trouble surviving in a freshwater habitat is that
(1) there are more carnivores in freshwater habitats
(2) salt water holds more nitrogen than fresh water
(3) more photosynthesis occurs in fresh water than in salt water
(4) water balance is affected by salt concentration

104. The chart below illustrates some methods of pest control.

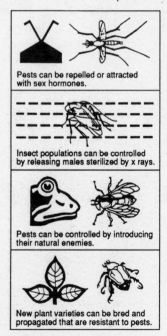

Pests can be repelled or attracted with sex hormones.

Insect populations can be controlled by releasing males sterilized by x rays.

Pests can be controlled by introducing their natural enemies.

New plant varieties can be bred and propagated that are resistant to pests.

One likely effect of using these methods of pest control will be to
(1) prevent the extinction of endangered species
(2) increase water pollution
(3) reduce pesticide contamination of the environment
(4) harm the atmosphere

Base your answers to questions 105 through 107 on the sequence of diagrams below and on your knowledge of biology.

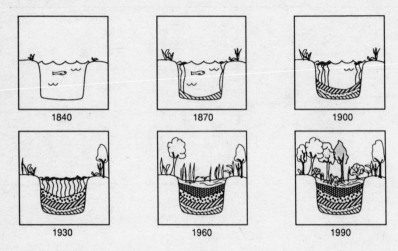

105. This sequence of diagrams best illustrates
     (1) ecological succession
     (2) organic evolution
     (3) the effects of acid rain
     (4) a food chain

106. If no human intervention or natural disaster occurs, by the year 2050 this area will most likely be a
     (1) lake
     (2) swamp
     (3) desert
     (4) forest

107. The natural increase in the amount of vegetation from 1840 to 1930 is related to the
     (1) decreasing water depth
     (2) increasing amount of sunlight
     (3) presence of bottom-feeding fish
     (4) use of the pond for fishing

108. In the nitrogen cycle, plants use nitrogen compounds to produce
     (1) glucose
     (2) starch
     (3) lipids
     (4) proteins

109. A flea in the fur of a mouse benefits at the mouse's expense. This type of relationship is known as
     (1) commensalism
     (2) parasitism
     (3) saprophytism
     (4) mutualism

PART III

This part consists of five groups. Choose three of these five groups. [15]

Group I

If you choose this group, be sure to answer questions 110–114.

Base your answers to questions 110 through 114 on the reading passage below and on your knowledge of biology.

Viruses

Most viruses are little more than strands of genetic material surrounded by a protein coat. Given the opportunity to enter a living cell, a virus springs into action and is reproduced.

Researchers have long known that viruses reproduce by using some of the cell's enzymes and protein-making structures. However, the precise details of the process remain unclear. Microbiologists have recently enabled viruses to reproduce outside a living cell, in a test-tube medium containing crushed human cells, salts, ATP, amino acids, and nucleotides.

In the test tube, the viral genetic material was replicated and new viral proteins were synthesized. These new proteins were then organized into coats around the newly formed genetic material. Complete viruses were formed, demonstrating that a virus can be active outside the cell if given the right environment.

110. When a virus enters a human cell, it may
    (1) control photosynthesis   (3) reproduce
    (2) copy the DNA of the cell   (4) enlarge

111. Microbiologists were able to grow viruses in a test tube containing
    (1) crushed human cells   (3) glucose
    (2) nutrient agar   (4) ammonia

112. Using one or more complete sentences, describe a possible reason that the microbiologists added ATP to the test-tube medium.

113. Using one or more complete sentences, explain the function of the new viral proteins.

114. Using one or more complete sentences, state a valid conclusion that can be drawn from this research about viruses.

Group 2

If you choose this group, be sure to answer questions 115–119.

Base your answers to questions 115 through 119 on the information below and on your knowledge of biology.

To measure glucose use in a human, a blood sample was taken from a vein, and the amount of glucose in the sample was determined. A glucose solution was then ingested by the person being tested. Blood samples were taken periodically for 5 hours and tested to determine the amount of glucose present. Results from the tests were used to construct the data table below.

Data Table

Time (hours)	Glucose (mg/100 dL)
0	80
0.5	170
1	120
2	90
3	80
4	70
5	70

Directions (115–116): Using the information in the data table, construct a line graph on the grid provided.

115. Mark an appropriate scale on each of the labeled axes.

116. Plot the data from the data table. Surround each point with a small circle and connect the points.
     Example:

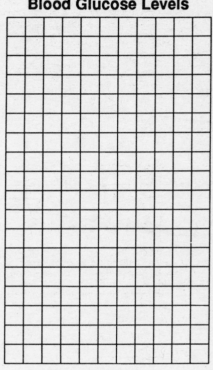

Blood Glucose Levels

Glucose (mg/100 dL)

Time (hours)

117. Using one or more complete sentences, give a possible explanation for the drop in the glucose level between 0.5 and 1 hour after the glucose was ingested.

118. Using one or more complete sentences, state a function of glucose in the human body.

119. Based on the information given, how much glucose would most likely be present in 100 deciliters (dL) of the blood 1.5 hours after the glucose was ingested?
     (1) 90 mg   (3) 120 mg
     (2) 105 mg   (4) 170 mg

Group 3

If you choose this group, be sure to answer questions 120–124.

120. Forty bean seeds were planted in 40 different pots containing soil of the same composition and moisture level. All seeds were of the same age and plant species. The pots were divided into four groups of 10, and each group was kept at a different temperature: 5°C, 10°C, 15°C, and 20°C, respectively, for a period of 30 days. All other environmental conditions were kept constant.

Using one or more complete sentences, state a problem being investigated in this experimental setup.

121. Choose one of the labeled animal cell parts from the diagram below. In the space provided on the separate answer paper, write the letter of the part you have chosen and, using one or more complete sentences, identify the part and state one of its functions.

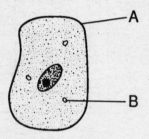

122. Twenty-five geranium plants were placed in each of four closed containers and then exposed to the light conditions shown in the data table below. All other environmental conditions were held constant for a period of 2 days. At the beginning of the investigation, the quantity of CO_2 present in each closed container was 250 cubic centimeters. The data table shows the amount of CO_2 remaining in each container at the end of 2 days.

Data Table

Container	Color of Light	CO_2 (cm^3)
1	blue	75
2	red	50
3	green	200
4	orange	150

The variable in this investigation was the
(1) type of plant
(2) color of light
(3) amount of CO_2 in each container at the beginning of the investigation
(4) number of days needed to complete the investigation

123. In the diagram at the right, the view of the insect specimen can best be described as
    (1) a ventral view, with the posterior end to the right of the page
    (2) an external view showing the ventral side of the abdomen
    (3) a dorsal view, with the anterior end to the left of the page
    (4) an internal view showing the dorsal side of the head region

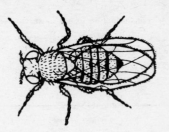

124. In addition to an indicator and proper safety equipment, which pieces of equipment shown below should be used to test for the presence of glucose in apple juice?

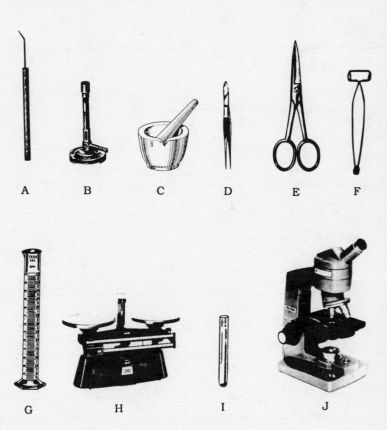

A   B   C   D   E   F

G   H   I   J

(1) *A, D,* and *E*
(2) *B, F,* and *I*

(3) *C, G,* and *H*
(4) *A, B,* and *J*

Group 4

If you choose this group, be sure to answer questions 125–129.

Base your answers to questions 125 through 129 on the information below and on your knowledge of biology.

A human was fed a meal containing measured amounts of proteins, starch, and fats. Eight hours later, a 10-milliliter sample of fluid was removed from the human's small intestine for analysis.

Note that question 125 has only three choices.

125. Based on the relative amounts of nutrients present, which graph best represents the results of the analysis?

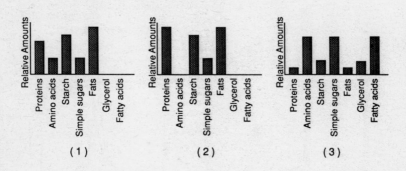

126. Which piece of equipment should be used to accurately measure the 10-milliliter sample for analysis?
   (1) triple-beam balance
   (2) graduated cylinder
   (3) large test tube
   (4) metric ruler

127. Which indicators could be used to test for the presence of some of the substances in the fluid sample?
   (1) Benedict's solution and Lugol's iodine
   (2) bromthymol blue solution and pH paper
   (3) Fehling's solution and bromthymol blue solution
   (4) pH paper and Lugol's iodine

128. Using one or more complete sentences, describe *one* safety precaution that a technician should use while analyzing the sample of intestinal fluid.

129. Using one or more complete sentences, describe *one* way that the results of the analysis would be different if the human was fed a single boiled potato instead of the meal containing measured amounts of proteins, starch, and fats.

Group 5

If you choose this group, be sure to answer questions 130–134.

Base your answers to questions 130 through 134 on the photograph below and on your knowledge of biology. The photograph shows onion root-tip tissue viewed under the high-power objective of a compound light microscope.

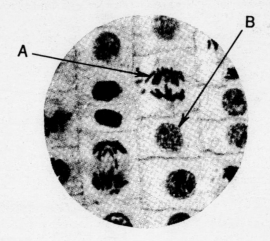

130. The photograph illustrates stages in the process of
    (1) meiosis in root tips
    (2) mitotic cell division in plants
    (3) water conduction in onions
    (4) chlorophyll production in chloroplasts

131. Identify the structure indicated by arrow *A*.

132. Identify the structure indicated by arrow *B*.

133. Using one or more sentences, describe one adjustment that could be made to the microscope to make the field of view brighter.

134. When viewed with a compound light microscope, which letter would best illustrate that the microscope inverts and reverses an image?
    (1) A
    (2) W
    (3) F
    (4) D

BIOLOGY

June 21, 1995

PART I

Answer all 75 questions in this part. [75]

Directions (1–75): For *each* statement or question followed by four choices, select the word or expression that, of those given, best completes the statement or answers the question. For other types of questions, follow the directions given.

1. The organ system represented in the diagram below contains specialized cells.

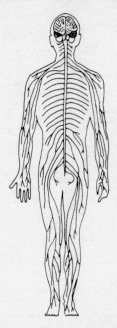

The function of these cells is most closely associated with the process of
   (1) regulation   (3) synthesis
   (2) growth   (4) hydrolysis

2. Members of a population of grey squirrels, *Sciurus carolinensis*, are classified in the same species because they
   (1) obtain their food in the same manner
   (2) can mate and produce fertile offspring
   (3) produce enzymes by synthesis
   (4) live in the same area

3. A fine network of channels within cells aids in the movement of substances. This network is known as the
   (1) endoplasmic reticulum   (3) cell wall
   (2) mitochondria   (4) ribosomes

4. Which statements listed below are associated with the cell theory?

    (A) Cells are the basic units of structure in living things.
    (B) Cells are the basic units of function in living things.
    (C) Cells come from preexisting cells.

  (1) statements A and B, only   (3) statements B and C, only
  (2) statements A and C, only   (4) statements A, B, and C

5. Which substance is classified as an inorganic compound?
  (1) glucose   (3) water
  (2) fat   (4) protein

6. A chain of chemically bonded amino acid molecules forms a compound known as a
  (1) polypeptide   (3) nucleotide
  (2) monosaccharide   (4) lipid

7. After it is produced by an autotroph, glucose can be
  (1) converted into storage products by hydrolysis
  (2) utilized to capture light energy from the Sun
  (3) combined with three fatty acids to form a lipid
  (4) used as an energy source in cellular respiration

8. Which structures are adaptations for nutrition in the paramecium?
  (1) pseudopodia and food vacuoles
  (2) oral groove and cilia
  (3) flagellum and eyespot
  (4) contractile vacuoles and oral groove

9. The fact that amylase in the human small intestine works best at normal body temperature suggests that
  (1) amylase is denatured at temperatures below 37°C
  (2) amylase can function only in the small intestine
  (3) the optimum temperature for amylase is 37°C
  (4) the pH of the small intestine does not affect amylase

Directions (10–11): For *each* phrase in questions 10 and 11 select the summary word equation, *chosen from the list below,* that is best described by that phrase.

Summary Word Equations

  (1) water + carbon dioxide ⟶
      glucose + oxygen + water
  (2) glucose + glucose ⟶
      maltose + water
  (3) glucose ⟶
      alcohol + carbon dioxide + ATP
  (4) glucose + oxygen ⟶
      carbon dioxide + water + ATP

10. The process that most directly supplies energy for metabolic activities in humans

11. A process that directly requires light energy

12. Two demonstrations were performed as described below.

Demonstration A	Demonstration B
Two drops of sucrase solution were placed on a sugar cube.	A sugar cube was crushed with a hammer.

The two demonstrations were most likely used to illustrate the difference between
(1) chemical and mechanical digestion
(2) photosynthesis and hydrolysis
(3) chemical digestion and hydrolysis
(4) mechanical digestion and synthesis

13. The end products of digestion enter the fluids and cells of an organism by the process of
(1) egestion
(2) fermentation
(3) absorption
(4) locomotion

14. Most mosses grow to be only a few inches tall, but ferns often grow to be several feet tall. This difference exists because mosses lack
(1) chlorophyll
(2) enzymes
(3) cell walls
(4) vascular tissue

15. Which statement best describes the products of excretion?
(1) They have no value to other living things.
(2) They result from extracellular digestion.
(3) They result from cellular metabolism.
(4) They are not toxic to living tissues.

16. Four terms associated with the process of regulation are listed in the chart below.

Term	Examples
(A) Receptors	Leg muscles and testes
(B) Stimuli	Temperature and light
(C) Impulses	Skin and eyes
(D) Effectors	Neurotransmitters and auxins

Which term is correctly paired with a set of examples?
(1) A
(2) B
(3) C
(4) D

17. The diagram below represents a demonstration involving two plant seedlings, *A* and *B*.

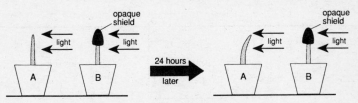

The demonstration was most likely set up to show the effect of
(1) sunlight on stomate size
(2) darkness on palisade cells
(3) sunlight on auxins
(4) darkness on water transport

18. The diagram below represents a cyclic event in the process of cellular respiration.

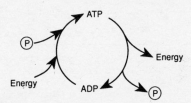

This cycle is important to living organisms because it
(1) is a nonreversible process that produces energy for the cell
(2) converts the potential energy of organic molecules to a form that can readily be used or stored
(3) transforms adenosine triphosphate molecules into protein molecules that cells can use for energy
(4) is the only process in cells that does not require enzymes

19. In the nervous system of a multicellular animal, synapses are located directly between
(1) axons and terminal branches
(2) impulses and receptors
(3) dendrites and cytons
(4) terminal branches and dendrites

20. The diagram below represents a cell in water. Formulas of molecules that can move freely across the membrane are shown. Some molecules are located inside the cell and others are in the water outside the cell.

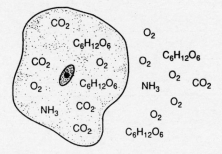

Based on the distribution of molecules, what would most likely happen to these molecules after a few hours?
(1) The concentration of $C_6H_{12}O_6$ will increase inside the cell.
(2) The concentration of CO_2 will increase outside the cell.
(3) The concentration of NH_3 will increase inside the cell.
(4) The concentration of O_2 will increase outside the cell.

21. A plant tissue specialized for transport of water and minerals from the roots to the leaves is known as
    (1) xylem
    (2) cambium
    (3) phloem
    (4) epidermis

22. Locomotion in the earthworm is accomplished by the combined action of
    (1) cilia and setae
    (2) muscles and setae
    (3) muscles and nephrons
    (4) flagella and muscles

23. Which statement best describes the nervous system of the organism shown in the diagram below?

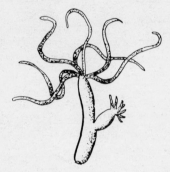

    (1) It has a highly developed brain and a dorsal nerve cord.
    (2) It has a primitive brain and few neurons.
    (3) It has fused ganglia and a ventral nerve cord.
    (4) It has a nerve net and no brain cells.

24. Which substance is normally absorbed by the large intestine?
    (1) water
    (2) glycogen
    (3) protein
    (4) cellulose

25. The diagram below represents a portion of the human digestive tract.

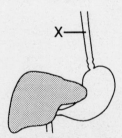

    The muscular contractions that occur in the region labeled X are known as
    (1) cyclosis
    (2) hydrolysis
    (3) synthesis
    (4) peristalsis

26. A portion of the human respiratory tract is represented in the diagram below.

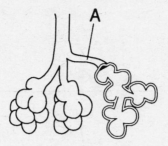

Which structure is indicated by letter *A*?
(1) trachea
(2) pharynx
(3) alveolus
(4) bronchiole

27. Which statement *most completely* describes the function of regulation in humans?
(1) The circulatory system transports hormones to various glands, stimulating their activity.
(2) The nervous system sends impulses to coordinate all body systems.
(3) The nervous and endocrine systems work together to maintain homeostasis.
(4) The large intestine stores undigested materials before they are eliminated from the body.

28. Which letter in the diagram below indicates the organ that is involved in the deamination of amino acids?

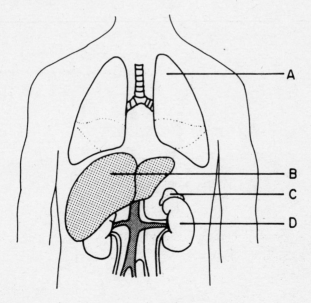

(1) *A*
(2) *B*
(3) *C*
(4) *D*

29. Which structures shown in the diagram below contract when the arm moves?

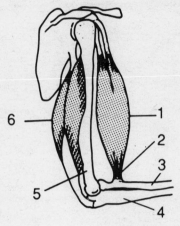

(1) 1 and 5   (3) 2 and 4
(2) 1 and 6   (4) 3 and 4

Base your answers to questions 30 through 32 on the diagram below and on your knowledge of biology.

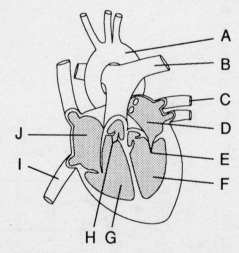

30. A valve that prevents the backflow of blood into an atrium is indicated by letter
    (1) *I*   (3) *C*
    (2) *H*   (4) *E*

31. The right ventricle is indicated by letter
    (1) *J*   (3) *F*
    (2) *G*   (4) *D*

32. Which structures contain oxygenated blood?
    (1) *A, C, D,* and *F*   (3) *B, C, F,* and *G*
    (2) *A, B, C,* and *I*   (4) *B, F, G,* and *J*

Base your answers to questions 33 through 35 on the diagram below and on your knowledge of biology.

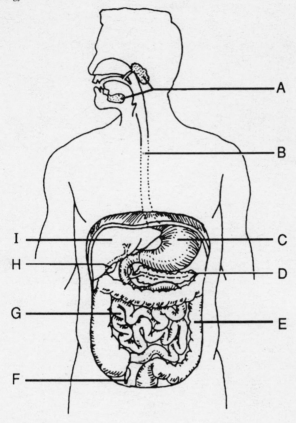

33. The end products of lipid digestion diffuse into the lacteals that are present in the lining of structure
    (1) *H*   (3) *C*
    (2) *G*   (4) *E*

34. Which organs are involved in the storage of glycogen?
    (1) *A* and *E*   (3) *C* and *H*
    (2) *B* and *F*   (4) *D* and *I*

35. Clinical studies have indicated that an increase in retention time of material in structure *E* is related to the occurrence of colon and rectal cancer. What could a person do to help decrease retention time in this structure?
    (1) limit the amount of physical activity before meals
    (2) increase protein consumption and decrease carbohydrate consumption
    (3) consume more fruits, vegetables, and grains
    (4) decrease intake of unsaturated fats and increase intake of saturated fats

36. An exact duplication of the complete set of chromosomes of a cell followed by the separation of these duplicate sets into two daughter cells is known as
    (1) mitotic cell division   (3) internal fertilization
    (2) zygote formation   (4) reduction division

37. Reproduction in many vertebrates is characterized by external fertilization. This type of fertilization is usually associated with the production of large numbers of eggs. These statements best describe reproduction in
    (1) reptiles   (3) amphibians
    (2) birds   (4) mammals

Base your answers to questions 38 through 40 on the diagrams below and on your knowledge of biology.

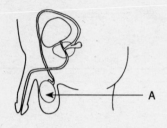 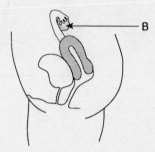

Directions (38–40): For *each* statement in questions 39 through 40 select the sentence, *chosen from the list below,* that best applies to that statement.

Sentences
    (1) The statement is correct for both structures *A* and *B*.
    (2) The statement is incorrect for both structures *A* and *B*.
    (3) The statement is correct for structure *A*, only.
    (4) The statement is correct for structure *B*, only.

38. Estrogen and progesterone are produced.

39. A substance is produced that influences the development of secondary sex characteristics.

40. This structure may contain a corpus luteum.

41. In which pattern of development do the wastes that are formed by a vertebrate embryo diffuse through a membrane into the external aquatic habitat?
    (1) external fertilization and external development
    (2) external fertilization and internal development
    (3) internal fertilization and external development
    (4) internal fertilization and internal development

42. In flowering plants, gametogenesis occurs within the
    (1) root tip and cambium layer   (3) anther and filament
    (2) ovary and anther   (4) xylem tissue and phloem tissue

43. The diagram below represents a longitudinal section of an apple.

X—

In the diagram, the structure indicated by letter X normally contains a
(1) diploid pollen grain
(2) monoploid seed
(3) diploid embryo
(4) monoploid zygote

Base your answers to questions 44 through 46 on the diagrams below which represent three different embryos and on your knowledge of biology.

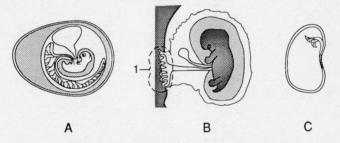

1—

A   B   C

44. Oxygen is required for aerobic respiration during the development of
(1) embryo A, only
(2) embryo B, only
(3) embryos A and B, only
(4) embryos A, B, and C

45. Nitrogenous wastes are removed by the mother during the development of
(1) embryo A, only
(2) embryo B, only
(3) embryo C, only
(4) embryos A and B

46. Which process essential to the survival of the embryo takes place in region 1 of diagram B?
(1) exchange of blood cells
(2) exchange of genes
(3) diffusion of nutrients
(4) digestion of food

47. Which embryonic process is illustrated in the diagram below?

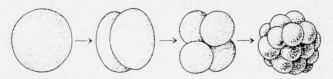

(1) cleavage
(2) fertilization
(3) specialization
(4) meiosis

48. A gene mutation may be transmitted to offspring if the mutation occurs within
    (1) an egg cell
    (2) muscle cells
    (3) cells of the uterus
    (4) blood cells

49. Some human *Y*-chromosomes contain a gene for a trait called hairy pinna, which produces massive hair growth on the outer ear. Since the corresponding gene is not found on the *X*-chromosome, which statement is most likely true?
    (1) Males with a normal *X*-chromosome and the gene for hairy pinna on the *Y*-chromosome do not have hairy ears.
    (2) The gene for hairy pinna is an autosomal recessive gene.
    (3) Females will not express the gene for hairy pinna.
    (4) Half as many women as men will carry the gene for hairy pinna.

Base your answers to questions 50 and 51 on the information below and on your knowledge of biology.

The pedigree chart below shows the inheritance of handedness in humans over three generations. The gene for right-handedness (*R*) is dominant over the gene for left-handedness (*r*).

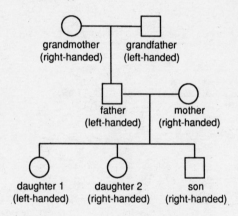

50. For which individual is *Rr* the most probable genotype?
    (1) grandfather
    (2) grandmother
    (3) father
    (4) daughter 1

51. Which two individuals have identical genotypes for handedness?
    (1) grandmother and grandfather
    (2) mother and father
    (3) daughter 1 and daughter 2
    (4) mother and son

52. Which statement best describes evolution?
    (1) Evolution is a predictable change from simple to complex organisms.
    (2) Evolution is a process of change through time.
    (3) Evolution often proceeds from complex to simpler organisms.
    (4) Evolution causes organisms to develop characteristics they need.

53. In the diagram below, which letter indicates a section of the molecule that includes all the components of a nucleotide?

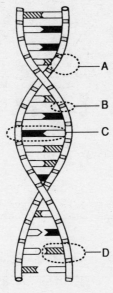

(1) *A*   (3) *C*
(2) *B*   (4) *D*

54. Which factor may have played a role in the development of the polar bear in Alaska and the brown bear in Russia into separate species?
(1) geographic isolation
(2) mitotic cell division
(3) asexual reproduction
(4) artificial selection

55. According to current evolutionary theory, which of Darwin's concepts is best explained by mutations and sexual reproduction?
(1) competition
(2) variation
(3) overproduction of a species
(4) reproductive isolation

Base your answers to questions 56 through 58 on the photographs below of chromosomes from a human male and on your knowledge of biology.

56. The arrangement of chromosomes in the diagram is known as a
    (1) karyotype
    (2) phenotype
    (3) mutation rate
    (4) genotype

57. The arrangement of chromosomes in the diagram is a method used in the identification of
    (1) phenylketonuria
    (2) blood type
    (3) Down syndrome
    (4) hemophilia

58. If the chromosomes of a female were arranged in chart form like the chromosomes of this male, the chart would
    (1) be identical to that of the male
    (2) appear different in one chromosome pair
    (3) contain more chromosomes
    (4) have one-half the number of chromosomes

Base your answers to questions 59 through 62 on the diagram below and on your knowledge of biology. The diagram represents some steps in a metabolic process.

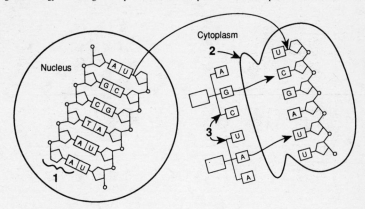

59. The structure indicated by number 1 most likely represents
    (1) an amino acid molecule
    (2) a messenger-RNA molecule
    (3) part of a transfer-RNA molecule
    (4) part of a DNA molecule

60. The structure indicated by number 2 is known as a
    (1) mitochondrion
    (2) chloroplast
    (3) ribosome
    (4) vacuole

61. The process represented in the diagram is most closely associated with
    (1) protein synthesis
    (2) starch hydrolysis
    (3) gene replication
    (4) artificial selection

62. The molecules indicated by number 3 are most likely
    (1) enzymes
    (2) transfer-RNA molecules
    (3) messenger-RNA molecules
    (4) proteins

63. Although three different bird species all inhabit the same type of tree in an area, competition between the birds rarely occurs. The most likely explanation for this lack of competition is that these birds
    (1) have different ecological niches
    (2) share food with each other
    (3) have a limited supply of food
    (4) are unable to interbreed

64. Which statement describes an activity that is directly involved in the nitrogen cycle?
    (1) A crow uses carbohydrates for cell metabolism.
    (2) A trout excretes carbon dioxide into the water.
    (3) Soil bacteria convert nitrogenous wastes into materials usable by autotrophs.
    (4) Plants release water into the atmosphere from the process of transpiration.

65. The diagrams below represent stages in the embryonic development of four organisms.

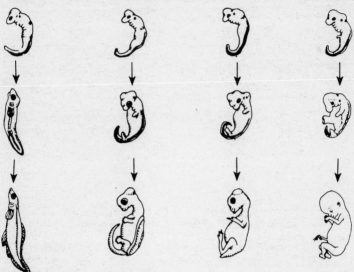

The similarities in embryonic development shown in the diagrams suggest that these organisms
(1) are all members of the same species
(2) all undergo external development
(3) may have evolved from a common ancestor
(4) have adaptations for the same environment as adults

66. In the diagram below of a whale, the bones labeled "pelvis" and "femur" appear to be useless.

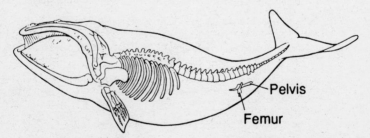

The possibility that these bones were once useful gives support to the concept of
(1) modern evolutionary theory
(2) fossil formation
(3) unfavorable variations
(4) stable gene frequencies

67. The chart below represents characteristics necessary for the maintenance of a self-sustaining ecosystem.

Ecosystem Characteristics

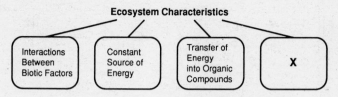

| Interactions Between Biotic Factors | Constant Source of Energy | Transfer of Energy into Organic Compounds | X |

Which characteristic is most likely represented by letter *X*?
(1) Lack of Abiotic Factors
(2) Cycling of Materials
(3) Few Biotic Factors
(4) Symbiotic Relationships

68. Which organisms in the diagram below are components of the same food chain?

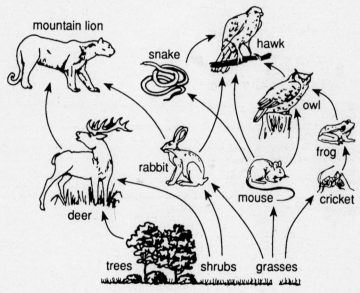

(1) trees, mountain lion, snake, and hawk
(2) trees, rabbit, deer, and shrubs
(3) grasses, cricket, frog, and mouse
(4) grasses, mouse, snake, and hawk

69. Which graph best represents the rate of evolution described by the concept of punctuated equilibrium?

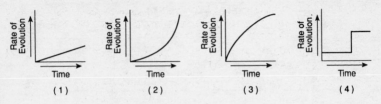

(1)   (2)   (3)   (4)

70. Which concept does the diagram below represent?

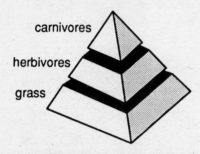

(1) the relative elevation of different organisms living at high altitudes
(2) the direct relationship between abiotic and biotic factors in an ecosystem
(3) the reduction in energy at each successive feeding level of a food chain
(4) the imbalance in ecosystems caused by low numbers of carnivores

71. When Mount Saint Helens erupted in 1980, a portion of the surrounding area was covered by lava, which buried all of the vegetation. Four months later, *Anaphalis margaritacea* plants were found growing out of lava rock crevices. The beginning of plant regrowth in this area is part of the process known as

(1) species preservation   (3) biotic competition
(2) organic evolution   (4) ecological succession

72. The graph below shows data on the average life expectancy of humans.

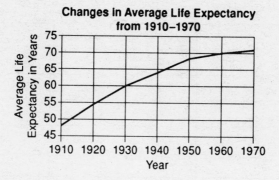

Changes in Average Life Expectancy from 1910–1970

The change in life expectancy is most likely the result of
(1) poor land-use management that has affected the quality of topsoil
(2) oversights that have had an impact on air quality
(3) a decrease in natural checks such as disease on the population
(4) widespread use of biocides such as DDT in water supplies

Base your answers to questions 73 through 75 on the information below and on your knowledge of biology.

For 25 years, hay was cut from the same 10 acres on a farm. During these years, shrews, grasshoppers, spiders, and mice were seen in this hayfield. After the farmer retired, he no longer cut the hay and the field was left unattended.

73. What will most likely occur in the former hayfield over the next few decades?
(1) The plant species will change, but the animal species will remain the same.
(2) The animal species will change, but the plant species will remain the same.
(3) Neither the plant species nor the animal species will change.
(4) Both the plant species and the animal species will change.

74. The grasshoppers, spiders, shrews, and other organisms, along with the soil, minerals, and amount of rainfall, constitute
(1) a community
(2) a population
(3) an ecosystem
(4) a food web

75. Just before he retired, the farmer determined the population size of several of the field species during the months of May, July, and August. The results are recorded in the table below.

Field Species	Number of Organisms		
	May	July	August
grasshoppers	1,000	5,000	1,500
birds	250	100	100
grasses	7,000	20,000	6,000
spiders	75	200	500

Which graph best represents the relative population size of the field species for May?

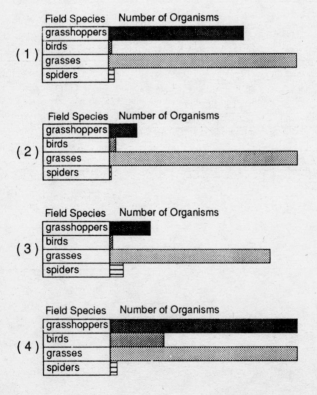

PART II

This part consists of five groups. Choose three of these five groups. [15]

Group 1

If you choose this group, be sure to answer questions 76–80.

Base your answers to questions 76 and 77 on the photographs below and on your knowledge of biology. The photographs show two views of a microorganism observed with a compound light microscope.

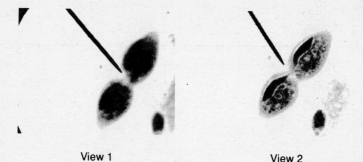

View 1   View 2

76. Which adjustment must be made to the microscope to make the image in view 1 as clear as the image in view 2?
    (1) remove the eyepiece
    (2) turn the fine adjustment
    (3) change from low power to high power
    (4) close the diaphragm opening

77. If the organism indicated by the pointer is 100 micrometers long before fission, the length of each new individual immediately after fission would be closest to
    (1) 1.0 millimeter   (3) 50 millimeters
    (2) 100 millimeters   (4) 0.05 millimeter

78. When compared to the image of a specimen observed with a compound light microscope under low power, the image of the specimen observed under high power will appear
    (1) larger and lighter   (3) smaller and darker
    (2) smaller and lighter   (4) larger and darker

79. Photographs of cells from two different organisms are shown below.

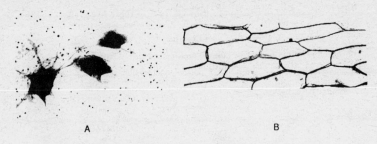

A   B

Which cell feature is a part of the cells shown in photograph *B*, but is *not* a part of the cells shown in photograph *A*?
(1) plasma membrane   (3) cell wall
(2) cytoplasm   (4) nucleus

80. The diagram below represents a compound light microscope.

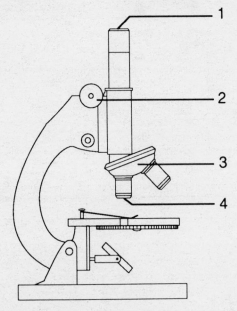

The observation of a specimen under both high and low power could be interfered with by a spot on the surface of which structure?
(1) 1   (3) 3
(2) 2   (4) 4

Group 2

If you choose this group, be sure to answer questions 81–85.

Base your answers to questions 81 through 84 on the information and data table below and on your knowledge of biology.

Certain chemicals cause mutations in cells by breaking chromosomes into pieces. Cells containing such broken chromosomes are known as mutated cells. Certain nutrients, such as beta carotene (a form of vitamin A), have the ability to prevent chromosome breakage by such mutagenic chemicals.

The results of an investigation of the effect of beta carotene in preventing chromosome damage are represented in the data table below. In this investigation, varying amounts of beta carotene per kilogram of body weight were added to the diets of hamsters. A mutagenic chemical was also added to the diets of the hamsters at a constant dose rate.

Data Table

Amount of Beta Carotene Added to Diet per kg of Hamster's Body Weight	Percentage of Mutated Cells
0 mg	11.5
20 mg	11.0
30 mg	8.0
40 mg	7.0
50 mg	4.5
75 mg	3.5
100 mg	2.0
150 mg	1.5

Directions (81–82): Using the information in the data table, construct a line graph on the grid provided.

81. Mark an appropriate scale on each of the labeled axes.

82. Plot the data from the data table. Surround each point with a small circle and connect the points.

Example: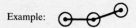

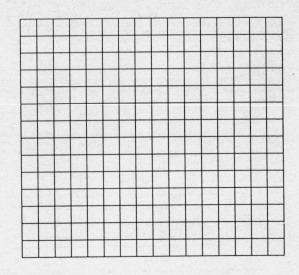

**Amount of Beta Carotene Added to Diet
(mg/kg of body weight)**

(vertical axis label: Percentage of Mutated Cells*)*

83. The greatest effect of added beta carotene on the percentage of mutated cells occurred as the dose rate increased from
    (1) 0 to 10 mg
    (2) 20 to 30 mg
    (3) 50 to 75 mg
    (4) 100 to 150 mg

84. Vitamin A was used in this experiment. Which conclusion can best be made concerning the effect of vitamin E on the production of mutated cells in hamsters exposed to this mutagenic chemical?
    (1) Vitamin E will increase the percentage of mutated cells produced.
    (2) Vitamin E will decrease the percentage of mutated cells produced.
    (3) There will be no measurable effect of vitamin E on the percentage of mutated cells produced.
    (4) No valid conclusion can be made concerning the effect of vitamin E on the percentage of mutated cells produced.

85. Which experimental procedure would best determine the effectiveness of a vaccine for preventing a certain disease in pigeons?
    (1) Expose 100 pigeons to the disease and then inoculate all 100 pigeons with the vaccine.
    (2) Expose 100 pigeons to the disease and then inoculate 50 of these pigeons with the vaccine.
    (3) Inoculate 10 pigeons with the vaccine and 90 pigeons with a harmless solution and then expose all 100 pigeons to the disease.
    (4) Inoculate 50 pigeons with the vaccine and 50 pigeons with a harmless solution and then expose all 100 pigeons to the disease.

Group 3

If you choose this group, be sure to answer questions 86–90.

Base your answers to questions 86 through 89 on the reading passage below and on your knowledge of biology.

Get the Lead Out

Researchers have recently determined that children scored better on intelligence tests after the amount of lead in their blood was reduced. This study offers hope that the effects of lead poisoning can be reversed.

Lead poisoning can cause mental retardation, learning disabilities, stunted growth, hearing loss, and behavior problems. Scientists estimate that at least 3 million children in the United States have lead concentrations above the danger level of 10 micrograms per deciliter of blood. Researchers found an average increase of one point on an index scale for intelligence for every decrease of 3 micrograms per deciliter in blood concentration.

A common source of lead poisoning is peeling or chipping paint in buildings constructed before 1960. Also, soil near heavily traveled roads may have been contaminated by the exhaust from older cars burning leaded gasoline.

In a recent related study, another group of researchers concluded that removing lead-contaminated soil does not reduce blood lead levels enough to justify its cost. The children in the study began with blood levels of 7 to 24 micrograms per deciliter. Replacing the lead-contaminated soil resulted in a reduction in blood lead levels of 0.8 to 1.6 micrograms per deciliter in 152 children under the age of 4.

These studies are not conclusive. Results indicate a need for further studies to determine if reducing environmental lead levels will significantly reduce lead levels in the blood.

86. One effect of lead poisoning is
    (1) an increase in growth
    (2) a decrease in platelet numbers
    (3) a decrease in learning problems
    (4) an increase in behavior problems

87. A decrease of 9 micrograms per deciliter in blood lead level would most likely lead to an average
    (1) increase of one point on an index scale for intelligence
    (2) increase of three points on an index scale for intelligence
    (3) decrease of three points on an index scale for intelligence
    (4) decrease of six points on an index scale for intelligence

88. The part of the nervous system most affected by high levels of lead in the blood is the
    (1) cerebrum   (3) spinal cord
    (2) cerebellum   (4) medulla

89. Using one or more complete sentences, state one practice that could be used to reduce lead in the home environment.

90. A laboratory demonstration was set up and maintained at 2°C for 2 hours. The results are shown in the diagram below.

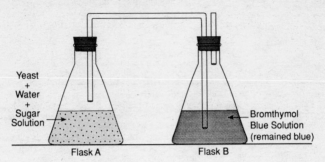

Yeast + Water + Sugar Solution

Bromthymol Blue Solution (remained blue)

Flask A   Flask B

According to the graph at the right, if the demonstration had been maintained at 40°C for 2 hours, the contents of flask *B* would most likely have

(1) turned yellow, and no gas bubbles would have been produced
(2) remained blue, and gas bubbles would have been produced
(3) turned yellow, and gas bubbles would have been produced
(4) remained blue, and no gas bubbles would have been produced

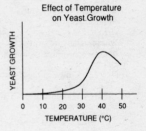

Effect of Temperature on Yeast Growth

Group 4

If you choose this group, be sure to answer questions 91–95.

91. The diagram below shows four setups used in an attempt to investigate the release of a gas during photosynthesis. Each setup was maintained at 25°C for a period of 10 hours.

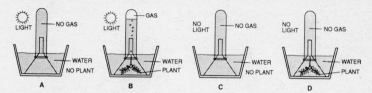

What was a variable in this experiment?
(1) water
(2) temperature
(3) time
(4) light

92. Which statement correctly describes the location of structures A and B in the diagram at the right?
(1) Structure A is dorsal to structure B.
(2) Structure B is posterior to structure A.
(3) Structure A is ventral to structure B.
(4) Structure B is anterior to structure A.

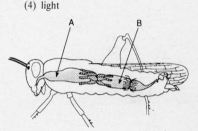

93. The best estimate of the number of ovules found in the ovary of a gladiolus flower would be determined by averaging the data from
(1) 10 students each counting the ovules in 10 different ovaries
(2) 2 students each counting the ovules in the same ovary 50 times
(3) 1 student counting the ovules in the same ovary 100 times
(4) 10 students each counting the ovules in the same ovary 10 times

94. To investigate the effect of a substance on plant growth, two bean plants of the same species were grown under identical conditions with the substance added to the soil of one of the plants. At the end of 2 weeks, the plant grown with the substance was 12.5 centimeters tall and the plant grown without the substance was 12.2 centimeters tall. The researcher concluded that the presence of the substance causes plants to grow taller. Using one or more complete sentences, state one reason that this conclusion may not be valid.

95. Data from measurements of transpiration and water uptake in an ash tree are plotted in the graph below.

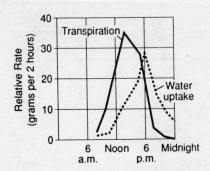

Which conclusion can correctly be drawn from the information in the graph?
(1) The rate of transpiration is not related to the amount of water uptake.
(2) Transpiration and water uptake are similar processes.
(3) Transpiration reaches a maximum rate faster than water uptake.
(4) As transpiration increases, the amount of water uptake decreases.

Group 5

If you choose this group, be sure to answer questions 96–100.

96. Pieces of pH paper were used to test the contents of three test tubes. The results are shown in the diagram below.

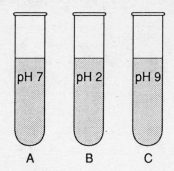

Which statement about the tubes is correct?
(1) Tube *A* contains a base.
(2) Tube *B* contains a base.
(3) Tube *B* contains an acid.
(4) Tube *C* contains an acid.

97. For what purpose would the equipment illustrated below most likely be used?

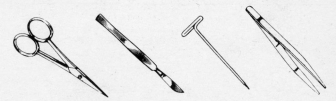

(1) dissecting a vertebrate
(2) extracting cell organelles
(3) identifying and classifying protists
(4) observing mitosis on prepared slides

98. To determine the effect of light on the germination of bean seeds, a student selected 12 healthy bean seeds and placed 6 of them in a petri dish in a dark closet and 6 of them in a petri dish on a windowsill. The experiment was conducted for 10 days at room temperature and no germination took place.

Using one or more complete sentences, describe one error in the experimental setup that resulted in the failure of the seeds to germinate.

99. A scientist performed an experiment using the following steps:

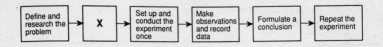

Using one or more complete sentences, identify the step that belongs in box *X*.

100. Which diagram shows a correct measurement?

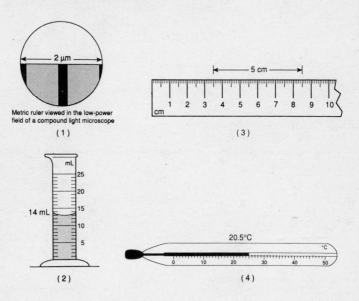

PYGMALION

Bernard Shaw was born in Dublin in 1856. Essentially shy, he yet created the persona of G.B.S., the showman, satirist, controversialist, critic, pundit, wit, intellectual buffoon and dramatist. Commentators brought a new adjective into English: Shavian, a term used to embody all his brilliant qualities.

After his arrival in London in 1876 he became an active Socialist and a brilliant platform speaker. He wrote on many social aspects of the day; on *Commonsense about the War* (1914), *How to Settle the Irish Question* (1917) and *The Intelligent Woman's Guide to Socialism, Capitalism, Sovietism and Fascism* (1928). He undertook his own education at the British Museum and consequently became keenly interested in cultural subjects. Thus his prolific output included music, art and theatre reviews, which were collected into several volumes, published as *Music In London 1890–1894* (3 vols., 1931); *Pen Portraits and Reviews* (1931); and *Our Theatres in the Nineties* (3 vols., 1931). He also wrote five novels and some shorter fiction, including *The Black Girl in Search of God and some Lesser Tales* and *Cashel Byron's Profession*, both published in Penguins.

He conducted a strong attack on the London theatre and was closely associated with the intellectual revival of British theatre. His many plays fall into several categories: 'Plays Pleasant'; 'Plays Unpleasant'; his comedies; chronicle-plays; 'metabiological Pentateuch' (*Back to Methuselah*, a series of plays) and 'political extravaganzas'. G.B.S. died in 1950.

PYGMALION

A ROMANCE IN FIVE ACTS

BERNARD SHAW

**WITH OVER
A HUNDRED DRAWINGS BY
FELIKS TOPOLSKI**

*

*DEFINITIVE TEXT
under the editorial supervision of
Dan H. Laurence*

PENGUIN BOOKS

PENGUIN BOOKS

Published by the Penguin Group
Penguin Books Ltd, 27 Wrights Lane, London W8 5TZ, England
Penguin Books USA Inc., 375 Hudson Street, New York, New York 10014, USA
Penguin Books Australia Ltd, Ringwood, Victoria, Australia
Penguin Books Canada Ltd, 10 Alcorn Avenue, Toronto, Ontario, Canada M4V 3B2
Penguin Books (NZ) Ltd, 182–190 Wairau Road, Auckland 10, New Zealand

Penguin Books Ltd, Registered Offices: Harmondsworth, Middlesex, England

The play first produced in London and New York 1914
First published 1916
The film first produced in London, 6 October 1938
The film version published in Penguin Books 1941
59 60 58

Printed in England by Clays Ltd, St Ives plc
Filmset in Monophoto Photina

PREFACE

A Professor of Phonetics

As will be seen later on, Pygmalion needs, not a preface, but a sequel, which I have supplied in its due place.

The English have no respect for their language, and will not teach their children to speak it. They cannot spell it because they have nothing to spell it with but an old foreign alphabet of which only the consonants – and not all of them – have any agreed speech value. Consequently no man can teach himself what it should sound like from reading it; and it is impossible for an Englishman to open his mouth without making some other Englishman despise him. Most European languages are now accessible in black and white to foreigners: English and French are not thus accessible even to Englishmen and Frenchmen. The reformer we need most today is an energetic phonetic enthusiast: that is why I have made such a one the hero of a popular play.

There have been heroes of that kind crying in the wilderness

5

for many years past. When I became interested in the subject towards the end of the eighteen-seventies, the illustrious Alexander Melville Bell, the inventor of Visible Speech, had emigrated to Canada, where his son invented the telephone; but Alexander J. Ellis was still a London patriarch, with an impressive head always covered by a velvet skull cap, for which he would apologize to public meetings in a very courtly manner. He and Tito Pagliardini, another phonetic veteran, were men whom it was impossible to dislike. Henry Sweet, then a young man, lacked their sweetness of character: he was about as conciliatory to conventional mortals as Ibsen or Samuel Butler. His great ability as a phonetician (he was, I think, the best of them all at his job) would have entitled him to high official recognition, and perhaps enabled him to popularize his subject, but for his Satanic contempt for all academic dignitaries and persons in general who thought more of Greek than of phonetics. Once, in the days when the Imperial Institute rose in South Kensington, and Joseph Chamberlain was booming the Empire, I induced the editor of a leading monthly review to commission an article from Sweet on the imperial importance of his subject. When it arrived, it contained nothing but a savagely derisive attack on a professor of language and literature whose chair Sweet regarded as proper to a phonetic expert only. The article, being libellous, had to be returned as impossible; and I had to renounce my dream of dragging its author into the limelight. When I met him afterwards, for the first time for many years, I found to my astonishment that he, who had been a quite tolerably presentable young man, had actually managed by sheer scorn to alter his personal appearance until he had become a sort of walking repudiation of Oxford and all its traditions. It must have been largely in his own despite that he was squeezed into something called a Readership of phonetics there. The future of phonetics rests probably with his pupils, who all swore by him; but nothing could bring the man himself into any sort of compliance with the university to which he nevertheless clung by divine right in an intensely Oxonian way. I daresay his papers, if he has left any, include some satires that may be published without too destructive results fifty years hence. He was, I believe, not in the least an ill-natured man: very much the opposite, I should say; but he would not suffer fools gladly; and to him all scholars who were not rabid phoneticians were fools.

Those who knew him will recognize in my third act the allusion to the Current Shorthand in which he used to write postcards. It may be acquired from a four and sixpenny manual published by the Clarendon Press. The postcards which Mrs Higgins describes are such as I have received from Sweet. I would decipher a sound which a cockney would represent by *zerr*, and a Frenchman by *seu*, and then write demanding with some heat what on earth it meant. Sweet, with boundless contempt for my stupidity, would reply that it not only meant but obviously was the word Result, as no other word containing that sound, and capable of making sense with the context, existed in any language spoken on earth. That less expert mortals should require fuller indications was beyond Sweet's patience. Therefore, though the whole point of his Current Shorthand is that it can express every sound in the language perfectly, vowels as well as consonants, and that your hand has to make no stroke except the easy and current ones with which you write m, n, and u, l, p, and q, scribbling them at whatever angle comes easiest to you, his unfortunate determination to make this remarkable and quite legible script serve also as a shorthand reduced it in his own practice to the most inscrutable of cryptograms. His true objective was the provision of a full, accurate, legible script for our language; but he was led past that by his contempt for the popular Pitman system of shorthand, which he called the Pitfall system. The triumph of Pitman was a triumph of business organization: there was a weekly paper to persuade you to learn Pitman: there were cheap textbooks and exercise books and transcripts of speeches for you to copy, and schools where experienced teachers coached you up to the necessary proficiency. Sweet could not organize his market in that fashion. He might as well have been the Sybil who tore up the leaves of prophecy that nobody would attend to. The four and sixpenny manual, mostly in his lithographed handwriting, that was never vulgarly advertized, may perhaps some day be taken up by a syndicate and pushed upon the public as The Times pushed the Encyclopædia Britannica; but until then it will certainly not prevail against Pitman. I have bought three copies of it during my lifetime; and I am informed by the publishers that its cloistered existence is still a steady and healthy one. I actually learned the system two several times; and yet the shorthand in which I am writing these lines is Pitman's. And the reason is, that my secretary cannot transcribe Sweet, having been perforce taught in the schools of Pitman. In America I could use the commercially organized Gregg shorthand, which has taken a hint from Sweet by making its letters writable (current, Sweet would have called them) instead of having to be geometrically drawn like Pitman's; but all these systems, including Sweet's, are spoilt by making them available for verbatim reporting, in which complete and exact spelling and word division are impossible. A complete and exact phonetic script is neither practicable nor necessary for ordinary use; but if we enlarge our alphabet to the Russian size, and make our spelling as phonetic as Spanish, the advance will be prodigious.

Pygmalion Higgins is not a portrait of Sweet, to whom the adventure of Eliza Doolittle would have been impossible; still, as will be seen, there are touches of Sweet in the play. With Higgins's physique and temperament Sweet might have set the Thames on fire. As it was, he impressed himself professionally on Europe to an extent that made his comparative personal obscurity, and the failure of Oxford to do justice to his eminence, a puzzle to foreign specialists in his subject. I do not blame Oxford, because I think Oxford is quite right in demanding a certain social amenity from its nurslings (heaven knows it is not exorbitant in its requirements!); for although I well know how hard it is for a man of genius with a seriously underrated subject to maintain serene and kindly relations with the men who underrate it, and who keep all the best places for less important subjects which they profess without originality and sometimes without much capacity for them, still, if he overwhelms them with wrath and disdain, he cannot expect them to heap honors on him.

Of the later generations of phoneticians I know little. Among them towered Robert Bridges, to whom perhaps Higgins may

8

owe his Miltonic sympathies, though here again I must disclaim all portraiture. But if the play makes the public aware that there are such people as phoneticians, and that they are among the most important people in England at present, it will serve its turn.

I wish to boast that Pygmalion has been an extremely successful play, both on stage and screen, all over Europe and North America as well as at home. It is so intensely and deliberately didactic, and its subject is esteemed so dry, that I delight in throwing it at the heads of the wiseacres who repeat the parrot cry that art should never be didactic. It goes to prove my contention that great art can never be anything else.

Finally, and for the encouragement of people troubled with accents that cut them off from all high employment, I may add that the change wrought by Professor Higgins in the flower-girl is neither impossible nor uncommon. The modern concierge's daughter who fulfils her ambition by playing the Queen of Spain in Ruy Blas at the Théâtre Français is only one of many thousands of men and women who have sloughed off their native dialects and acquired a new tongue. Our West End shop assistants and domestic servants are bi-lingual. But the thing has to be done scientifically, or the last state of the aspirant may be worse than the first. An honest slum dialect is more tolerable than the attempts of phonetically untaught persons to imitate the plutocracy. Ambitious flower-girls who read this play must not imagine that they can pass themselves off as fine ladies by untutored imitation. They must learn their alphabet over again, and different, from a phonetic expert. Imitation will only make them ridiculous.

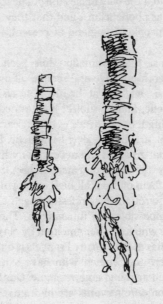

NOTE FOR TECHNICIANS. A complete representation of the play as printed for the first time in this edition is technically possible only on the cinema screen or on stages furnished with exceptionally elaborate machinery. For ordinary theatrical use the scenes separated by rows of asterisks are to be omitted.

In the dialogue an e upside down indicates the indefinite vowel, sometimes called obscure or neutral, for which, though it is one of the commonest sounds in English speech, our wretched alphabet has no letter.

PYGMALION

ACT ONE

London at 11.15 p.m. Torrents of heavy summer rain. Cab whistles blowing frantically in all directions. Pedestrians running for shelter into the portico of St Paul's church (not Wren's cathedral but Inigo Jones's church in Covent Garden vegetable market), among them a lady and her daughter in evening dress. All are peering out gloomily at the rain, except one man with his back turned to the rest, wholly preoccupied with a notebook in which he is writing.

The church clock strikes the first quarter.

THE DAUGHTER [*in the space between the central pillars, close to the one on her left*] I'm getting chilled to the bone. What can Freddy be doing all this time? He's been gone twenty minutes.

THE MOTHER [*on her daughter's right*] Not so long. But he ought to have got us a cab by this.

A BYSTANDER [*on the lady's right*] He wont get no cab not until half-past eleven, missus, when they come back after dropping their theatre fares.

THE MOTHER. But we must have a cab. We cant stand here until half-past eleven. It's too bad.

THE BYSTANDER. Well it aint my fault, missus.

THE DAUGHTER. If Freddy had a bit of gumption, he would have got one at the theatre door.

THE MOTHER. What could he have done, poor boy?

THE DAUGHTER. Other people get cabs. Why couldnt he?

Freddy rushes in out of the rain from the Southampton Street side, and comes between them closing a dripping umbrella. He is a young man of twenty, in evening dress, very wet round the ankles.

THE DAUGHTER. Well, havnt you got a cab?

FREDDY. Theres not one to be had for love or money.

THE MOTHER. Oh, Freddy, there must be one. You cant have tried.

THE DAUGHTER. It's too tiresome. Do you expect us to go and get one ourselves?

FREDDY. I tell you theyre all engaged. The rain was so sudden: nobody was prepared; and everybody had to take a cab. Ive been to Charing Cross one way and nearly to Ludgate Circus the other; and they were all engaged.

THE MOTHER. Did you try Trafalgar Square?

FREDDY. There wasnt one at Trafalgar Square.

THE DAUGHTER. Did you try?

FREDDY. I tried as far as Charing Cross Station. Did you expect me to walk to Hammersmith?

THE DAUGHTER. You havnt tried at all.

THE MOTHER. You really are very helpless, Freddy. Go again; and dont come back until you have found a cab.

FREDDY. I shall simply get soaked for nothing.

THE DAUGHTER. And what about us? Are we to stay here all night in this draught, with next to nothing on? You selfish pig –

FREDDY. Oh, very well: I'll go, I'll go. [*He opens his umbrella and dashes off Strandwards, but comes into collision with a flower girl who is hurrying in for shelter, knocking her basket out of her hands. A blinding flash of lightning, followed instantly by a rattling peal of thunder, orchestrates the incident*].

THE FLOWER GIRL. Nah then, Freddy: look wh' y' gowin, deah.

FREDDY. Sorry [*he rushes off*].

THE FLOWER GIRL [*picking up her scattered flowers and replacing them in the basket*] Theres menners f' yer! Tə-oo banches o voylets trod into the mad. [*She sits down on the plinth of the column, sorting her flowers, on the lady's right. She is not at all a romantic figure. She is perhaps eighteen, perhaps twenty, hardly older. She wears a little sailor hat of black straw that has long been exposed to the dust and soot of London and has seldom if ever been brushed. Her hair needs washing rather badly: its mousy color can hardly be natural. She wears a shoddy black coat that reaches nearly to her knees and is shaped to her waist. She has a brown skirt with a coarse apron. Her boots are much the worse for wear. She is no doubt as clean as she can afford to be; but compared to the ladies she is very dirty. Her features are no worse than theirs; but their condition leaves something to be desired; and she needs the services of a dentist].*

THE MOTHER. How do you know that my son's name is Freddy, pray?

THE FLOWER GIRL. Ow, eez, yə-ooa san, is e? Wal, fewd dan y' d-ooty bawmz a mather should, eed now bettern to spawl a pore gel's flahrzn than ran awy athaht pyin. Will ye-oo py me f'them? [*Here, with apologies, this desperate attempt to*

16

represent her dialect without a phonetic alphabet must be abandoned as unintelligible outside London].

THE DAUGHTER. Do nothing of the sort, mother. The idea!

THE MOTHER. Please allow me, Clara. Have you any pennies?

THE DAUGHTER. No. Ive nothing smaller than sixpence.

THE FLOWER GIRL [*hopefully*] I can give you change for a tanner, kind lady.

THE MOTHER [*to Clara*] Give it to me. [*Clara parts reluctantly*]. Now [*to the girl*] This is for your flowers.

THE FLOWER GIRL. Thank you kindly, lady.

THE DAUGHTER. Make her give you the change. These things are only a penny a bunch.

THE MOTHER. Do hold your tongue, Clara. [*To the girl*] You can keep the change.

THE FLOWER GIRL. Oh, thank you, lady.

THE MOTHER. Now tell me how you know that young gentleman's name.

THE FLOWER GIRL. I didnt.

THE MOTHER. I heard you call him by it. Dont try to deceive me.

THE FLOWER GIRL [*protesting*] Who's trying to deceive you? I called him Freddy or Charlie same as you might yourself if you was talking to a stranger and wished to be pleasant.

THE DAUGHTER. Sixpence thrown away! Really, mamma, you might have spared Freddy that. [*She retreats in disgust behind the pillar*].

An elderly gentleman of the amiable military type rushes into the shelter, and closes a dripping umbrella. He is in the same plight as Freddy, very wet about the ankles. He is in evening dress, with a light overcoat. He takes the place left vacant by the daughter.

THE GENTLEMAN. Phew!

THE MOTHER [*to the gentleman*] Oh, sir, is there any sign of its stopping?

THE GENTLEMAN. I'm afraid not. It started worse than ever about two minutes ago [*he goes to the plinth beside the flower girl; puts up his foot on it; and stoops to turn down his trouser ends*].

THE MOTHER. Oh dear! [*She retires sadly and joins her daughter*].

THR FLOWER GIRL [*taking advantage of the military gentleman's proximity to establish friendly relations with him*] If it's worse, it's a sign it's nearly over. So cheer up, Captain; and buy a flower off a poor girl.

THE GENTLEMAN. I'm sorry. I havnt any change.

THE FLOWER GIRL. I can give you change, Captain.

THE GENTLEMAN. For a sovereign? Ive nothing less.

THE FLOWER GIRL. Garn! Oh do buy a flower off me, Captain. I can change half-a-crown. Take this for tuppence.

THE GENTLEMAN. Now dont be troublesome: theres a good girl. [*Trying his pockets*] I really havnt any change – Stop: heres three hapence, if thats any use to you [*he retreats to the other pillar*].

THE FLOWER GIRL [*disappointed, but thinking three halfpence better than nothing*] Thank you, sir.

THE BYSTANDER [*to the girl*] You be careful: give him a flower for it. Theres a bloke here behind taking down every blessed word youre saying. [*All turn to the man who is taking notes*].

THE FLOWER GIRL [*springing up terrified*] I aint done nothing wrong by speaking to the gentleman. Ive a right to sell flowers if I keep off the kerb. [*Hysterically*] I'm a respectable girl: so

help me, I never spoke to him except to ask him to buy a flower off me.

General hubbub, mostly sympathetic to the flower girl, but deprecating her excessive sensibility. Cries of Dont start hollerin. Who's hurting you? Nobody's going to touch you. Whats the good of fussing? Steady on. Easy easy, etc., *come from the elderly staid spectators, who pat her comfortingly. Less patient ones bid her shut her head, or ask her roughly what is wrong with her. A remoter group, not knowing what the matter is, crowd in and increase the noise with question and answer*: Whats the row? What-she-do? Where is he? A tec taking her down. What! him? Yes: him over there: Took money off the gentleman, etc.

THE FLOWER GIRL [*breaking through them to the gentleman, crying wildly*] Oh, sir, dont let him charge me. You dunno what it means to me. Theyll take away my character and drive me on the streets for speaking to gentlemen. They –

THE NOTE TAKER [*coming forward on her right, the rest crowding after him*] There! there! there! there! who's hurting you, you silly girl? What do you take me for?

THE BYSTANDER. It's aw rawt: e's a genleman: look at his
bə-oots. [*Explaining to the note taker*] She thought you was
a copper's nark, sir.

THE NOTE TAKER [*with quick interest*] Whats a copper's nark?

THE BYSTANDER [*inapt at definition*] It's a – well, it's a copper's
nark, as you might say. What else would you call it? A sort
of informer.

THE FLOWER GIRL [*still hysterical*] I take my Bible oath I never said a word –

THE NOTE TAKER [*overbearing but good-humored*] Oh, shut up, shut up. Do I look like a policeman?

THE FLOWER GIRL [*far from reassured*] Then what did you take down my words for? How do I know whether you took me down right? You just shew me what youve wrote about me. [*The note taker opens his book and holds it steadily under her nose, though the pressure of the mob trying to read it over his shoulders would upset a weaker man*]. Whats that? That aint proper writing. I cant read that.

THE NOTE TAKER. I can. [*Reads, reproducing her pronunciation exactly*] 'Cheer ap, Keptin; n' baw ya flahr orf a pore gel.'

THE FLOWER GIRL [*much distressed*] It's because I called him Captain. I meant no harm. [*To the gentleman*] Oh, sir, dont let him lay a charge agen me for a word like that. You –

THE GENTLEMAN. Charge! I make no charge. [*To the note taker*] Really, sir, if you are a detective, you need not begin protecting me against molestation by young women until I ask you. Anybody could see that the girl meant no harm.

THE BYSTANDERS GENERALLY [*demonstrating against police espionage*] Course they could. What business is it of yours? You mind your own affairs. He wants promotion, he does. Taking down people's words! Girl never said a word to him. What harm if she did? Nice thing a girl cant shelter from

the rain without being insulted, etc., etc., etc. [*She is conducted by the more sympathetic demonstrators back to her plinth, where she resumes her seat and struggles with her emotion*].

THE BYSTANDER. He aint a tec. He's a blooming busy-body: thats what he is. I tell you, look at his bə-oots.

THE NOTE TAKER [*turning on him genially*] And how are all your people down at Selsey?

THE BYSTANDER [*suspiciously*] Who told you my people come from Selsey?

THE NOTE TAKER. Never you mind. They did. [*To the girl*] How do you come to be up so far east? You were born in Lisson Grove.

THE FLOWER GIRL [*appalled*] Oh, what harm is there in my leaving Lisson Grove? It wasnt fit for a pig to live in; and I had to pay four-and-six a week. [*In tears*] Oh, boo – hoo – oo –

THE NOTE TAKER. Live where you like; but stop that noise.

THE GENTLEMAN [*to the girl*] Come, come! he cant touch you: you have a right to live where you please.

A SARCASTIC BYSTANDER [*thrusting himself between the note taker and the gentleman*] Park Lane, for instance. I'd like to go into the Housing Question with you, I would.

THE FLOWER GIRL [*subsiding into a brooding melancholy over her basket, and talking very low-spiritedly to herself*] I'm a good girl, I am.

THE SARCASTIC BYSTANDER [*not attending to her*] Do you know where I come from?

THE NOTE TAKER [*promptly*] Hoxton.

Titterings. Popular interest in the note taker's performance increases.

THE SARCASTIC ONE [*amazed*] Well, who said I didnt? Bly me! you know everything, you do.

THE FLOWER GIRL [*still nursing her sense of injury*] Aint no call to meddle with me, he aint.

THE BYSTANDER [*to her*] Of course he aint. Dont you stand it from him. [*To the note taker*] See here: what call have you to know about people what never offered to meddle with you?

THE FLOWER GIRL. Let him say what he likes. I dont want to have no truck with him.

THE BYSTANDER. You take us for dirt under your feet, dont you? Catch you taking liberties with a gentleman!

THE SARCASTIC BYSTANDER. Yes: tell him where he come from if you want to go fortune-telling.

THE NOTE TAKER. Cheltenham, Harrow, Cambridge, and India.

THE GENTLEMAN. Quite right.

Great laughter. Reaction in the note taker's favor. Exclamations of He knows all about it. Told him proper. Hear him tell the toff where he come from? *etc.*

THE GENTLEMAN. May I ask, sir, do you do this for your living at a music hall?

THE NOTE TAKER. I've thought of that. Perhaps I shall some day.

The rain has stopped; and the persons on the outside of the crowd begin to drop off.

THE FLOWER GIRL [*resenting the reaction*] He's no gentleman, he aint, to interfere with a poor girl.

THE DAUGHTER [*out of patience, pushing her way rudely to the front and displacing the gentleman, who politely retires to the other side of the pillar*] What on earth is Freddy doing? I shall get pneumownia if I stay in this draught any longer.

THE NOTE TAKER [*to himself, hastily making a note of her pronunciation of 'monia'*] Earlscourt.

THE DAUGHTER [*violently*] Will you please keep your impertinent remarks to yourself.

THE NOTE TAKER. Did I say that out loud? I didnt mean to. I beg your pardon. Your mother's Epsom, unmistakeably.

THE MOTHER [*advancing between the daughter and the note taker*] How very curious! I was brought up in Largelady Park, near Epsom.

THE NOTE TAKER [*uproariously amused*] Ha! ha! what a devil of a name! Excuse me. [*To the daughter*] You want a cab, do you?

THE DAUGHTER. Dont dare speak to me.

THE MOTHER. Oh, please, please, Clara. [*Her daughter repudiates her with an angry shrug and retires haughtily*]. We should be so grateful to you, sir, if you found us a cab. [*The note taker produces a whistle*]. Oh, thank you. [*She joins her daughter*].

The note taker blows a piercing blast.

THE SARCASTIC BYSTANDER. There! I knowed he was a plainclothes copper.

THE BYSTANDER. That aint a police whistle: thats a sporting whistle.

THE FLOWER GIRL [*still preoccupied with her wounded feelings*] He's no right to take away my character. My character is the same to me as any lady's.

THE NOTE TAKER. I dont know whether youve noticed it; but the rain stopped about two minutes ago.

THE BYSTANDER. So it has. Why didnt you say so before? and us losing our time listening to your silliness! [*He walks off towards the Strand*].

THE SARCASTIC BYSTANDER. I can tell where you come from. You come from Anwell. Go back there.

THE NOTE TAKER [*helpfully*] Hanwell.

THE SARCASTIC BYSTANDER [*affecting great distinction of speech*] Thenk you, teacher. Haw haw! So long [*he touches his hat with mock respect and strolls off*].

THE FLOWER GIRL. Frightening people like that! How would he like it himself?

THE MOTHER. It's quite fine now, Clara. We can walk to a motor bus. Come. [*She gathers her skirts above her ankles and hurries off towards the Strand*].

THE DAUGHTER. But the cab — [*her mother is out of hearing*]. Oh, how tiresome! [*She follows angrily*].

All the rest have gone except the note taker, the gentleman, and the flower girl, who sits arranging her basket, and still pitying herself in murmurs.

THE FLOWER GIRL. Poor girl! Hard enough for her to live without being worrited and chivied.

THE GENTLEMAN [*returning to his former place on the note taker's left*] How do you do it, if I may ask?

THE NOTE TAKER. Simply phonetics. The science of speech. Thats my profession: also my hobby. Happy is the man who can make a living by his hobby! You can spot an Irishman or a Yorkshireman by his brogue. *I* can place any man within six miles. I can place him within two miles in London. Sometimes within two streets.

THE FLOWER GIRL. Ought to be ashamed of himself, unmanly coward!

THE GENTLEMAN. But is there a living in that?

THE NOTE TAKER. Oh, yes. Quite a fat one. This is an age of upstarts. Men begin in Kentish Town with £80 a year, and end in Park Lane with a hundred thousand. They want to drop Kentish Town; but they give themselves away every time they open their mouths. Now I can teach them –

THE FLOWER GIRL. Let him mind his own business and leave a poor girl –

THE NOTE TAKER [*explosively*] Woman: cease this detestable boohooing instantly; or else seek the shelter of some other place of worship.

THE FLOWER GIRL [*with feeble defiance*] Ive a right to be here if I like, same as you.

THE NOTE TAKER. A woman who utters such depressing and disgusting sounds has no right to be anywhere – no right to live. Remember that you are a human being with a soul and the divine gift of articulate speech: that your native language is the language of Shakespear and Milton and The Bible; and dont sit there crooning like a bilious pigeon.

THE FLOWER GIRL [*quite overwhelmed, looking up at him in mingled wonder and deprecation without daring to raise her head*] Ah-ah-ah-ow-ow-ow-oo!

THE NOTE TAKER [*whipping out his book*] Heavens! what a sound! [*He writes; then holds out the book and reads, reproducing her vowels exactly*] Ah-ah-ah-ow-ow-ow-oo!

THE FLOWER GIRL [*tickled by the performance, and laughing in spite of herself*] Garn!

THE NOTE TAKER. You see this creature with her kerbstone English: the English that will keep her in the gutter to the end of her days. Well, sir, in three months I could pass that girl off as a duchess at an ambassador's garden party. I could even get her a place as lady's maid or shop assistant, which requires better English.

THE FLOWER GIRL. What's that you say?

THE NOTE TAKER. Yes, you squashed cabbage leaf, you disgrace to the noble architecture of these columns, you incarnate insult to the English language: I could pass you off as the Queen of Sheba. [*To the Gentleman*] Can you believe that?

THE GENTLEMAN. Of course I can. I am myself a student of Indian dialects; and –

THE NOTE TAKER [*eagerly*] Are you? Do you know Colonel Pickering, the author of Spoken Sanscrit?

THE GENTLEMAN. I am Colonel Pickering. Who are you?

THE NOTE TAKER. Henry Higgins, author of Higgins's Universal Alphabet.

PICKERING [*with enthusiasm*] I came from India to meet you.

HIGGINS. I was going to India to meet you.

PICKERING. Where do you live?

HIGGINS. 27A Wimpole Street. Come and see me tomorrow.

PICKERING. I'm at the Carlton. Come with me now and lets have a jaw over some supper.

HIGGINS. Right you are.

THE FLOWER GIRL [*to Pickering, as he passes her*] Buy a flower, kind gentleman. I'm short for my lodging.

PICKERING. I really havnt any change. I'm sorry [*he goes away*].

HIGGINS [*shocked at the girl's mendacity*] Liar. You said you could change half-a-crown.

THE FLOWER GIRL [*rising in desperation*] You ought to be stuffed with nails, you ought. [*Flinging the basket at his feet*] Take the whole blooming basket for sixpence.

The church clock strikes the second quarter.

HIGGINS [*hearing in it the voice of God, rebuking him for his Pharisaic want of charity to the poor girl*] A reminder. [*He raises his hat solemnly; then throws a handful of money into the basket and follows Pickering*].

THE FLOWER GIRL [*picking up a half-crown*] Ah-ow-ooh! [*Picking up a couple of florins*] Aaah-ow-ooh! [*Picking up several coins*] Aaaaaah-ow-ooh! [*Picking up a half-sovereign*] Aaaaaaaaaaaah-ow-ooh!!!

FREDDY [*springing out of a taxicab*] Got one at last. Hallo! [*To the girl*] Where are the two ladies that were here?

THE FLOWER GIRL. They walked to the bus when the rain stopped.

FREDDY. And left me with a cab on my hands! Damnation!

THE FLOWER GIRL [*with grandeur*] Never mind, young man. I'm going home in a taxi. [*She sails off to the cab. The driver puts his hand behind him and holds the door firmly shut against her. Quite understanding his mistrust, she shews him her handful of money*]. A taxi fare aint no object to me, Charlie. [*He grins and opens the door*]. Here. What about the basket?

THE TAXIMAN. Give it here. Tuppence extra.

LIZA. No: I dont want nobody to see it. [*She crushes it into the cab and gets in, continuing the conversation through the window*] Goodbye, Freddy.

FREDDY [*dazedly raising his hat*] Goodbye.

TAXIMAN. Where to?

LIZA. Bucknam Pellis [Buckingham Palace].

TAXIMAN. What d'ye mean – Bucknam Pellis?

LIZA. Dont you know where it is? In the Green Park, where the King lives. Goodbye, Freddy. Dont let me keep you standing there. Goodbye.

FREDDY. Goodbye. [*He goes*].

TAXIMAN. Here? Whats this about Bucknam Pellis? What business have you at Bucknam Pellis?

LIZA. Of course I havnt none. But I wasnt going to let him know that. You drive me home.

29

TAXIMAN. And wheres home?

LIZA. Angel Court, Drury Lane, next Meiklejohn's oil shop.

TAXIMAN. That sounds more like it, Judy. [*He drives off*].

*   *   *

Let us follow the taxi to the entrance to Angel Court, a narrow little archway between two shops, one of them Meiklejohn's oil shop. When it stops there, Eliza gets out, dragging her basket with her.

LIZA. How much?

TAXIMAN [*indicating the taximeter*] Cant you read? A shilling.

LIZA. A shilling for two minutes!!

TAXIMAN. Two minutes or ten: it's all the same.

LIZA. Well, I dont call it right.

TAXIMAN. Ever been in a taxi before?

LIZA [*with dignity*] Hundreds and thousands of times, young man.

TAXIMAN [*laughing at her*] Good for you, Judy. Keep the shilling, darling, with best love from all at home. Good luck! [*He drives off*].

LIZA [*humiliated*] Impidence!

She picks up the basket and trudges up the alley with it to her

*lodging: a small room with very old wall paper hanging loose in
the damp places. A broken pane in the window is mended with
paper. A portrait of a popular actor and a fashion plate of ladies'
dresses, all wildly beyond poor Eliza's means, both torn from
newspapers, are pinned up on the wall. A birdcage hangs in the
window; but its tenant died long ago: it remains as a memorial
only.*

*These are the only visible luxuries: the rest is the irreducible
minimum of poverty's needs: a wretched bed heaped with all sorts
of coverings that have any warmth in them, a draped packing case
with a basin and jug on it and a little looking glass over it, a chair
and table, the refuse of some suburban kitchen, and an American
alarum clock on the shelf above the unused fireplace: the whole
lighted with a gas lamp with a penny in the slot meter. Rent: four
shillings a week.*

Here Eliza, chronically weary, but too excited to go to bed,
sits, counting her new riches and dreaming and planning
what to do with them, until the gas goes out, when she enjoys
for the first time the sensation of being able to put in another
penny without grudging it. This prodigal mood does not ex-
tinguish her gnawing sense of the need for economy
sufficiently to prevent her from calculating that she can dream

and plan in bed more cheaply and warmly than sitting up without a fire. So she takes off her shawl and skirt and adds them to the miscellaneous bedclothes. Then she kicks off her shoes and gets into bed without any further change.

ACT TWO

Next day at 11 *a.m. Higgins's laboratory in Wimpole Street. It is a room on the first floor, looking on the street, and was meant for the drawing room. The double doors are in the middle of the back wall; and persons entering find in the corner to their right two tall file cabinets at right angles to one another against the wall. In this corner stands a flat writing-table, on which are a phonograph, a laryngoscope, a row of tiny organ pipes with a bellows, a set of lamp chimneys for singing flames with burners attached to a gas plug in the wall by an indiarubber tube, several tuning-forks of different sizes, a life-size image of half a human head, shewing in section the vocal organs, and a box containing a supply of wax cylinders for the phonograph.*

Further down the room, on the same side, is a fireplace, with a comfortable leather-covered easy-chair at the side of the hearth nearest the door, and a coal-scuttle. There is a clock on the mantelpiece. Between the fireplace and the phonograph table is a stand for newspapers.

On the other side of the central door, to the left of the visitor, is a cabinet of shallow drawers. On it is a telephone and the telephone directory. The corner beyond, and most of the side wall, is occupied by a grand piano, with the keyboard at the end furthest from the door, and a bench for the player extending the full length of the keyboard. On the piano is a dessert dish heaped with fruit and sweets, mostly chocolates.

The middle of the room is clear. Besides the easy-chair, the piano bench, and two chairs at the phonograph table, there is one stray chair. It stands near the fireplace. On the walls, engravings: mostly Piranesis and mezzotint portraits. No paintings.

Pickering is seated at the table, putting down some cards and a tuning-fork which he has been using. Higgins is standing up near him, closing two or three file drawers which are hanging out. He appears in the morning light as a robust, vital, appetizing sort of man of forty or thereabouts, dressed in a professional-looking black frock-coat with a white linen collar and black silk tie. He is of the energetic scientific type, heartily, even violently interested in everything that can be studied as a scientific subject, and careless about himself and other people, including their feelings. He is, in fact, but for his years and size, rather like a very impetuous baby 'taking notice' eagerly and loudly, and requiring almost as much watching to keep him out of unintended mischief. His manner varies from genial bullying when he is in a good humor to stormy petulance when anything goes wrong; but he is so entirely frank and void of malice that he remains likeable even in his least reasonable moments.

HIGGINS [*as he shuts the last drawer*] Well, I think thats the whole show.

PICKERING. It's really amazing. I havnt taken half of it in, you know.

HIGGINS. Would you like to go over any of it again?

PICKERING [*rising and coming to the fireplace, where he plants himself with his back to the fire*] No, thank you: not now. I'm quite done up for this morning.

HIGGINS [*following him, and standing beside him on his left*] Tired of listening to sounds?

PICKERING. Yes. It's a fearful strain. I rather fancied myself because I can pronounce twenty-four distinct vowel sounds; but your hundred and thirty beat me. I cant hear a bit of difference between most of them.

HIGGINS [*chuckling, and going over to the piano to eat sweets*] Oh, that comes with practice. You hear no difference at first; but you keep on listening, and presently you find theyre

all as different as A from B. [*Mrs Pearce looks in: she is Higgins's housekeeper*]. Whats the matter?

MRS PEARCE [*hesitating, evidently perplexed*] A young woman asks to see you, sir.

HIGGINS. A young woman! What does she want?

MRS PEARCE. Well, sir, she says youll be glad to see her
when you know what she's come
about. She's quite a common
girl, sir. Very common indeed. I
should have sent her away, only
I thought perhaps you wanted
her to talk into your machines. I
hope Ive not done wrong; but
really you see such queer people
sometimes – youll excuse me, I'm
sure, sir –

HIGGINS. Oh, thats all right, Mrs
Pearce. Has she an interesting
accent?

MRS PEARCE. Oh, something dreadful, sir, really. I dont know
how you can take an interest in it.

HIGGINS [*to Pickering*] Lets have her up. Shew her up, Mrs
Pearce [*he rushes across to his working table and picks out a
cylinder to use on the phonograph*].

MRS PEARCE [*only half resigned to it*] Very well, sir. It's for
you to say. [*She goes downstairs*].

HIGGINS. This is rather a bit of luck. I'll shew you how I make
records. We'll set her talking; and I'll take it down first in
Bell's Visible Speech; then in broad Romic; and then we'll
get her on the phonograph so that you can turn her on as
often as you like with the written transcript before you.

MRS PEARCE [*returning*] This is the young woman, sir.

*The flower girl enters in state. She has a hat with three ostrich
feathers, orange, sky-blue, and red. She has a nearly clean apron
and the shoddy coat has been tidied a little. The pathos of this
deplorable figure, with its innocent vanity and consequential air,
touches Pickering, who has already straightened himself in the
presence of Mrs Pearce. But as to Higgins, the only distinction he
makes between men and women is that when he is neither bullying
nor exclaiming to the heavens against some featherweight cross,
he coaxes women as a child coaxes its nurse when it wants to get
anything out of her.*

HIGGINS [*brusquely, recognizing her with unconcealed disappointment, and at once, babylike, making an intolerable grievance of it*] Why, this is the girl I jotted down last night. She's no use: Ive got all the records I want of the Lisson Grove lingo; and

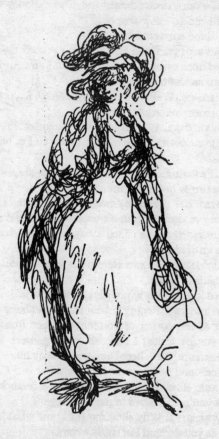

I'm not going to waste another cylinder on it. [*To the girl*] Be off with you: I dont want you.

THE FLOWER GIRL. Dont you be so saucy. You aint heard what I come for yet. [*To Mrs Pearce, who is waiting at the door for further instructions*] Did you tell him I come in a taxi?

MRS PEARCE. Nonsense, girl! what do you think a gentleman like Mr Higgins cares what you came in?

THE FLOWER GIRL. Oh, we are proud! He aint above giving lessons, not him: I heard him say so. Well, I aint come here to ask for any compliment; and if my money's not good enough I can go elsewhere.

HIGGINS. Good enough for what?

THE FLOWER GIRL. Good enough for yə-oo. Now you know, dont you? I'm coming to have lessons, I am. And to pay for em tə-oo: make no mistake.

HIGGINS [stupent] Well!!! [Recovering his breath with a gasp] What do you expect me to say to you?

THE FLOWER GIRL. Well, if you was a gentleman, you might ask me to sit down, I think. Dont I tell you I'm bringing you business?

HIGGINS. Pickering: shall we ask this baggage to sit down, or shall we throw her out of the window?

THE FLOWER GIRL [running away in terror to the piano, where she turns at bay] Ah-ah-oh-ow-ow-ow-oo! [Wounded and whimpering] I wont be called a baggage when Ive offered to pay like any lady.

Motionless, the two men stare at her from the other side of the room, amazed.

PICKERING [gently] But what is it you want?

THE FLOWER GIRL. I want to be a lady in a flower shop stead of sellin at the corner of Tottenham Court Road. But they wont take me unless I can talk more genteel. He said he could teach me. Well, here I am ready to pay him – not asking any favor – and he treats me zif I was dirt.

MRS PEARCE. How can you be such a foolish ignorant girl as to think you could afford to pay Mr Higgins?

THE FLOWER GIRL. Why shouldnt I? I know what lessons cost as well as you do; and I'm ready to pay.

HIGGINS. How much?

THE FLOWER GIRL [coming back to him, triumphant] Now youre talking! I thought youd come off it when you saw a chance of getting back a bit of what you chucked at me last night. [Confidentially] Youd had a drop in, hadnt you?

HIGGINS [*peremptorily*] Sit down.

THE FLOWER GIRL. Oh, if youre going to make a compliment of it –

HIGGINS [*thundering at her*] Sit down.

MRS PEARCE [*severely*] Sit down, girl. Do as youre told.

THE FLOWER GIRL. Ah-ah-ah-ow-ow-oo! [*She stands, half rebellious, half-bewildered*].

PICKERING [*very courteous*] Wont you sit down? [*He places the stray chair near the hearthrug between himself and Higgins*].

LIZA [*coyly*] Dont mind if I do. [*She sits down. Pickering returns to the hearthrug*].

HIGGINS. Whats your name?

THE FLOWER GIRL. Liza Doolittle.

HIGGINS [*declaiming gravely*]

> Eliza, Elizabeth, Betsy and Bess,
>   They went to the woods to get a bird's nes':

PICKERING. They found a nest with four eggs in it:

HIGGINS. They took one apiece, and left three in it.

> *They laugh heartily at their own fun.*

LIZA. Oh, dont be silly.

MRS PEARCE [*placing herself behind Eliza's chair*] You mustnt speak to the gentleman like that.

LIZA. Well, why wont he speak sensible to me?

HIGGINS. Come back to business. How much do you propose to pay me for the lessons?

LIZA. Oh, I know whats right. A lady friend of mine gets French lessons for eighteenpence an hour from a real French gentleman. Well, you wouldnt have the face to ask me the same for teaching me my own language as you would for French; so I wont give more than a shilling. Take it or leave it.

HIGGINS [*walking up and down the room, rattling his keys and his cash in his pockets*] You know, Pickering, if you consider a shilling, not as a simple shilling, but as a percentage of this girl's income, it works out as fully equivalent to sixty or seventy guineas from a millionaire.

PICKERING. How so?

HIGGINS. Figure it out. A millionaire has about £150 a day. She earns about half-a-crown.

LIZA [*haughtily*] Who told you I only –

HIGGINS [*continuing*] She offers me two-fifths of her day's income for a lesson. Two-fifths of a millionaire's income for a day would be somewhere about £60. It's handsome. By George, it's enormous! it's the biggest offer I ever had.

LIZA [*rising, terrified*] Sixty pounds! What are you talking about? I never offered you sixty pounds. Where would I get –

HIGGINS. Hold your tongue.

LIZA [*weeping*] But I aint got sixty pounds. Oh –

MRS PEARCE. Dont cry, you silly girl. Sit down. Nobody is going to touch your money.

HIGGINS. Somebody is going to touch you, with a broomstick, if you dont stop snivelling. Sit down.

LIZA [*obeying slowly*] Ah-ah-ah-ow-oo-o! One would think you was my father.

HIGGINS. If I decide to teach you, I'll be worse than two fathers to you. Here [*he offers her his silk handkerchief*]!

LIZA. Whats this for?

HIGGINS. To wipe your eyes. To wipe any part of your face that feels moist. Remember: thats your handkerchief; and thats your sleeve. Dont mistake the one for the other if you wish to become a lady in a shop.

  Liza, utterly bewildered, stares helplessly at him.

MRS PEARCE. It's no use talking to her like that, Mr Higgins: she doesnt understand you. Besides, youre quite wrong: she doesnt do it that way at all [*she takes the handkerchief*].

LIZA [*snatching it*] Here! You give me that handkerchief. He gev it to me, not to you.

PICKERING [*laughing*] He did. I think it must be regarded as her property, Mrs Pearce.

MRS PEARCE [*resigning herself*] Serve you right, Mr Higgins.

PICKERING. Higgins: I'm interested. What about the ambassador's garden party? I'll say youre the greatest teacher alive if you make that good. I'll bet you all the expenses of the experiment you cant do it. And I'll pay for the lessons.

LIZA. Oh, you are real good. Thank you, Captain.

HIGGINS [*tempted, looking at her*] It's almost irresistible. She's so deliciously low – so horribly dirty –

LIZA [*protesting extremely*] Ah-ah-ah-ah-ow-ow-oo-oo!!! I aint dirty: I washed my face and hands afore I come, I did.

PICKERING. Youre certainly not going to turn her head with flattery, Higgins.

MRS PEARCE [*uneasy*] Oh, dont say that, sir: theres more ways than one of turning a girl's head; and nobody can do it better than Mr Higgins, though he may not always mean it. I do hope, sir, you wont encourage him to do anything foolish.

HIGGINS [*becoming excited as the idea grows on him*] What is life but a series of inspired follies? The difficulty is to find them to do. Never lose a chance: it doesnt come every day. I shall make a duchess of this draggletailed guttersnipe.

LIZA [*strongly deprecating this view of her*] Ah-ah-ah-ow-ow-oo!

HIGGINS [*carried away*] Yes: in six months – in three if she has a good ear and a quick tongue – I'll take her anywhere and pass her off as anything. We'll start today: now! this moment! Take her away and clean her, Mrs Pearce. Monkey Brand, if it wont come off any other way. Is there a good fire in the kitchen?

MRS PEARCE [*protesting*] Yes; but –

HIGGINS [*storming on*] Take all her clothes off and burn them. Ring up Whiteley or somebody for new ones. Wrap her up in brown paper til they come.

LIZA. Youre no gentleman, youre not, to talk of such things. I'm a good girl, I am; and I know what the like of you are, I do.

HIGGINS. We want none of your Lisson Grove prudery here, young woman. Youve got to learn to behave like a duchess. Take her away, Mrs Pearce. If she gives you any trouble, wallop her.

LIZA [*springing up and running between Pickering and Mrs Pearce for protection*] No! I'll call the police, I will.

MRS PEARCE. But Ive no place to put her.

HIGGINS. Put her in the dustbin.

LIZA. Ah-ah-ah-ow-ow-oo!

PICKERING. Oh come, Higgins! be reasonable.

MRS PEARCE [*resolutely*] You must be reasonable, Mr Higgins: really you must. You cant walk over everybody like this.

Higgins, thus scolded, subsides. The hurricane is succeeded by a zephyr of amiable surprise.

HIGGINS [*with professional exquisiteness of modulation*] I walk over everybody! My dear Mrs Pearce, my dear Pickering, I never had the slightest intention of walking over anyone. All I propose is that we should be kind to this poor girl. We must help her to prepare and fit herself for her new station in life. If I did not express myself clearly it was because I did not wish to hurt her delicacy, or yours.

Liza, reassured, steals back to her chair.

MRS PEARCE [*to Pickering*] Well, did you ever hear anything like that, sir?

PICKERING [*laughing heartily*] Never, Mrs Pearce: never.

HIGGINS [*patiently*] Whats the matter?

MRS PEARCE. Well, the matter is, sir, that you cant take a girl up like that as if you were picking up a pebble on the beach.

HIGGINS. Why not?

MRS PEARCE. Why not! But you dont know anything about her. What about her parents? She may be married.

LIZA. Garn!

HIGGINS. There! As the girl very properly says, Garn! Married indeed! Dont you know that a woman of that class looks a worn out drudge of fifty a year after she's married?

LIZA. Whood marry me?

HIGGINS [*suddenly resorting to the most thrillingly beautiful low tones in his best elocutionary style*] By George, Eliza, the streets will be strewn with the bodies of men shooting themselves for your sake before Ive done with you.

MRS PEARCE. Nonsense, sir. You mustnt talk like that to her.

LIZA [*rising and squaring herself determinedly*] I'm going away. He's off his chump, he is. I dont want no balmies teaching me.

HIGGINS [*wounded in his tenderest point by her insensibility to his elocution*] Oh, indeed! I'm mad, am I? Very well, Mrs Pearce: you neednt order the new clothes for her. Throw her out.

LIZA [*whimpering*] Nah-ow. You got no right to touch me.

MRS PEARCE. You see now what comes of being saucy. [*Indicating the door*] This way, please.

LIZA [*almost in tears*] I didnt want no clothes. I wouldnt have taken them [*she throws away the handkerchief*]. I can buy my own clothes.

HIGGINS [*deftly retrieving the handkerchief and intercepting her on her reluctant way to the door*] Youre an ungrateful wicked girl. This is my return for offering to take you out of the gutter and dress you beautifully and make a lady of you.

MRS PEARCE. Stop, Mr Higgins. I wont allow it. It's you that are wicked. Go home to your parents, girl; and tell them to take better care of you.

LIZA. I aint got no parents. They told me I was big enough to earn my own living and turned me out.

MRS PEARCE. Wheres your mother?

LIZA. I aint got no mother. Her that turned me out was my sixth stepmother. But I done without them. And I'm a good girl, I am.

HIGGINS. Very well, then, what on earth is all this fuss about? The girl doesnt belong to anybody – is no use to anybody but me. [*He goes to Mrs Pearce and begins coaxing*]. You can adopt her, Mrs Pearce: I'm sure a daughter would be a great amusement to you. Now dont make any more fuss. Take her downstairs; and –

MRS PEARCE. But whats to become of her? Is she to be paid anything? Do be sensible, sir.

HIGGINS. Oh, pay her whatever is necessary: put it down in the housekeeping book. [*Impatiently*] What on earth will she want with money? She'll have her food and her clothes. She'll only drink if you give her money.

LIZA [*turning on him*] Oh you are a brute. It's a lie: nobody ever saw the sign of liquor on me. [*To Pickering*] Oh, sir: youre a gentleman: dont let him speak to me like that.

PICKERING [*in good-humored remonstrance*] Does it occur to you, Higgins, that the girl has some feelings?

HIGGINS [*looking critically at her*] Oh no, I dont think so. Not any feelings that we need bother about. [*Cheerily*] Have you, Eliza?

LIZA. I got my feelings same as anyone else.

HIGGINS [*to Pickering, reflectively*] You see the difficulty?

PICKERING. Eh? What difficulty?

HIGGINS. To get her to talk grammar. The mere pronunciation is easy enough.

LIZA. I dont want to talk grammar. I want to talk like a lady in a flower-shop.

MRS PEARCE. Will you please keep to the point, Mr Higgins. I want to know on what terms the girl is to be here. Is she to have any wages? And what is to become of her when youve finished your teaching? You must look ahead a little.

HIGGINS [*impatiently*] Whats to become of her if I leave her in the gutter? Tell me that, Mrs Pearce.

MRS PEARCE. Thats her own business, not yours, Mr Higgins.

HIGGINS. Well, when Ive done with her, we can throw her back into the gutter; and then it will be her own business again; so thats all right.

LIZA. Oh, youve no feeling heart in you: you dont care for nothing but yourself. [*She rises and takes the floor resolutely*]. Here! Ive had enough of this. I'm going [*making for the door*]. You ought to be ashamed of yourself, you ought.

HIGGINS [*snatching a chocolate cream from the piano, his eyes suddenly beginning to twinkle with mischief*] Have some chocolates, Eliza.

LIZA [*halting, tempted*] How do I know what might be in them? Ive heard of girls being drugged by the like of you.

Higgins whips out his penknife; cuts a chocolate in two; puts one half into his mouth and bolts it; and offers her the other half.

HIGGINS. Pledge of good faith, Eliza. I eat one half: you eat the other. [*Liza opens her mouth to retort: he pops the half chocolate into it*]. You shall have boxes of them, barrels of them, every day. You shall live on them. Eh?

LIZA [*who has disposed of the chocolate after being nearly choked by it*] I wouldnt have ate it, only I'm too ladylike to take it out of my mouth.

HIGGINS. Listen, Eliza. I think you said you came in a taxi.

LIZA. Well, what if I did? Ive as good a right to take a taxi as anyone else.

HIGGINS. You have, Eliza; and in future you shall have as many taxis as you want. You shall go up and down and round the town in a taxi every day. Think of that, Eliza.

MRS PEARCE. Mr Higgins: youre tempting the girl. It's not right. She should think of the future.

HIGGINS. At her age! Nonsense! Time enough to think of the future when you havnt any future to think of. No, Eliza: do as this lady does: think of other people's futures; but never think of your own. Think of chocolates, and taxis, and gold, and diamonds.

LIZA. No: I dont want no gold and no diamonds. I'm a good girl, I am. [*She sits down again, with an attempt at dignity*].

HIGGINS. You shall remain so, Eliza, under the care of Mrs Pearce. And you shall marry an officer in the Guards, with a beautiful moustache: the son of a marquis, who will disinherit him for marrying you, but will relent when he sees your beauty and goodness –

PICKERING. Excuse me, Higgins; but I really must interfere. Mrs Pearce is quite right. If this girl is to put herself in your hands for six months for an experiment in teaching, she must understand thoroughly what she's doing.

HIGGINS. How can she? She's incapable of understanding anything. Besides, do any of us understand what we are doing? If we did, would we ever do it?

PICKERING. Very clever, Higgins; but not to the present point. [*To Eliza*] Miss Doolittle –

LIZA [*overwhelmed*] Ah-ah-ow-oo!

HIGGINS. There! Thats all youll get out of Eliza. Ah-ah-ow-oo! No use explaining. As a military man you ought to know that. Give her her orders: thats enough for her. Eliza: you are to live here for the next six months, learning how to speak beautifully, like a lady in a florist's shop. If youre good and do whatever youre told, you shall sleep in a proper bedroom, and have lots to eat, and money to buy chocolates and take rides in taxis. If youre naughty and idle you will sleep in the back kitchen among the black beetles, and be walloped by Mrs Pearce with a broomstick. At the end of six months you shall go to Buckingham Palace in a carriage, beautifully dressed. If the King finds out youre not a lady, you will be taken by the police to the Tower of London, where your head will be cut off as a warning to other presumptuous flower girls. If you are not found out, you shall have a present of seven-and-sixpence to start life with as a lady in a shop. If you refuse this offer you will be a most ungrateful wicked girl; and the angels will weep for you. [*To Pickering*] Now are you satisfied, Pickering? [*To Mrs Pearce*] Can I put it more plainly and fairly, Mrs Pearce?

MRS PEARCE [*patiently*] I think youd better let me speak to the girl properly in private. I dont know that I can take charge of her or consent to the arrangement at all. Of course I know you dont mean her any harm; but when you get what you call interested in people's accents, you never think or care what may happen to them or you. Come with me, Eliza.

HIGGINS. Thats all right. Thank you, Mrs Pearce. Bundle her off to the bathroom.

LIZA [*rising reluctantly and suspiciously*] Youre a great bully, you are. I wont stay here if I dont like. I wont let nobody wallop me. I never asked to go to Bucknam Palace, I didnt. I was never in trouble with the police, not me. I'm a good girl –

MRS PEARCE. Dont answer back, girl. You dont understand the gentleman. Come with me. [*She leads the way to the door, and holds it open for Eliza*].

LIZA [*as she goes out*] Well, what I say is right. I wont go near the King, not if I'm going to have my head cut off. If I'd known what I was letting myself in for, I wouldnt have come here. I always been a good girl; and I never offered to say a word to him; and I dont owe him nothing; and I dont care; and I wont be put upon; and I have my feelings the same as anyone else –

Mrs Pearce shuts the door; and Eliza's plaints are no longer audible.

*　　*　　*

Eliza is taken upstairs to the third floor greatly to her surprise; for she expected to be taken down to the scullery.

There Mrs Pearce opens a door and takes her into a spare bedroom.

MRS PEARCE. I will have to put you here. This will be your bedroom.

LIZA. O-h, I couldnt sleep here, missus. It's too good for the likes of me. I should be afraid to touch anything. I aint a duchess yet, you know.

MRS PEARCE. You have got to make yourself as clean as the room: then you wont be afraid of it. And you must call me Mrs Pearce, not missus. [*She throws open the door of the dressing-room, now modernized as a bathroom*].

LIZA. Gawd! whats this? Is this where you wash clothes? Funny sort of copper I call it.

MRS PEARCE. It is not a copper. This is where we wash ourselves, Eliza, and where I am going to wash you.

LIZA. You expect me to get into that and wet myself all over! Not me. I should catch my death. I knew a woman did it every Saturday night; and she died of it.

MRS PEARCE. Mr Higgins has the gentlemen's bathroom downstairs; and he has a bath every morning, in cold water.

LIZA. Ugh! He's made of iron, that man.

MRS PEARCE. If you are to sit with him and the Colonel and be taught you will have to do the same. They wont like the smell of you if you dont. But you can have the water as hot as you like. There are two taps: hot and cold.

LIZA [*weeping*] I couldnt. I dursnt. Its not natural: it would kill me. Ive never had a bath in my life: not what youd call a proper one.

MRS PEARCE. Well, dont you want to be clean and sweet and decent, like a lady? You know you cant be a nice girl inside if youre a dirty slut outside.

LIZA. Boohoo!!!!

MRS PEARCE. Now stop crying and go back into your room and take off all your clothes. Then wrap yourself in this [*taking down a gown from its peg and handing it to her*] and come back to me. I will get the bath ready.

LIZA [*all tears*] I cant. I wont. I'm not used to it. Ive never took off all my clothes before. It's not right: it's not decent.

MRS PEARCE. Nonsense, child. Dont you take off all your clothes every night when you go to bed?

LIZA [*amazed*] No. Why should I? I should catch my death. Of course I take off my skirt.

MRS PEARCE. Do you mean that you sleep in the underclothes you wear in the daytime?

LIZA. What else have I to sleep in?

MRS PEARCE. You will never do that again as long as you live here. I will get you a proper nightdress.

LIZA. Do you mean change into cold things and lie awake shivering half the night? You want to kill me, you do.

MRS PEARCE. I want to change you from a frowzy slut to a clean respectable girl fit to sit with the gentlemen in the study. Are you going to trust me and do what I tell you or be thrown out and sent back to your flower basket?

LIZA. But you dont know what the cold is to me. You dont know how I dread it.

MRS PEARCE. Your bed wont be cold here: I will put a hot water bottle in it. [*Pushing her into the bedroom*] Off with you and undress.

LIZA. Oh, if only I'd a known what a dreadful thing it is to be clean I'd never have come. I didnt know when I was well off. I – [*Mrs Pearce pushes her through the door, but leaves it partly open lest her prisoner should take to flight*].

Mrs Pearce puts on a pair of white rubber sleeves, and fills the bath, mixing hot and cold, and testing the result with the bath thermometer. She perfumes it with a handful of bath salts and adds a palmful of mustard. She then takes a formidable looking long handled scrubbing brush and soaps it profusely with a ball of scented soap.

Eliza comes back with nothing on but the bath gown huddled tightly round her, a piteous spectacle of abject terror.

MRS PEARCE. Now come along. Take that thing off.

LIZA. Oh I couldnt, Mrs Pearce: I reely couldnt. I never done such a thing.

MRS PEARCE. Nonsense. Here: step in and tell me whether it's hot enough for you.

LIZA. Ah-oo! Ah-oo! It's too hot.

MRS PEARCE [*deftly snatching the gown away and throwing Eliza down on her back*] It wont hurt you. [*She sets to work with the scrubbing brush*].

    Eliza's screams are heartrending.

*   *   *

    Meanwhile the Colonel has been having it out with Higgins about Eliza. Pickering has come from the hearth to the chair and seated himself astride of it with his arms on the back to cross-examine him.

PICKERING. Excuse the straight question, Higgins. Are you a man of good character where women are concerned?

HIGGINS [*moodily*] Have you ever met a man of good character where women are concerned?

PICKERING. Yes: very frequently.

HIGGINS [*dogmatically, lifting himself on his hands to the level of the piano, and sitting on it with a bounce*] Well, I havnt. I find that the moment I let a woman make friends with me, she becomes jealous, exacting, suspicious, and a damned nuisance. I find that the moment I let myself make friends with a woman, I become selfish and tyrannical. Women upset everything. When you let them into your life, you find that the woman is driving at one thing and youre driving at another.

PICKERING. At what, for example?

HIGGINS [*coming off the piano restlessly*] Oh, Lord knows! I suppose the woman wants to live her own life; and the man wants to live his; and each tries to drag the other on to the wrong track. One wants to go north and the other south; and the result is that both have to go east, though they both hate the east wind. [*He sits down on the bench at the keyboard*]. So here I am, a confirmed old bachelor, and likely to remain so.

PICKERING [*rising and standing over him gravely*] Come, Higgins! You know what I mean. If I'm to be in this business I shall feel responsible for that girl. I hope it's understood that no advantage is to be taken of her position.

HIGGINS. What! That thing! Sacred, I assure you. [*Rising to explain*] You see, she'll be a pupil; and teaching would be impossible unless pupils were sacred. Ive taught scores of American millionairesses how to speak English: the best looking women in the world. I'm seasoned. They might as well be blocks of wood. *I* might as well be a block of wood. It's –

Mrs Pearce opens the door. She has Eliza's hat in her hand. Pickering retires to the easy-chair at the hearth and sits down.

HIGGINS [*eagerly*] Well, Mrs Pearce: is it all right?

MRS PEARCE [*at the door*] I just wish to trouble you with a word, if I may, Mr Higgins.

HIGGINS. Yes, certainly. Come in. [*She comes forward*] Dont burn that, Mrs Pearce. I'll keep it as a curiosity. [*He takes the hat*].

MRS PEARCE. Handle it carefully, sir, please. I had to promise her not to burn it; but I had better put it in the oven for a while.

HIGGINS [*putting it down hastily on the piano*] Oh! thank you. Well, what have you to say to me?

PICKERING. Am I in the way?

MRS PEARCE. Not at all, sir. Mr Higgins: will you please be very particular what you say before the girl?

HIGGINS [*sternly*] Of course. I'm always particular about what I say. Why do you say this to me?

MRS PEARCE [*unmoved*] No sir: youre not at all particular when youve mislaid anything or when you get a little impatient. Now it doesnt matter before me: I'm used to it. But you really must not swear before the girl.

HIGGINS [*indignantly*] I swear! [*Most emphatically*] I never swear. I detest the habit. What the devil do you mean?

MRS PEARCE [*stolidly*] Thats what I mean, sir. You swear a great deal too much. I dont mind your damning and blasting, and what the devil and where the devil and who the devil –

HIGGINS. Mrs Pearce: this language from your lips! Really!

MRS PEARCE [*not to be put off*] – but there is a certain word I must ask you not to use. The girl used it herself when she began to enjoy the bath. It begins with the same letter as bath. She knows no better: she learnt it at her mother's knee. But she must not hear it from your lips.

HIGGINS [*loftily*] I cannot charge myself with having ever uttered it, Mrs Pearce. [*She looks at him steadfastly. He adds, hiding an uneasy conscience with a judicial air*] Except perhaps in a moment of extreme and justifiable excitement.

MRS PEARCE. Only this morning, sir, you applied it to your boots, to the butter, and to the brown bread.

HIGGINS. Oh, that! Mere alliteration, Mrs Pearce, natural to a poet.

MRS PEARCE. Well, sir, whatever you choose to call it, I beg you not to let the girl hear you repeat it.

HIGGINS. Oh, very well, very well. Is that all?

MRS PEARCE. No, sir. We shall have to be very particular with this girl as to personal cleanliness.

HIGGINS. Certainly. Quite right. Most important.

MRS PEARCE. I mean not to be slovenly about her dress or untidy in leaving things about.

HIGGINS [*going to her solemnly*] Just so. I intended to call your attention to that. [*He passes on to Pickering, who is enjoying the conversation immensely*]. It is these little things that matter, Pickering. Take care of the pence and the pounds will take care of themselves is as true of personal habits as of money. [*He comes to anchor on the hearthrug, with the air of a man in an unassailable position*].

MRS PEARCE. Yes, sir. Then might I ask you not to come down to breakfast in your dressing-gown, or at any rate not to use it as a napkin to the extent you do, sir. And if you would be so good as not to eat everything off the same plate, and to remember not to put the porridge saucepan out of your hand on the clean tablecloth, it would be a better example to the girl. You know you nearly choked yourself with a fishbone in the jam only last week.

HIGGINS [*routed from the hearthrug and drifting back to the piano*] I may do these things sometimes in absence of mind; but surely I dont do them habitually. [*Angrily*] By the way: my dressing-gown smells most damnably of benzine.

MRS PEARCE. No doubt it does, Mr Higgins. But if you will wipe your fingers –

HIGGINS [*yelling*] Oh very well, very well: I'll wipe them in my hair in future.

MRS PEARCE. I hope youre not offended, Mr Higgins.

HIGGINS [*shocked at finding himself thought capable of an unamiable sentiment*] Not at all, not at all. Youre quite right, Mrs Pearce: I shall be particularly careful before the girl. Is that all?

MRS PEARCE. No, sir. Might she use some of those Japanese dresses you brought from abroad? I really cant put her back into her old things.

HIGGINS. Certainly. Anything you like. Is that all?

MRS PEARCE. Thank you, sir. Thats all. [*She goes out*].

HIGGINS. You know, Pickering, that woman has the most extraordinary ideas about me. Here I am, a shy, diffident sort of man. Ive never been able to feel really grown-up and tremendous, like other chaps. And yet she's firmly persuaded that I'm an arbitrary overbearing bossing kind of person. I cant account for it.

Mrs Pearce returns.

MRS PEARCE. If you please, sir, the trouble's beginning already.

Theres a dustman downstairs, Alfred Doolittle, wants to see you. He says you have his daughter here.

PICKERING [*rising*] Phew! I say!

HIGGINS [*promptly*] Send the blackguard up.

MRS PEARCE. Oh, very well, sir. [*She goes out*].

PICKERING. He may not be a blackguard, Higgins.

HIGGINS. Nonsense. Of course he's a blackguard.

PICKERING. Whether he is or not, I'm afraid we shall have some trouble with him.

HIGGINS [*confidently*] Oh no: I think not. If theres any trouble he shall have it with me, not I with him. And we are sure to get something interesting out of him.

PICKERING. About the girl?

HIGGINS. No. I mean his dialect.

PICKERING. Oh!

MRS PEARCE [*at the door*] Doolittle, sir. [*She admits Doolittle and retires*].

Alfred Doolittle is an elderly but vigorous dustman, clad in the costume of his profession, including a hat with a back brim covering his neck and shoulders. He has well marked and rather interesting features, and seems equally free from fear and conscience. He has a remarkably expressive voice, the result of a habit of giving vent to his feelings without reserve. His present pose is that of wounded honor and stern resolution.

DOOLITTLE [*at the door, uncertain which of the two gentlemen is his man*] Professor Iggins?

HIGGINS. Here. Good morning. Sit down.

DOOLITTLE. Morning, Governor. [*He sits down magisterially*] I come about a very serious matter, Governor.

HIGGINS [*to Pickering*] Brought up in Hounslow. Mother Welsh, I should think. [*Doolittle opens his mouth, amazed. Higgins continues*] What do you want, Doolittle?

DOOLITTLE [*menacingly*] I want my daughter: thats what I want. See?

HIGGINS. Of course you do. Youre her father, arnt you? You dont suppose anyone else wants her, do you? I'm glad to see you have some spark of family feeling left. She's upstairs. Take her away at once.

DOOLITTLE [*rising, fearfully taken aback*] What!

HIGGINS. Take her away. Do you suppose I'm going to keep your daughter for you?

DOOLITTLE [*remonstrating*] Now, now, look here, Governor. Is

this reasonable? Is it fairity to take advantage of a man like this? The girl belongs to me. You got her. Where do I come in? [*He sits down again*].

HIGGINS. Your daughter had the audacity to come to my house and ask me to teach her how to speak properly so that she could get a place in a flower-shop. This gentleman and my housekeeper have been here all the time. [*Bullying him*] How dare you come here and attempt to blackmail me? You sent her here on purpose.

DOOLITTLE [*protesting*] No, Governor.

HIGGINS. You must have. How else could you possibly know that she is here?

DOOLITTLE. Dont take a man up like that, Governor.

HIGGINS. The police shall take you up. This is a plant – a plot to extort money by threats. I shall telephone for the police [*he goes resolutely to the telephone and opens the directory*].

DOOLITTLE. Have I asked you for a brass farthing? I leave it to the gentleman here: have I said a word about money?

HIGGINS [*throwing the book aside and marching down on Doolittle with a poser*] What else did you come for?

DOOLITTLE [*sweetly*] Well, what would a man come for? Be human, Governor.

HIGGINS [*disarmed*] Alfred: did you put her up to it?

DOOLITTLE. So help me, Governor, I never did. I take my Bible oath I aint seen the girl these two months past.

HIGGINS. Then how did you know she was here?

DOOLITTLE [*'most musical, most melancholy'*] I'll tell you, Governor, if youll only let me get a word in. I'm willing to tell you. I'm wanting to tell you. I'm waiting to tell you.

HIGGINS. Pickering: this chap has a certain natural gift of rhetoric. Observe the rhythm of his native woodnotes wild. 'I'm willing to tell you: I'm wanting to tell you: I'm waiting to tell you.' Sentimental rhetoric! thats the Welsh strain in him. It also accounts for his mendacity and dishonesty.

PICKERING. Oh, please, Higgins: I'm west country myself. [*To Doolittle*] How did you know the girl was here if you didnt send her?

DOOLITTLE. It was like this, Governor. The girl took a boy in the taxi to give him a jaunt. Son of her landlady, he is. He hung about on the chance of her giving him another ride home. Well, she sent him back for her luggage when she heard you was willing for her to stop here. I met the boy at the corner of Long Acre and Endell Street.

HIGGINS. Public house. Yes?

DOOLITTLE. The poor man's club, Governor: why shouldnt I?

PICKERING. Do let him tell his story, Higgins.

DOOLITTLE. He told me what was up. And I ask you, what was my feelings and my duty as a father? I says to the boy, 'You bring me the luggage,' I says –

PICKERING. Why didnt you go for it yourself?

DOOLITTLE. Landlady wouldnt have trusted me with it, Governor. She's that kind of woman: you know. I had to give the boy a penny afore he trusted me with it, the little swine. I brought it to her just to oblige you like, and make myself agreeable. Thats all.

HIGGINS. How much luggage?

DOOLITTLE. Musical instrument, Governor. A few pictures, a trifle of jewelry, and a bird-cage. She said she didn't want no clothes. What was I to think from that, Governor? I ask you as a parent what was I to think?

HIGGINS. So you came to rescue her from worse than death eh?

DOOLITTLE [appreciatively: relieved at being so well understood] Just so, Governor. Thats right.

PICKERING. But why did you bring her luggage if you intended to take her away?

DOOLITTLE. Have I said a word about taking her away? Have I now?

HIGGINS [determinedly] Youre going to take her away, double quick. [He crosses to the hearth and rings the bell].

DOOLITTLE [rising] No, Governor. Dont say that. I'm not the man to stand in my girl's light. Heres a career opening for her as you might say; and –

Mrs Pearce opens the door and awaits orders.

HIGGINS. Mrs Pearce: this is Eliza's father. He has come to take her away. Give her to him. [He goes back to the piano, with an air of washing his hands of the whole affair].

DOOLITTLE. No. This is a misunderstanding. Listen here –

MRS PEARCE. He cant take her away, Mr Higgins: how can he? You told me to burn her clothes.

DOOLITTLE. Thats right. I cant carry the girl through the streets like a blooming monkey, can I? I put it to you.

HIGGINS. You have put it to me that you want your daughter. Take your daughter. If she has no clothes go out and buy her some.

DOOLITTLE [*desperate*] Wheres the clothes she come in? Did I burn them or did your missus here?

MRS PEARCE. I am the housekeeper, if you please. I have sent for some clothes for the girl. When they come you can take her away. You can wait in the kitchen. This way, please.

Doolittle, much troubled, accompanies her to the door; then hesitates: finally turns confidentially to Higgins.

DOOLITTLE. Listen here, Governor. You and me is men of the world, aint we?

HIGGINS. Oh! Men of the world, are we? Youd better go, Mrs Pearce.

MRS PEARCE. I think so, indeed, sir. [*She goes, with dignity*].

PICKERING. The floor is yours, Mr Doolittle.

DOOLITTLE [*to Pickering*] I thank you, Governor. [*To Higgins, who takes refuge on the piano bench, a little overwhelmed by the proximity of his visitor; for Doolittle has a professional flavor of dust about him*]. Well, the truth is, Ive taken a sort of fancy to you, Governor; and if you want the girl, I'm not so set on having her back home again but what I might be open to an arrangement. Regarded in the light of a young woman, she's a fine handsome girl. As a daughter she's not worth her keep; and so I tell you straight. All I ask is my rights as a father; and youre the last man alive to expect me to let her go for nothing; for I can see youre one of the straight sort, Governor. Well, whats a five-pound note to you? and whats Eliza to me? [*He turns to his chair and sits down judicially*].

PICKERING. I think you ought to know, Doolittle, that Mr Higgins's intentions are entirely honorable.

DOOLITTLE. Course they are, Governor. If I thought they wasn't, I'd ask fifty.

HIGGINS [*revolted*] Do you mean to say that you would sell your daughter for £50?

DOOLITTLE. Not in a general way I wouldnt; but to oblige

a gentleman like you I'd do a good deal, I do assure you.

PICKERING. Have you no morals, man?

DOOLITTLE [*unabashed*] Cant afford them, Governor. Neither could you if you was as poor as me. Not that I mean any harm, you know. But if Liza is going to have a bit out of this, why not me too?

HIGGINS [*troubled*] I dont know what to do, Pickering. There can be no question that as a matter of morals it's a positive crime to give this chap a farthing. And yet I feel a sort of rough justice in his claim.

DOOLITTLE. Thats it, Governor. Thats all I say. A father's heart, as it were.

PICKERING. Well, I know the feeling; but really it seems hardly right –

DOOLITTLE. Dont say that, Governor. Dont look at it that way. What am I, Governors both? I ask you, what am I? I'm one of the undeserving poor: thats what I am. Think of what that means to a man. It means that he's up agen middle class morality all the time. If theres anything going, and I put in for a bit of it, it's always the same story: 'Youre undeserving; so you cant have it.' But my needs is as great as the most deserving widow's that ever got money out of six different charities in one week for the death of the same husband. I dont need less than a deserving man: I need more. I dont eat less hearty than him; and I drink a lot more. I want a bit of amusement, cause I'm a thinking man. I want cheerfulness and a song and a band when I feel low. Well, they charge me just the same for everything as they charge the deserving. What is middle class morality? Just an excuse for never giving me anything. Therefore, I ask you, as two gentlemen, not to play that game on me. I'm playing straight with you. I aint pretending to be deserving. I'm undeserving; and I mean to go on being undeserving. I like it; and thats the truth. Will you take advantage of a man's nature to do him out of the price of his own daughter what he's brought up and fed and clothed by the sweat of his brow until she's growed big enough to be interesting to you two gentlemen? Is five pounds unreasonable? I put it to you; and I leave it to you.

HIGGINS [*rising, and going over to Pickering*] Pickering: if we were to take this man in hand for three months, he could choose between a seat in the Cabinet and a popular pulpit in Wales.

PICKERING. What do you say to that, Doolittle?

DOOLITTLE. Not me, Governor, thank you kindly. Ive heard all the preachers and all the prime ministers – for I'm a thinking man and game for politics or religion or social reform same as all the other amusements – and I tell you it's a dog's life any way you look at it. Undeserving poverty is my line. Taking one station in society with another, it's – it's – well, it's the only one that has any ginger in it, to my taste.

HIGGINS. I suppose we must give him a fiver.

PICKERING. He'll make a bad use of it, I'm afraid.

DOOLITTLE. Not me, Governor, so help me I wont. Dont you be afraid that I'll save it and spare it and live idle on it. There wont be a penny of it left by Monday: I'll have to go to work same as if I'd never had it. It wont pauperize me, you bet. Just one good spree for myself and the missus, giving pleasure to ourselves and employment to others, and satisfaction to you to think it's not been throwed away. You couldnt spend it better.

HIGGINS [*taking out his pocket book and coming between Doolittle and the piano*] This is irresistible. Lets give him ten. [*He offers two notes to the dustman*].

DOOLITTLE. No, Governor. She wouldnt have the heart to spend ten; and perhaps I shouldnt neither. Ten pounds is a lot of money: it makes a man feel prudent like; and then goodbye to happiness. You give me what I ask you, Governor: not a penny more, and not a penny less.

PICKERING. Why dont you marry that missus of yours? I rather draw the line at encouraging that sort of immorality.

DOOLITTLE. Tell her so, Governor: tell her so. *I*'m willing. It's me that suffers by it. Ive no hold on her. I got to be agreeable to her. I got to give her presents. I got to buy her clothes something sinful. I'm a slave to that woman,

Governor, just because I'm not her lawful husband. And she knows it too. Catch her marrying me! Take my advice, Governor – marry Eliza while she's young and dont know no better. If you dont youll be sorry for it after. If you do, she'll be sorry for it after; but better her than you, because youre a man, and she's only a woman and dont know how to be happy anyhow.

HIGGINS. Pickering: If we listen to this man another minute, we shall have no convictions left. [*To Doolittle*] Five pounds I think you said.

DOOLITTLE. Thank you kindly, Governor.

HIGGINS. Youre sure you wont take ten?

DOOLITTLE. Not now. Another time, Governor.

HIGGINS [*handing him a five-pound note*] Here you are.

DOOLITTLE. Thank you, Governor. Good morning. [*He hurries to the door, anxious to get away with his booty. When he opens it he is confronted with a dainty and exquisitely clean young Japanese lady in a simple blue cotton kimono printed cunningly with small white jasmine blossoms. Mrs Pearce is with her. He gets out of her way deferentially and apologizes*]. Beg pardon, miss.

THE JAPANESE LADY. Garn! Dont you know your own daughter?

DOOLITTLE ⎧ *exclaiming* ⎫ Bly me! it's Eliza!
HIGGINS ⎨ *simul-* ⎬ Whats that? This!
PICKERING ⎩ *taneously* ⎭ By Jove!

LIZA. Dont I look silly?

HIGGINS. Silly?

MRS PEARCE [*at the door*] Now, Mr Higgins, please dont say anything to make the girl conceited about herself.

HIGGINS [*conscientiously*] Oh! Quite right, Mrs Pearce. [*To Eliza*] Yes: damned silly.

MRS PEARCE. Please, sir.

HIGGINS [*correcting himself*] I mean extremely silly.

LIZA. I should look all right with my hat on. [*She takes up her hat; puts it on; and walks across the room to the fireplace with a fashionable air*].

HIGGINS. A new fashion, by George! And it ought to look horrible!

DOOLITTLE [*with fatherly pride*] Well, I never thought she'd clean up as good looking as that, Governor. She's a credit to me, aint she?

LIZA. I tell you, it's easy to clean up here. Hot and cold water on tap, just as much as you like, there is. Woolly towels, there is; and a towel horse so hot, it burns your fingers. Soft brushes to scrub yourself, and a wooden bowl of soap smelling like primroses. Now I know why ladies is so clean. Washing's a treat for them. Wish they could see what it is for the like of me!

HIGGINS. I'm glad the bathroom met with your approval.

LIZA. It didnt: not all of it; and I dont care who hears me say it. Mrs Pearce knows.

HIGGINS. What was wrong, Mrs Pearce?

MRS PEARCE [*blandly*] Oh, nothing, sir. It doesnt matter.

LIZA. I had a good mind to break it. I didn't know which way to look. But I hung a towel over it, I did.

HIGGINS. Over what?

MRS PEARCE. Over the looking-glass sir.

HIGGINS. Doolittle: you have brought your daughter up too strictly.

DOOLITTLE. Me! I never brought her up at all, except to give her a lick of a strap now and again. Dont put it on me, Governor. She aint accustomed to it, you see: thats all. But she'll soon pick up your free-and-easy ways.

LIZA. I'm a good girl, I am; and I wont pick up no free-and-easy ways.

HIGGINS. Eliza: if you say again that youre a good girl, your father shall take you home.

LIZA. Not him. You dont know my father. All he come here for was to touch you for some money to get drunk on.

DOOLITTLE. Well, what else would I want money for? To put into the plate in church, I suppose. [*She puts out her tongue at him. He is so incensed by this that Pickering presently finds*

61

it necessary to step between them]. Dont you give me none of your lip; and dont let me hear you giving this gentleman any of it neither, or youll hear from me about it. See?

HIGGINS. Have you any further advice to give her before you go, Doolittle? Your blessing, for instance.

DOOLITTLE. No, Governor: I aint such a mug as to put up my children to all I know myself. Hard enough to hold them in without that. If you want Eliza's mind improved, Governor, you do it yourself with a strap. So long, gentlemen. [*He turns to go*].

HIGGINS [*impressively*] Stop. Youll come regularly to see your daughter. It's your duty, you know. My brother is a clergyman; and he could help you in your talks with her.

DOOLITTLE [*evasively*] Certainly, I'll come, Governor. Not just this week, because I have a job at a distance. But later on you may depend on me. Afternoon, gentlemen. Afternoon, maam. [*He touches his hat to Mrs Pearce, who disdains the salutation and goes out. He winks at Higgins, thinking him probably a fellow-sufferer from Mrs Pearce's difficult disposition, and follows her*].

LIZA. Dont you believe the old liar. He'd as soon you set a bull-dog on him as a clergyman. You wont see him again in a hurry.

HIGGINS. I dont want to, Eliza. Do you?

LIZA. Not me. I dont want never to see him again, I dont. He's a disgrace to me, he is, collecting dust, instead of working at his trade.

PICKERING. What is his trade, Eliza?

LIZA. Talking money out of other people's pockets into his own. His proper trade's a navvy; and he works at it sometimes too – for exercise – and earns good money at it. Aint you going to call me Miss Doolittle any more?

PICKERING. I beg your pardon, Miss Doolittle. It was a slip of the tongue.

LIZA. Oh, I dont mind; only it sounded so genteel. I should just like to take a taxi to the corner of Tottenham Court Road and get out there and tell it to wait for me, just to put the girls in their place a bit. I wouldnt speak to them, you know.

PICKERING. Better wait til we get you something really fashionable.

HIGGINS. Besides, you shouldnt cut your old friends now that you have risen in the world. Thats what we call snobbery.

LIZA. You dont call the like of them my friends now, I should hope. Theyve took it out of me often enough with their ridicule when they had the chance; and now I mean to get a bit of my own back. But if I'm to have fashionable clothes, I'll wait. I should like to have some. Mrs Pearce says youre going to give me some to wear in bed at night different to what I wear in the daytime; but it do seem a waste of money when you could get something to shew. Besides, I never could fancy changing into cold things on a winter night.

MRS PEARCE [*coming back*] Now, Eliza. The new things have come for you to try on.

LIZA. Ah-ow-oo-ooh! [*She rushes out*].

MRS PEARCE [*following her*] Oh, dont rush about like that, girl. [*She shuts the door behind her*].

HIGGINS. Pickering: we have taken on a stiff job.

PICKERING [*with conviction*] Higgins: we have.

* * *

There seems to be some curiosity as to what Higgins's lessons to Eliza were like. Well, here is a sample: the first one.

Picture Eliza, in her new clothes, and feeling her inside put out of step by a lunch, dinner, and breakfast of a kind to which it is unaccustomed, seated with Higgins and the Colonel in the study, feeling like a hospital out-patient at a first encounter with the doctors.

Higgins, constitutionally unable to sit still, discomposes her still more by striding restlessly about. But for the reassuring presence and quietude of her friend the Colonel she would run for her life, even back to Drury Lane.

HIGGINS. Say your alphabet.

LIZA. I know my alphabet. Do you think I know nothing? I dont need to be taught like a child.

HIGGINS [*thundering*] Say your alphabet.

PICKERING. Say it, Miss Doolittle. You will understand

presently. Do what he tells you; and let him teach you in his own way.

LIZA. Oh well, if you put it like that – Ahyee, bəyee, cəyee, dəyee –

HIGGINS [*with the roar of a wounded lion*] Stop. Listen to this, Pickering. This is what we pay for as elementary education. This unfortunate animal has been locked up for nine years in school at our expense to teach her to speak and read the language of Shakespear and Milton. And the result is Ahyee, Bə-yee, Cə-yee, Də-yee. [*To Eliza*] Say A, B, C, D.

LIZA [*almost in tears*] But I'm saying it. Ahyee, Bəyee, Cə-yee –

HIGGINS. Stop. Say a cup of tea.

LIZA. A cappətə-ee.

HIGGINS. Put your tongue forward until it squeezes against the top of your lower teeth. Now say cup.

LIZA. C-c-c – I cant. C-Cup.

PICKERING. Good. Splendid, Miss Doolittle.

HIGGINS. By Jupiter, she's done it at the first shot. Pickering: we shall make a duchess of her. [*To Eliza*] Now do you think you could possibly say tea? Not tə-yee, mind: if you ever say bə-yee cə-yee də-yee again you shall be dragged round the room three times by the hair of your head. [*Fortissimo*] T, T, T, T.

LIZA [*weeping*] I cant hear no difference cep that it sounds more genteel-like when you say it.

HIGGINS. Well, if you can hear that difference, what the devil are you crying for? Pickering: give her a chocolate.

PICKERING. No, no. Never mind crying a little, Miss Doolittle: you are doing very well; and the lessons wont hurt. I promise you I wont let him drag you round the room by your hair.

HIGGINS. Be off with you to Mrs Pearce and tell her about it. Think about it. Try to do it by yourself: and keep your tongue well forward in your mouth instead of trying to roll it up and swallow it. Another lesson at half-past four this afternoon. Away with you.

    Eliza, still sobbing, rushes from the room.

    And that is the sort of ordeal poor Eliza has to go through for months before we meet her again on her first appearance in London society of the professional class.

ACT THREE

It is Mrs Higgins's at-home day. Nobody has yet arrived. Her drawing room, in a flat on Chelsea Embankment, has three windows looking on the river; and the ceiling is not so lofty as it would be in an older house of the same pretension. The windows are open, giving access to a balcony with flowers in pots. If you stand with your face to the windows, you have the fireplace on your left and the door in the right-hand wall close to the corner nearest the windows.

Mrs Higgins was brought up on Morris and Burne Jones; and her room, which is very unlike her son's room in Wimpole Street, is not crowded with furniture and little tables and nicknacks. In the middle of the room there is a big ottoman; and this, with the carpet, the Morris wallpapers, and the Morris chintz window curtains and brocade covers of the ottoman and its cushions, supply all the ornament, and are much too handsome to be hidden by odds and ends of useless things. A few good oil-paintings from the exhibitions in the Grosvenor Gallery thirty years ago (the Burne Jones, not the Whistler side of them) are on the walls. The only landscape is a Cecil Lawson on the scale of a Rubens. There is a portrait of Mrs Higgins as she was when she defied the fashion in her youth in one of the beautiful Rossettian costumes which, when caricatured by people who did not understand, led to the absurdities of popular estheticism in the eighteen-seventies.

In the corner diagonally opposite the door Mrs Higgins, now over sixty and long past taking the trouble to dress out of the fashion, sits writing at an elegantly simple writing-table with a bell button

within reach of her hand. There is a Chippendale chair further back in the room between her and the window nearest her side. At the other side of the room, further forward, is an Elizabethan chair roughly carved in the taste of Inigo Jones. On the same side a piano in a decorated case. The corner between the fireplace and the window is occupied by a divan cushioned in Morris chintz.

It is between four and five in the afternoon.

The door is opened violently; and Higgins enters with his hat on.

MRS HIGGINS [*dismayed*] Henry! [*Scolding him*] What are you doing here today? It is my at-home day: you promised not to come. [*As he bends to kiss her, she takes his hat off, and presents it to him*].

HIGGINS. Oh bother! [*He throws the hat down on the table*].

MRS HIGGINS. Go home at once.

HIGGINS [*kissing her*] I know, mother. I came on purpose.

MRS HIGGINS. But you mustnt. I'm serious, Henry. You offend all my friends: they stop coming whenever they meet you.

HIGGINS. Nonsense! I know I have no small talk; but people dont mind. [*He sits on the settee*].

MRS HIGGINS. Oh! dont they? Small talk indeed! What about your large talk? Really, dear, you mustnt stay.

HIGGINS. I must. Ive a job for you. A phonetic job.

MRS HIGGINS. No use, dear. I'm sorry; but I cant get round your vowels; and though I like to get pretty postcards in your patent shorthand, I always have to read the copies in ordinary writing you so thoughtfully send me.

HIGGINS. Well, this isnt a phonetic job.

MRS HIGGINS. You said it was.

HIGGINS. Not your part of it. Ive picked up a girl.

MRS HIGGINS. Does that mean that some girl has picked you up?

HIGGINS. Not at all. I dont mean a love affair.

MRS HIGGINS. What a pity!

HIGGINS. Why?

MRS HIGGINS. Well, you never fall in love with anyone under forty-five. When will you discover that there are some rather nice-looking young women about?

HIGGINS. Oh, I cant be bothered with young women. My idea of a lovable woman is somebody as like you as possible. I shall never get into the way of seriously liking young women: some habits lie too deep to be changed. [*Rising abruptly and walking about, jingling his money and his keys in his trouser pockets*] Besides, theyre all idiots.

MRS HIGGINS. Do you know what you would do if you really loved me, Henry?

HIGGINS. Oh bother! What? Marry, I suppose.

MRS HIGGINS. No. Stop fidgeting and take your hands out of your pockets. [*With a gesture of despair, he obeys and sits down again*]. Thats a good boy. Now tell me about the girl.

HIGGINS. She's coming to see you.

MRS HIGGINS. I dont remember asking her.

HIGGINS. You didnt. *I* asked her. If youd known her you wouldnt have asked her.

MRS HIGGINS. Indeed! Why?

HIGGINS. Well, it's like this. She's a common flower girl. I picked her off the kerbstone.

MRS HIGGINS. And invited her to my at-home!

HIGGINS [*rising and coming to her to coax her*] Oh, thatll be all right. Ive taught her to speak properly; and she has strict orders as to her behavior. She's to keep to two subjects: the weather and everybody's health – Fine day and How do you do, you know – and not to let herself go on things in general. That will be safe.

MRS HIGGINS. Safe! To talk about our health! about our insides! perhaps about our outsides! How could you be so silly, Henry?

HIGGINS [*impatiently*] Well, she must talk about something. [*He controls himself and sits down again*]. Oh, she'll be all right: dont you fuss. Pickering is in it with me. Ive a sort of bet on that I'll pass her off as a duchess in six months. I started on her some months ago; and she's getting on like a house on fire. I shall win my bet. She has a quick ear; and she's been easier to teach than my middle-class pupils because she's had to learn a complete new language. She talks English almost as you talk French.

MRS HIGGINS. Thats satisfactory, at all events.

HIGGINS. Well, it is and it isnt.

MRS HIGGINS. What does that mean?

HIGGINS. You see, Ive got her pronunciation all right; but you have to consider not only how a girl pronounces, but what she pronounces; and thats where –

They are interrupted by the parlormaid, announcing guests.

THE PARLORMAID. Mrs and Miss Eynsford Hill. [*She withdraws*].

HIGGINS. Oh Lord! [*He rises: snatches his hat from the table; and makes for the door; but before he reaches it his mother introduces him*].

Mrs and Miss Eynsford Hill are the mother and daughter who sheltered from the rain in Covent Garden. The mother is well bred, quiet, and has the habitual anxiety of straitened means. The daughter has acquired a gay air of being very much at home in society: the bravado of genteel poverty.

MRS EYNSFORD HILL [*to Mrs Higgins*] How do you do? [*They shake hands*].

MISS EYNSFORD HILL. How d'you do? [*She shakes*].

MRS HIGGINS [*introducing*] My son Henry.

MRS EYNSFORD HILL. Your celebrated son! I have so longed to meet you, Professor Higgins.

HIGGINS [*glumly, making no movement in her direction*] Delighted. [*He backs against the piano and bows brusquely*].

MISS EYNSFORD HILL [*going to him with confident familiarity*] How do you do?

HIGGINS [*staring at her*] Ive seen you before somewhere. I havnt the ghost of a notion where; but Ive heard your voice. [*Drearily*] It doesnt matter. Youd better sit down.

MRS HIGGINS. I'm sorry to say that my celebrated son has no manners. You mustnt mind him.

MISS EYNSFORD HILL [*gaily*] I dont. [*She sits in the Elizabethan chair*].

MRS EYNSFORD HILL [*a little bewildered*] Not at all. [*She sits on the ottoman between her daughter and Mrs Higgins, who has turned her chair away from the writing-table*].

HIGGINS. Oh, have I been rude? I didnt mean to be.

He goes to the central window, through which, with his back to the company, he contemplates the river and the flowers in Battersea Park on the opposite bank as if they were a frozen desert.

The parlormaid returns, ushering in Pickering.

THE PARLORMAID. Colonel Pickering. [*She withdraws*].

PICKERING. How do you do, Mrs Higgins?

MRS HIGGINS. So glad youve come. Do you know Mrs Eynsford Hill – Miss Eynsford Hill? [*Exchange of bows. The Colonel brings the Chippendale chair a little forward between Mrs Hill and Mrs Higgins, and sits down*].

PICKERING. Has Henry told you what weve come for?

HIGGINS [*over his shoulder*] We were interrupted: damn it!

MRS HIGGINS. Oh Henry, Henry, really!

MRS EYNSFORD HILL [*half rising*] Are we in the way?

MRS HIGGINS [*rising and making her sit down again*] No, no. You couldnt have come more fortunately: we want you to meet a friend of ours.

HIGGINS [*turning hopefully*] Yes, by George! We want two or three people. Youll do as well as anybody else.

The parlormaid returns, ushering Freddy.

THE PARLORMAID. Mr Eynsford Hill.

HIGGINS [*almost audibly, past endurance*] God of Heaven! another of them.

FREDDY [*shaking hands with Mrs Higgins*] Ahdedo?

MRS HIGGINS. Very good of you to come. [*Introducing*] Colonel Pickering.

FREDDY [*bowing*] Ahdedo?

MRS HIGGINS. I dont think you know my son, Professor Higgins.

FREDDY [*going to Higgins*] Ahdedo?

HIGGINS [*looking at him much as if he were a pickpocket*] I'll take my oath Ive met you before somewhere. Where was it?

FREDDY. I dont think so.

HIGGINS [*resignedly*] It dont matter, anyhow. Sit down.

He shakes Freddy's hand and almost slings him on to the ottoman with his face to the window; then comes round to the other side of it.

HIGGINS. Well, here we are, anyhow! [*He sits down on the ottoman next Mrs Eynsford Hill, on her left*]. And now, what the devil are we going to talk about until Eliza comes?

72

MRS HIGGINS. Henry: you are the life and soul of the Royal Society's soirées; but really youre rather trying on more commonplace occasions.

HIGGINS. Am I? Very sorry. [*Beaming suddenly*] I suppose I am, you know. [*Uproariously*] Ha, ha!

MISS EYNSFORD HILL [*who considers Higgins quite eligible matrimonially*] I sympathize. *I* havnt any small talk. If people would only be frank and say what they really think!

HIGGINS [*relapsing into gloom*] Lord forbid!

MRS EYNSFORD HILL [*taking up her daughter's cue*] But why?

HIGGINS. What they think they ought to think is bad enough, Lord knows; but what they really think would break up the whole show. Do you suppose it would be really agreeable if I were to come out now with what I really think?

MISS EYNSFORD HILL [*gaily*] Is it so very cynical?

HIGGINS. Cynical! Who the dickens said it was cynical? I mean it wouldnt be decent.

MRS EYNSFORD HILL [*seriously*] Oh! I'm sure you dont mean that, Mr Higgins.

HIGGINS. You see, we're all savages, more or less. We're supposed to be civilized and cultured – to know all about poetry and philosophy and art and science, and so on; but how many of us know even the meanings of these names? [*To Miss Hill*] What do you know of poetry? [*To Mrs Hill*] What do you know of science? [*Indicating Freddy*] What does h e know of art or science or anything else? What the devil do you imagine I know of philosophy?

MRS HIGGINS [*warningly*] Or of manners, Henry?

THE PARLORMAID [*opening the door*] Miss Doolittle. [*She withdraws*].

HIGGINS [*rising hastily and running to Mrs Higgins*] Here she is, mother. [*He stands on tiptoe and makes signs over his mother's head to Eliza to indicate to her which lady is her hostess*].

Eliza, who is exquisitely dressed, produces an impression of such remarkable distinction and beauty as she enters that they all rise, quite fluttered. Guided by Higgins's signals, she comes to Mrs Higgins with studied grace.

LIZA [*speaking with pedantic correctness of pronunciation and great beauty of tone*] How do you do, Mrs Higgins? [*She gasps slightly in making sure of the H in Higgins, but is quite successful*]. Mr Higgins told me I might come.

MRS HIGGINS [*cordially*] Quite right: I'm very glad indeed to see you.

PICKERING. How do you do, Miss Doolittle?

LIZA [*shaking hands with him*] Colonel Pickering, is it not?

MRS EYNSFORD HILL. I feel sure we have met before, Miss Doolittle. I remember your eyes.

LIZA. How do you do? [*She sits down on the ottoman gracefully in the place just left vacant by Higgins*].

MRS FYNSFORD HILL [*introducing*] My daughter Clara.

LIZA. How do you do?

CLARA [*impulsively*] How do you do? [*She sits down on the ottoman beside Eliza, devouring her with her eyes*].

FREDDY [*coming to their side of the ottoman*] Ive certainly had the pleasure.

MRS EYNSFORD HILL [*introducing*] My son Freddy.

LIZA. How do you do?

Freddy bows and sits down in the Elizabethan chair, infatuated.

HIGGINS [*suddenly*] By George, yes: it all comes back to me! [*They stare at him*]. Covent Garden! [*Lamentably*] What a damned thing!

MRS HIGGINS. Henry, please! [*He is about to sit on the edge of the table*] Dont sit on my writing-table: youll break it.

HIGGINS [*sulkily*] Sorry.

He goes to the divan, stumbling into the fender and over the fire-irons on his way; extricating himself with muttered imprecations; and finishing his disastrous journey by throwing himself so impatiently on the divan that he almost breaks it. Mrs Higgins looks at him, but controls herself and says nothing.

A long and painful pause ensues.

MRS HIGGINS [*at last, conversationally*] Will it rain, do you think?

LIZA. The shallow depression in the west of these islands is likely to move slowly in an easterly direction. There are no indications of any great change in the barometrical situation.

FREDDY. Ha! ha! how awfully funny!

LIZA. What is wrong with that, young man? I bet I got it right.

FREDDY. Killing!

MRS EYNSFORD HILL. I'm sure I hope it wont turn cold. Theres so much influenza about. It runs right through our whole family regularly every spring.

LIZA [*darkly*] My aunt died of influenza: so they said.

MRS EYNSFORD HILL [*clicks her tongue sympathetically*]!!!

LIZA [*in the same tragic tone*] But it's my belief they done the old woman in.

MRS HIGGINS [*puzzled*] Done her in?

LIZA. Y-e-e-e-es, Lord love you! Why should she die of influenza? She come through diphtheria right enough the year before. I saw her with my own eyes. Fairly blue with it, she was. They all thought she was dead; but my father he kept ladling gin down her throat til she came to so sudden that she bit the bowl off the spoon.

MRS EYNSFORD HILL [*startled*] Dear me!

LIZA [*piling up the indictment*] What call would a woman with that strength in her have to die of influenza? What become of her new straw hat that should have come to me? Somebody pinched it; and what I say is, them as pinched it done her in.

MRS EYNSFORD HILL. What does doing her in mean?

HIGGINS [*hastily*] Oh, thats the new small talk. To do a person in means to kill them.

MRS EYNSFORD HILL [*to Eliza, horrified*] You surely dont believe that your aunt was killed?

LIZA. Do I not! Them she lived with would have killed her for a hat-pin, let alone a hat.

MRS EYNSFORD HILL. But it cant have been right for your father to pour spirits down her throat like that. It might have killed her.

LIZA. Not her. Gin was mother's milk to her. Besides, he'd poured so much down his own throat that he knew the good of it.

MRS EYNSFORD HILL. Do you mean that he drank?

LIZA. Drank! My word! Something chronic.

MRS EYNSFORD HILL. How dreadful for you!

LIZA. Not a bit. It never did him no harm what I could see. But then he did not keep it up regular. [*Cheerfully*] On the burst, as you might say, from time to time. And always more agreeable when he had a drop in. When he was out of work, my mother used to give him fourpence and tell him to go out and not come back until he'd drunk himself cheerful and loving-like. Theres lots of women has to make their husbands drunk to make them fit to live with. [*Now quite at her ease*] You see, it's like this. If a man has a bit of a conscience, it always  takes him when he's sober; and then it makes him low-spirited. A drop of booze just takes that off and makes him happy. [*To Freddy, who is in convulsions of suppressed laughter*] Here! what are you sniggering at?

FREDDY. The new small talk. You do it so awfully well.

LIZA. If I was doing it proper, what was you laughing at? [*To Higgins*] Have I said anything I oughtnt?

MRS HIGGINS [*interposing*] Not at all, Miss Doolittle.

LIZA. Well, thats a mercy, anyhow. [*Expansively*] What I always say is –

HIGGINS [*rising and looking at his watch*] Ahem!

LIZA [*looking round at him; taking the hint; and rising*] Well: I must go. [*They all rise. Freddy goes to the door*]. So pleased to have met you. Goodbye. [*She shakes hands with Mrs Higgins*].

MRS HIGGINS. Goodbye.

LIZA. Goodbye, Colonel Pickering.

PICKERING. Goodbye, Miss Doolittle. [*They shake hands*].

LIZA [*nodding to the others*] Goodbye, all.

FREDDY [*opening the door for her*] Are you walking across the Park, Miss Doolittle? If so –

LIZA [*perfectly elegant diction*] Walk! Not bloody likely. [*Sensation*]. I am going in a taxi. [*She goes out*].

Pickering gasps and sits down. Freddy goes out on the balcony to catch another glimpse of Eliza.

MRS EYNSFORD HILL [*suffering from shock*] Well, I really cant get used to the new ways.

CLARA [*throwing herself discontentedly into the Elizabethan chair*] Oh, it's all right, mamma, quite right. People will think we never go anywhere or see anybody if you are so old-fashioned.

MRS EYNSFORD HILL. I daresay I am very old-fashioned; but I do hope you wont begin using that expression, Clara. I have got accustomed to hear you talking about men as rotters, and calling everything filthy and beastly; though I do think it horrible and unladylike. But this last is really too much. Dont you think so, Colonel Pickering?

PICKERING. Dont ask me. Ive been away in India for several years; and manners have changed so much that I sometimes dont know whether I'm at a respectable dinner-table or in a ship's forecastle.

CLARA. It's all a matter of habit. Theres no right or wrong in  it. Nobody means anything by it. And it's so quaint, and gives such a smart emphasis to things that are not in themselves very witty. I find the new small talk delightful and quite innocent.

MRS EYNSFORD HILL [*rising*] Well, after that, I think it's time for us to go.

> *Pickering and Higgins rise.*

CLARA [*rising*] Oh yes: we have three at-homes to go to still. Goodbye, Mrs Higgins. Goodbye, Colonel Pickering. Goodbye, Professor Higgins.

HIGGINS [*coming grimly at her from the divan, and accompanying her to the door*] Goodbye. Be sure you try on that small talk at the three at-homes. Dont be nervous about it. Pitch it in strong.

CLARA [*all smiles*] I will. Goodbye. Such nonsense, all this early Victorian prudery!

HIGGINS [*tempting her*] Such damned nonsense!

CLARA. Such bloody nonsense!

MRS EYNSFORD HILL [*convulsively*] Clara!

CLARA. Ha! ha! [*She goes out radiant, conscious of being thoroughly up to date, and is heard descending the stairs in a stream of silvery laughter*].

FREDDY [*to the heavens at large*] Well, I ask you – [*He gives it up, and comes to Mrs Higgins*]. Goodbye.

MRS HIGGINS [*shaking hands*] Goodbye. Would you like to meet Miss Doolittle again?

FREDDY [*eagerly*] Yes, I should, most awfully.

MRS HIGGINS. Well, you know my days.

FREDDY. Yes. Thanks awfully. Goodbye. [*He goes out*].

MRS EYNSFORD HILL. Goodbye, Mr Higgins.

HIGGINS. Goodbye. Goodbye.

MRS EYNSFORD HILL [to Pickering] It's no use. I shall never be able to bring myself to use that word.

PICKERING. Dont. It's not compulsory, you know. Youll get on quite well without it.

MRS EYNSFORD HILL. Only, Clara is so down on me if I am not positively reeking with the latest slang. Goodbye.

PICKERING. Goodbye. [They shake hands].

MRS EYNSFORD HILL [to Mrs Higgins] You mustnt mind Clara. [Pickering, catching from her lowered tone that this is not meant for him to hear, discreetly joins Higgins at the window]. We're so poor! and she gets so few parties, poor child! She doesnt quite know. [Mrs Higgins, seeing that her eyes are moist, takes her hand sympathetically and goes with her to the door]. But the boy is nice. Dont you think so?

MRS HIGGINS. Oh, quite nice. I shall always be delighted to see him.

MRS EYNSFORD HILL. Thank you, dear. Goodbye. [She goes out].

HIGGINS [eagerly] Well? Is Eliza presentable [he swoops on his mother and drags her to the ottoman, where she sits down in Eliza's place with her son on her left]?

  Pickering returns to his chair on her right.

MRS HIGGINS. You silly boy, of course she's not presentable. She's a triumph of your art and of her dressmaker's; but if you suppose for a moment that she doesnt give herself away in every sentence she utters, you must be perfectly cracked about her.

PICKERING. But dont you think something might be done? I mean something to eliminate the sanguinary element from her conversation.

MRS HIGGINS. Not as long as she is in Henry's hands.

HIGGINS [aggrieved] Do you mean that my language is improper?

MRS HIGGINS. No. dearest: it would be quite proper – say on a canal barge; but it would not be proper for her at a garden party.

HIGGINS [deeply injured] Well I must say –

PICKERING [interrupting him] Come, Higgins: you must learn

to know yourself. I havnt heard such language as yours since we used to review the volunteers in Hyde Park twenty years ago.

HIGGINS [*sulkily*] Oh, well, if you say so, I suppose I dont always talk like a bishop.

MRS HIGGINS [*quieting Henry with a touch*] Colonel Pickering: will you tell me what is the exact state of things in Wimpole Street?

PICKERING [*cheerfully: as if this completely changed the subject*] Well, I have come to live there with Henry. We work together at my Indian Dialects; and we think it more convenient –

MRS HIGGINS. Quite so. I know all about that: it's an excellent arrangement. But where does this girl live?

HIGGINS. With us, of course. Where should she live?

MRS HIGGINS. But on what terms? Is she a servant? If not, what is she?

PICKERING [*slowly*] I think I know what you mean, Mrs Higgins.

HIGGINS. Well, dash me if *I* do! Ive had to work at the girl every day for months to get her to her present pitch. Besides, she's useful. She knows where my things are, and remembers my appointments and so forth.

MRS HIGGINS. How does your housekeeper get on with her?

HIGGINS. Mrs Pearce? Oh, she's jolly glad to get so much taken off her hands; for before Eliza came, she used to have to find things and remind me of my appointments. But she's got some silly bee in her bonnet about Eliza. She keeps saying 'You dont think, sir': doesnt she, Pick?

PICKERING. Yes: thats the formula. 'You dont think, sir.' Thats the end of every conversation about Eliza.

HIGGINS. As if I ever stop thinking about the girl and her confounded vowels and consonants. I'm worn out, thinking about her, and watching her lips and her teeth and her tongue, not to mention her soul, which is the quaintest of the lot.

MRS HIGGINS. You certainly are a pretty pair of babies, playing with your live doll.

HIGGINS. Playing! The hardest job I ever tackled: make no mistake about that, mother. But you have no idea how frightfully interesting it is to take a human being and change her into a quite different human being by creating a new speech for her. It's filling up the deepest gulf that separates class from class and soul from soul.

PICKERING [*drawing his chair closer to Mrs Higgins and bending over to her eagerly*] Yes: it's enormously interesting. I assure you, Mrs Higgins, we take Eliza very seriously. Every week – every day almost – there is some new change. [*Closer again*] We keep records of every stage – dozens of gramophone disks and photographs –

HIGGINS [*assailing her at the other ear*] Yes, by George: it's the most absorbing experiment I ever tackled. She regularly fills our lives up: doesnt she, Pick?

PICKERING. We're always talking Eliza.

HIGGINS. Teaching Eliza.

PICKERING. Dressing Eliza.

MRS HIGGINS. What!

HIGGINS. Inventing new Elizas.

HIGGINS.	[*speaking together*]	You know, she has the most extra-ordinary quickness of ear:
PICKERING.		I assure you, my dear Mrs Higgins, that girl
HIGGINS.		just like a parrot. Ive tried her with every
PICKERING.		is a genius. She can play the piano quite beautifully.
HIGGINS.		possible sort of sound that a human being can make –
PICKERING.		We have taken her to classical concerts and to music
HIGGINS.		Continental dialects, African dialects, Hottentot
PICKERING.		halls; and it's all the same to her: she plays everything
HIGGINS.		clicks, things it took me years to get hold of; and
PICKERING.		she hears right off when she comes home, whether it's

HIGGINS.		she picks them up like a shot, right away, as if she had
	[speaking	
PICKERING.	together]	Beethoven and Brahms or Lehar and Lionel Monckton;
HIGGINS.		been at it all her life.
PICKERING.		though six months ago, she'd never as much as touched a piano –

MRS HIGGINS [putting her fingers in her ears, as they are by this time shouting one another down with an intolerable noise] Sh-sh-sh – sh!

[They stop].

PICKERING. I beg your pardon. [He draws his chair back apologetically].

HIGGINS. Sorry. When Pickering starts shouting nobody can get a word in edgeways.

MRS HIGGINS. Be quiet, Henry. Colonel Pickering: dont you realize that when Eliza walked into Wimpole Street, something walked in with her?

PICKERING. Her father did. But Henry soon got rid of him.

MRS HIGGINS. It would have been more to the point if her mother had. But as her mother didnt something else did.

PICKERING. But what?

83

MRS HIGGINS [*unconsciously dating herself by the word*] A problem.

PICKERING. Oh I see. The problem of how to pass her off as a lady.

HIGGINS. I'll solve that problem. Ive half solved it already.

MRS HIGGINS. No, you two infinitely stupid male creatures: the problem of what is to be done with her afterwards.

HIGGINS. I dont see anything in that. She can go her own way, with all the advantages I have given her.

MRS HIGGINS. The advantages of that poor woman who was here just now! The manners and habits that disqualify a fine lady from earning her own living without giving her a fine lady's income! Is that what you mean?

PICKERING [*indulgently, being rather bored*] Oh, that will be all right, Mrs Higgins. [*He rises to go*].

HIGGINS [*rising also*] We'll find her some light employment.

PICKERING. She's happy enough. Dont you worry about her. Goodbye. [*He shakes hands as if he were consoling a frightened child, and makes for the door*].

HIGGINS. Anyhow, theres no good bothering now. The thing's done. Goodbye, mother. [*He kisses her, and follows Pickering*].

PICKERING [*turning for a final consolation*] There are plenty of openings. We'll do whats right. Goodbye.

HIGGINS [*to Pickering as they go out together*] Lets take her to the Shakespear exhibition at Earls Court.

PICKERING. Yes: lets. Her remarks will be delicious.

HIGGINS. She'll mimic all the people for us when we get home.

PICKERING. Ripping. [*Both are heard laughing as they go downstairs*].

MRS HIGGINS [*rises with an impatient bounce, and returns to her work at the writing-table. She sweeps a litter of disarranged papers out of the way; snatches a sheet of paper from her stationery case; and tries resolutely to write. At the third time she gives it up; flings down her pen; grips the table angrily and exclaims*] Oh, men! men!! men!!!

*   *   *

Clearly Eliza will not pass as a duchess yet; and Higgins's bet remains unwon. But the six months are not yet exhausted; and just in time Eliza does actually pass as a princess. For a glimpse of how she did it imagine an Embassy in London one summer evening after dark. The hall door has an awning and a carpet across the sidewalk to the kerb, because a grand reception is in progress. A small crowd is lined up to see the guests arrive.

A Rolls-Royce car drives up. Pickering in evening dress, with medals and orders, alights, and hands out Eliza, in opera cloak, evening dress, diamonds, fan, flowers and all accessories. Higgins follows. The car drives off; and the three go up the steps and into the house, the door opening for them as they approach.

Inside the house they find themselves in a spacious hall from which the grand staircase rises. On the left are the

arrangements for the gentlemen's cloaks. The male guests are
depositing their hats and wraps there.

On the right is a door leading to the ladies' cloakroom. Ladies
are going in cloaked and coming out in splendor. Pickering

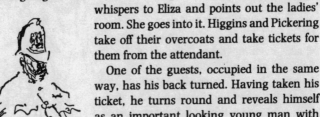

whispers to Eliza and points out the ladies'
room. She goes into it. Higgins and Pickering
take off their overcoats and take tickets for
them from the attendant.

One of the guests, occupied in the same
way, has his back turned. Having taken his
ticket, he turns round and reveals himself
as an important looking young man with
an astonishingly hairy face. He has an enormous moustache, flowing out into luxuriant
whiskers. Waves of hair cluster on his brow.

86

His hair is cropped closely at the back, and glows with oil. Otherwise he is very smart. He wears several worthless orders. He is evidently a foreigner, guessable as a whiskered Pandour from Hungary; but in spite of the ferocity of his moustache he is amiable and genially voluble.

Recognizing Higgins, he flings his arms wide apart and approaches him enthusiastically.

WHISKERS. Maestro, maestro [*he embraces Higgins and kisses him on both cheeks*]. You remember me?

HIGGINS. No I dont. Who the devil are you?

WHISKERS. I am your pupil: your first pupil, your best and greatest pupil. I am little Nepommuck, the marvellous boy. I have made your name famous throughout Europe. You teach me phonetic. You cannot forget ME.

HIGGINS. Why dont you shave?

NEPOMMUCK. I have not your imposing appearance, your chin, your brow. Nobody notices me when I shave. Now I am famous: they call me Hairy Faced Dick.

HIGGINS. And what are you doing here among all these swells?

NEPOMMUCK. I am interpreter. I speak 32 languages. I am indispensable at these international parties. You are great cockney specialist: you place a man anywhere in London the moment he open his mouth. I place any man in Europe.

A footman hurries down the grand staircase and comes to Nepommuck.

FOOTMAN. You are wanted upstairs. Her Excellency cannot understand the Greek gentleman.

NEPOMMUCK. Thank you, yes, immediately.

The footman goes and is lost in the crowd.

NEPOMMUCK [*to Higgins*] This Greek diplomatist pretends he cannot speak nor understand English. He cannot deceive me. He is the son of a Clerkenwell watchmaker. He speaks English so villainously that he dare not utter a word of it without betraying his origin. I help him to pretend; but I make him

pay through the nose. I make them all pay. Ha ha! [*He hurries upstairs*].

PICKERING. Is this fellow really an expert? Can he find out Eliza and blackmail her?

HIGGINS. We shall see. If he finds her out I lose my bet.

Eliza comes from the cloakroom and joins them.

PICKERING. Well, Eliza, now for it. Are you ready?

LIZA. Are you nervous, Colonel?

PICKERING. Frightfully. I feel exactly as I felt before my first battle. It's the first time that frightens.

LIZA. It is not the first time for me, Colonel. I have done this fifty times – hundreds of times – in my little piggery in Angel Court in my day-dreams. I am in a dream now. Promise me not to let Professor Higgins wake me; for if he does I shall forget everything and talk as I used to in Drury Lane.

PICKERING. Not a word, Higgins. [*To Eliza*] Now ready?

LIZA. Ready.

PICKERING. Go.

They mount the stairs, Higgins last. Pickering whispers to the footman on the first landing.

FIRST LANDING FOOTMAN. Miss Doolittle, Colonel Pickering, Professor Higgins.

SECOND LANDING FOOTMAN. Miss Doolittle, Colonel Pickering, Professor Higgins.

At the top of the staircase the Ambassador

*and his wife, with Nepommuck at her elbow, are
receiving.*

HOSTESS [*taking Eliza's hand*] How d'ye do?

HOST [*same play*] How d'ye do? How d'ye do,
Pickering?

LIZA [*with a beautiful gravity that awes her hostess*]
How do you do? [*She passes on to the drawing
room*].

HOSTESS. Is that your adopted daughter, Colonel
Pickering? She will make a sensation.

PICKERING. Most kind of you to invite her for me.
[*He passes on*].

HOSTESS [*to Nepommuck*] Find out all about her.

NEPOMMUCK [*bowing*] Excellency – [*he goes into
the crowd*].

HOST. How d'ye do, Higgins? You have a rival here tonight.
He introduced himself as your pupil. Is he any good?

HIGGINS. He can learn a language in a fortnight – knows dozens
of them. A sure mark of a fool. As a
phonetician, no good whatever.

HOSTESS. How d'ye do, Professor?

HIGGINS. How do you do? Fearful bore for
you this sort of thing. Forgive my part in
it. [*He passes on*].

In the drawing room and its suite of
salons the reception is in full swing. Eliza
passes through. She is so intent on her
ordeal that she walks like a somnambulist
in a desert instead of a débutante in a
fashionable crowd. They stop talking to
look at her, admiring her dress, her jewels,
and her strangely attractive self. Some of
the younger ones at the back stand on
their chairs to see.

The Host and Hostess come in from the
staircase and mingle with their guests.
Higgins, gloomy and contemptuous of the whole business,
comes into the group where they are chatting.

HOSTESS. Ah, here is Professor Higgins: he will tell us. Tell us all about the wonderful young lady, Professor.

HIGGINS [*almost morosely*] What wonderful young lady?

HOSTESS. You know very well. They tell me there has been nothing like her in London since people stood on their chairs to look at Mrs Langtry.

Nepommuck joins the group, full of news.

HOSTESS. Ah, here you are at last, Nepommuck. Have you found out all about the Doolittle lady?

NEPOMMUCK. I have found out all about her. She is a fraud.

HOSTESS. A fraud! Oh no.

NEPOMMUCK. YES, yes. She cannot deceive me. Her name cannot be Doolittle.

HIGGINS. Why?

NEPOMMUCK. Because Doolittle is an English name. And she is not English.

HOSTESS. Oh, nonsense! She speaks English perfectly.

NEPOMMUCK. Too perfectly. Can you shew me any English woman who speaks English as it should be spoken? Only foreigners who have been taught to speak it speak it well.

HOSTESS. Certainly she terrified me by the way she said How d'ye do. I had a schoolmistress who talked like that; and I was mortally afraid of her. But if she is not English what is she?

NEPOMMUCK. Hungarian.

ALL THE REST. Hungarian!

NEPOMMUCK. Hungarian. And of royal blood. I am Hungarian. My blood is royal.

HIGGINS. Did you speak to her in Hungarian?

NEPOMMUCK. I did. She was very clever. She said 'Please speak to me in English: I do not understand French.' French! She pretends not to know the difference between Hungarian and French. Impossible: she knows both.

HIGGINS. And the blood royal? How did you find that out?

NEPOMMUCK. Instinct, maestro, instinct. Only the Magyar races can produce that air of the divine right, those resolute eyes. She is a princess.

HOST. What do you say, Professor?

HIGGINS. I say an ordinary London girl out of the gutter and taught to speak by an expert. I place her in Drury Lane.

NEPOMMUCK. Ha ha ha! Oh, maestro, maestro, you are mad on the subject of cockney dialects. The London gutter is the whole world for you.

HIGGINS [*to the Hostess*] What does your Excellency say?

HOSTESS. Oh, of course I agree with Nepommuck. She must be a princess at least.

HOST. Not necessarily legitimate, of course. Morganatic perhaps. But that is undoubtedly her class.

HIGGINS. I stick to my opinion.

HOSTESS. Oh, you are incorrigible.

    The group breaks up, leaving Higgins isolated. Pickering joins him.

PICKERING. Where is Eliza? We must keep an eye on her.

    Eliza joins them.

LIZA. I dont think I can bear much more. The people all stare so at me. An old lady has just told me that I speak exactly like Queen Victoria. I am sorry if I have lost your bet. I have done my best; but nothing can make me the same as these people.

PICKERING. You have not lost it, my dear. You have won it ten times over.

HIGGINS. Let us get out of this. I have had enough of chattering to these fools.

PICKERING. Eliza is tired; and I am hungry. Let us clear out and have supper somewhere.

ACT FOUR

The Wimpole Street laboratory. Midnight. Nobody in the room. The clock on the mantelpiece strikes twelve. The fire is not alight: it is a summer night.

Presently Higgins and Pickering are heard on the stairs.

HIGGINS [*calling down to Pickering*] I say, Pick: lock up, will you? I shant be going out again.

PICKERING. Right. Can Mrs Pearce go to bed? We dont want anything more, do we?

HIGGINS. Lord, no!

Eliza opens the door and is seen on the lighted landing in all the finery in which she has just won Higgins's bet for him. She comes to the hearth, and switches on the electric lights there. She is tired: her pallor contrasts strongly with her dark eyes and hair; and her expression is almost tragic. She takes off her cloak; puts her fan and gloves on the piano; and sits down on the bench, brooding and silent. Higgins, in evening dress, with overcoat and hat, comes in, carrying a smoking jacket which he has picked up downstairs.

96

He takes off the hat and overcoat; throws them carelessly on the newspaper stand; disposes of his coat in the same way; puts on the smoking jacket; and throws himself wearily into the easy-chair at the hearth. Pickering, similarly attired, comes in. He also takes off his hat and overcoat, and is about to throw them on Higgins's when he hesitates.

PICKERING. I say: Mrs Pearce will row if we leave these things lying about in the drawing room.

HIGGINS. Oh, chuck them over the bannisters into the hall. She'll find them there in the morning and put them away all right. She'll think we were drunk.

PICKERING. We are, slightly. Are there any letters?

HIGGINS. I didnt look. [*Pickering takes the overcoats and hats and goes downstairs. Higgins begins half singing half yawning an air from La Fanciulla del Golden West. Suddenly he stops and exclaims*] I wonder where the devil my slippers are!

    Eliza looks at him darkly; then rises suddenly and leaves the room.

    Higgins yawns again, and resumes his song.

    Pickering returns, with the contents of the letterbox in his hand.

PICKERING. Only circulars, and this coroneted billet-doux for you. [*He throws the circulars into the fender, and posts himself on the hearthrug, with his back to the grate*].

HIGGINS [*glancing at the billet-doux*] Money-lender. [*He throws the letter after the circulars*].

    Eliza returns with a pair of large down-at-heel slippers. She places them on the carpet before Higgins, and sits as before without a word.

HIGGINS [*yawning again*] Oh Lord! What an evening! What a crew! What a silly tomfoolery! [*He raises his shoe to unlace it, and catches sight of the slippers. He stops unlacing and*

looks at them as if they had appeared there of their own accord].
Oh! theyre there, are they?

PICKERING [*stretching himself*] Well, I feel a bit tired. It's been a long day. The garden party, a dinner party, and the reception! Rather too much of a good thing. But youve won your bet, Higgins. Eliza did the trick, and something to spare, eh?

HIGGINS [*fervently*] Thank God it's over!

Eliza flinches violently; but they take no notice of her; and she recovers herself and sits stonily as before.

PICKERING. Were you nervous at the garden party? *I* was. Eliza didnt seem a bit nervous.

HIGGINS. Oh, she wasnt nervous. I knew she'd be all right. No: it's the strain of putting the job through all these months that has told on me. It was interesting enough at first, while we were at the phonetics; but after that I got deadly sick of it. If I hadnt backed myself to do it I should have chucked the whole thing up two months ago. It was a silly notion: the whole thing has been a bore.

PICKERING. Oh come! the garden party was frightfully exciting. My heart began beating like anything.

HIGGINS. Yes, for the first three minutes. But when I saw we were going to win hands down, I felt like a bear in a cage, hanging about doing nothing. The dinner was worse: sitting gorging there for over an hour, with nobody but a damned fool of a fashionable woman to talk to! I tell you, Pickering, never again for me. No more artificial duchesses. The whole thing has been simple purgatory.

PICKERING. Youve never been broken in properly to the social routine. [*Strolling over to the piano*] I rather enjoy dipping into it occasionally myself: it makes me feel young again. Anyhow, it was a great success: an immense success. I was quite frightened once or twice because Eliza was doing it so well. You see, lots of the real people cant do it at all: theyre such fools that they think style comes by nature to people in their position; and so they never learn. Theres always something professional about doing a thing superlatively well.

HIGGINS. Yes: thats what drives me mad: the silly people dont know their own silly business. [*Rising*] However, it's over and done with; and now I can go to bed at last without dreading tomorrow.

Eliza's beauty becomes murderous.

PICKERING. I think I shall turn in too. Still, it's been a great occasion: a triumph for you. Goodnight. [*He goes*].

HIGGINS [*following him*] Goodnight. [*Over his shoulder, at the door*] Put out the lights, Eliza; and tell Mrs Pearce not to make coffee for me in the morning: I'll take tea. [*He goes out*].

Eliza tries to control herself and feel indifferent as she rises and walks across to the hearth to switch off the lights. By the time she gets there she is on the point of screaming. She sits down in Higgins's chair and holds on hard to the arms. Finally she gives way and flings herself furiously on the floor, raging.

HIGGINS [*in despairing wrath outside*] What the devil have I done with my slippers? [*He appears at the door*].

LIZA [*snatching up the slippers, and hurling them at him one after the other with all her force*] There are your slippers. And there. Take your slippers; and may you never have a day's luck with them!

HIGGINS [*astounded*] What on earth – ! [*He comes to her*]. Whats the matter? Get up. [*He pulls her up*]. Anything wrong?

LIZA [*breathless*] Nothing wrong – with you. Ive won your bet for you, havnt I? Thats enough for you. *I* dont matter, I suppose.

HIGGINS. You won my bet! You! Presumptuous insect! *I* won it. What did you throw those slippers at me for?

LIZA. Because I wanted to smash your face. I'd like to kill you, you selfish brute. Why didnt you leave me where you picked me out of – in the gutter? You thank God it's all over, and that now you can throw me back again there, do you? [*She crisps her fingers frantically*].

HIGGINS [*looking at her in cool wonder*] The creature is nervous, after all.

LIZA [*gives a suffocated scream of fury, and instinctively darts her nails at his face*]!!

HIGGINS [*catching her wrists*] Ah! would you? Claws in, you cat. How dare you shew your temper to me? Sit down and be quiet. [*He throws her roughly into the easy-chair*].

LIZA [*crushed by superior strength and weight*] Whats to become of me? Whats to become of me?

HIGGINS. How the devil do I know whats to become of you? What does it matter what becomes of you?

LIZA. You dont care. I know you dont care. You wouldnt care if I was dead. I'm nothing to you – not so much as them slippers.

HIGGINS [*thundering*] Those slippers.

LIZA [*with bitter submission*] Those slippers. I didnt think it made any difference now.

A pause. Eliza hopeless and crushed. Higgins a little uneasy.

HIGGINS [*in his loftiest manner*] Why have you begun going on like this? May I ask whether you complain of your treatment here?

LIZA. No.

HIGGINS. Has anybody behaved badly to you? Colonel Pickering? Mrs Pearce? Any of the servants?

LIZA. No.

HIGGINS. I presume you dont pretend that *I* have treated you badly?

LIZA. No.

HIGGINS. I am glad to hear it. [*He moderates his tone*]. Perhaps youre tired after the strain of the day. Will you have a glass of champagne? [*He moves towards the door*].

LIZA. No. [*Recollecting her manners*] Thank you.

HIGGINS. [*good-humored again*] This has been coming on you for some days. I suppose it was natural for you to be anxious about the garden party. But thats all over now. [*He pats her kindly on the shoulder. She writhes*]. Theres nothing more to worry about.

LIZA. No. Nothing more for you to worry about. [*She suddenly rises and gets away from him by going to the piano bench, where she sits and hides her face*]. Oh God! I wish I was dead.

HIGGINS [*staring after her in sincere surprise*] Why? In heaven's name, why? [*Reasonably, going to her*] Listen to me, Eliza. All this irritation is purely subjective.

LIZA. I dont understand. I'm too ignorant.

HIGGINS. It's only imagination. Low spirits and nothing else. Nobody's hurting you. Nothing's wrong. You go to bed like a good girl and sleep it off. Have a little cry and say your prayers: that will make you comfortable.

LIZA. I heard your prayers. 'Thank God it's all over!'

HIGGINS [*impatiently*] Well, dont you thank God it's all over? Now you are free and can do what you like.

LIZA [*pulling herself together in desperation*] What am I fit for? What have you left me fit for? Where am I to go? What am I to do? Whats to become of me?

HIGGINS [*enlightened, but not at all impressed*] Oh, thats whats worrying you, is it? [*He thrusts his hands into his pockets, and walks about in his usual manner, rattling the contents of his pockets, as if condescending to a trivial subject out of pure kindness*]. I shouldnt bother about it if I were you. I should imagine you wont have much difficulty in settling yourself somewhere or other, though I hadnt quite realized that you were going away. [*She looks quickly at him: he does not look at her, but examines the dessert stand on the piano and decides that he will eat an apple*]. You might marry, you know. [*He bites a large piece out of the apple and munches it noisily*]. You see, Eliza, all men are not confirmed old bachelors like me and the Colonel. Most men are the marrying sort (poor devils!); and youre not bad-looking: it's quite a pleasure to look at you sometimes − not now, of course, because youre crying and looking as ugly as the very devil; but when youre all right and quite yourself, youre what I should call attractive. That is, to the people in the marrying line, you understand. You go to bed and have a good nice rest; and then get up and look at yourself in the glass; and you wont feel so cheap.

Eliza again looks at him, speechless, and does not stir.

The look is quite lost on him: he eats his apple with a dreamy expression of happiness, as it is quite a good one.

HIGGINS [*a genial afterthought occurring to him*] I daresay my mother could find some chap or other who would do very well.

LIZA. We were above that at the corner of Tottenham Court Road.

HIGGINS [*waking up*] What do you mean?

LIZA. I sold flowers. I didnt sell myself. Now youve made a lady of me I'm not fit to sell anything else. I wish youd left me where you found me.

HIGGINS [*slinging the core of the apple decisively into the grate*] Tosh, Eliza. Dont you insult human relations by dragging all this cant about buying and selling into it. You neednt marry the fellow if you dont like him.

LIZA. What else am I to do?

HIGGINS. Oh, lots of things. What about your old idea of a florist's shop? Pickering could set you up in one: he has lots of money. [*Chuckling*] He'll have to pay for all those togs you have been wearing today; and that, with the hire of the jewellery, will make a big hole in two hundred pounds. Why, six months ago you would have thought it the millennium to have a flower shop of your own. Come! youll be all right. I must clear off to bed: I'm devilish sleepy. By the way, I came down for something: I forget what it was.

LIZA. Your slippers.

HIGGINS. Oh yes, of course. You shied them at me. [*He picks them up, and is going out when she rises and speaks to him*].

LIZA. Before you go, sir –

HIGGINS [*dropping the slippers in his surprise at her calling him Sir*] Eh?

LIZA. Do my clothes belong to me or to Colonel Pickering?

HIGGINS [*coming back into the room as if her question were the very climax of unreason*] What the devil use would they be to Pickering?

LIZA. He might want them for the next girl you pick up to experiment on.

HIGGINS [*shocked and hurt*] Is that the way you feel towards us?

LIZA. I dont want to hear anything more about that. All I want to know is whether anything belongs to me. My own clothes were burnt.

HIGGINS. But what does it matter? Why need you start bothering about that in the middle of the night?

LIZA. I want to know what I may take away with me. I dont want to be accused of stealing.

HIGGINS [*now deeply wounded*] Stealing! You shouldnt have said that, Eliza. That shews a want of feeling.

LIZA. I'm sorry. I'm only a common ignorant girl; and in my station I have to be careful. There cant be any feelings between the like of you and the like of me. Please will you tell me what belongs to me and what doesnt?

HIGGINS [*very sulky*] You may take the whole damned houseful if you like. Except the jewels. Theyre hired. Will that satisfy you? [*He turns on his heel and is about to go in extreme dudgeon*].

LIZA [*drinking in his emotion like nectar, and nagging him to provoke a further supply*] Stop, please. [*She takes off her jewels*]. Will you take these to your room and keep them safe? I dont want to run the risk of their being missing.

HIGGINS [*furious*] Hand them over. [*She puts them into his hands*]. If these belonged to me instead of to the jeweller, I'd ram them down your ungrateful throat. [*He perfunctorily thrusts them into his pockets, unconsciously decorating himself with the protruding ends of the chains*].

LIZA [*taking a ring off*] This ring isnt the jeweller's: it's the one you bought me in Brighton. I dont want it now. [*Higgins dashes the ring violently into the fireplace, and turns on her so threateningly that she crouches over the piano with her hands over her face, and exclaims*] Dont you hit me.

HIGGINS. Hit you! You infamous creature, how dare you accuse me of such a thing? It is you who have hit me. You have wounded me to the heart.

LIZA [*thrilling with hidden joy*] I'm glad. Ive got a little of my own back, anyhow.

HIGGINS [*with dignity, in his finest professional style*] You have caused me to lose my temper: a thing that has hardly ever happened to me before. I prefer to say nothing more tonight. I am going to bed.

LIZA [*pertly*] Youd better leave a note for Mrs Pearce about the coffee; for she wont be told by me.

HIGGINS [*formally*] Damn Mrs Pearce; and damn the coffee; and damn you; and [*wildly*] damn my own folly in having lavished my hard-earned knowledge and the treasure of my regard and intimacy on a heartless guttersnipe. [*He goes out with impressive decorum, and spoils it by slamming the door savagely*].

Eliza goes down on her knees on the hearthrug to look for the ring. When she finds it she considers for a moment what to do with it. Finally she flings it down on the dessert stand and goes upstairs in a tearing rage.

* * *

The furniture of Eliza's room has been increased by a big wardrobe and a sumptuous dressing-table. She comes in and switches on the electric light. She goes to the wardrobe; opens it; and pulls out a walking dress, a hat, and a pair of shoes, which she throws on the bed. She takes off her evening dress and shoes; then takes a padded hanger from the wardrobe; adjusts it carefully in the evening dress; and hangs it in the wardrobe, which she shuts with a slam. She puts on her walking shoes, her walking dress, and hat. She takes her wrist watch from the dressing-table and fastens it on. She pulls on her gloves; takes her vanity bag; and looks into it to see that her purse is there before hanging it on her wrist. She makes for the door. Every movement expresses her furious resolution.

She takes a last look at herself in the glass.

She suddenly puts out her tongue at herself; then leaves the room, switching off the electric light at the door.

Meanwhile, in the street outside,

Freddy Eynsford Hill, lovelorn, is gazing up at the second floor, in which one of the windows is still lighted.

The light goes out.

FREDDY. Goodnight, darling, darling, darling.

Eliza comes out, giving the door a considerable bang behind her.

LIZA. Whatever are you doing here?

FREDDY. Nothing. I spend most of my nights here. It's the only place where I'm happy. Dont laugh at me, Miss Doolittle.

LIZA. Dont you call me Miss Doolittle, do you hear? Liza's good enough for me. [*She breaks down and grabs him by the shoulders*] Freddy: you dont think I'm a heartless guttersnipe, do you?

FREDDY. Oh no, no, darling: how can you imagine such a thing? You are the loveliest, dearest –

He loses all self-control and smothers her with kisses. She, hungry for comfort, responds. They stand there in one another's arms.

An elderly police constable arrives.

CONSTABLE [*scandalized*] Now then! Now then!! Now then!!!

They release one another hastily.

FREDDY. Sorry, constable. Weve only just become engaged.

They run away.

The constable shakes his head, reflecting on his own courtship and on the vanity of human hopes. He moves off in the opposite direction with slow professional steps.

The flight of the lovers takes them to Cavendish Square. There they halt to consider their next move.

LIZA [*out of breath*] He didnt half give me a fright, that copper. But you answered him proper.

FREDDY. I hope I havnt taken you out of your way. Where were
you going?

LIZA. To the river.

FREDDY. What for?

LIZA. To make a hole in it.

FREDDY [*horrified*] Eliza, darling. What do you mean? What's
the matter?

LIZA. Never mind. It doesnt matter now. Theres nobody in the world now but you and me, is there?

FREDDY. Not a soul.

They indulge in another embrace, and are again surprised by a much younger constable.

SECOND CONSTABLE. Now then, you two! What's this? Where do you think you are? Move along here, double quick.

FREDDY. As you say, sir, double quick.

They run away again, and are in Hanover Square before they stop for another conference.

FREDDY. I had no idea the police were so devilishly prudish.

LIZA. It's their business to hunt girls off the streets.

FREDDY. We must go somewhere. We cant wander about the streets all night.

LIZA. Cant we? I think it'd be lovely to wander about for ever.

FREDDY. Oh, darling.

> *They embrace again, oblivious of the arrival of a crawling taxi. It stops.*

TAXIMAN. Can I drive you and the lady anywhere, sir?

> *They start asunder.*

LIZA. Oh, Freddy, a taxi. The very thing.

FREDDY. But, damn it, Ive no money.

LIZA. I have plenty. The Colonel thinks you should never go out without ten pounds in your pocket. Listen. We'll drive about all night; and in the morning I'll call on old Mrs Higgins and ask her what I ought to do. I'll tell you all about it in the cab. And the police wont touch us there.

FREDDY. Righto! Ripping. [*To the Taximan*] Wimbledon Common. [*They drive off*].

ACT FIVE

Mrs Higgins's drawing room. She is at her writing-table as before. The parlormaid comes in.

THE PARLORMAID [*at the door*] Mr Henry, maam, is downstairs with Colonel Pickering.

MRS HIGGINS. Well, shew them up.

THE PARLORMAID. Theyre using the telephone, maam. Telephoning to the police, I think.

MRS HIGGINS. What!

THE PARLORMAID [*coming further in and lowering her voice*] Mr Henry is in a state, maam. I thought I'd better tell you.

MRS HIGGINS. If you had told me that Mr Henry was not in a state it would have been more surprising. Tell them to come up when theyve finished with the police. I suppose he's lost something.

THE PARLORMAID. Yes, maam [*going*].

MRS HIGGINS. Go upstairs and tell Miss Doolittle that Mr Henry and the Colonel are here. Ask her not to come down til I send for her.

THE PARLORMAID. Yes, maam.

*Higgins bursts in. He is, as the parlormaid
has said, in a state.*

HIGGINS. Look here, mother: heres a confounded thing!

MRS HIGGINS. Yes, dear. Good morning. [*He
checks his impatience and kisses her, whilst the
parlormaid goes out*]. What is it?

HIGGINS. Eliza's bolted.

MRS HIGGINS [*calmly continuing her writing*]
You must have frightened her.

HIGGINS. Frightened her! nonsense! She was
left last night, as usual, to turn out the lights
and all that; and instead of going to bed she
changed her clothes and went right off: her
bed wasnt slept in. She came in a cab for
her things before seven this morning; and
that fool Mrs Pearce let her have them without telling me a
word about it. What am I to do?

MRS HIGGINS. Do without, I'm afraid, Henry. The girl has a
perfect right to leave if she chooses.

HIGGINS [*wandering distractedly across the room*] But I cant find
anything. I dont know what appointments Ive got. I'm –
[*Pickering comes in. Mrs Higgins puts down her pen and turns
away from the writing-table*].

PICKERING [*shaking hands*] Good morning, Mrs Higgins. Has
Henry told you? [*He sits down on the ottoman*].

HIGGINS. What does that ass of an inspector say? Have you
offered a reward?

MRS HIGGINS [*rising in indignant amazement*] You dont mean to
say you have set the police after Eliza?

HIGGINS. Of course. What are the police for? What else could
we do? [*He sits in the Elizabethan chair*].

PICKERING. The inspector made a lot of difficulties. I really
think he suspected us of some improper purpose.

MRS HIGGINS. Well, of course he did. What right have you to
go to the police and give the girl's name as if she were a thief,

or a lost umbrella, or something? Really! [*She sits down again, deeply vexed*].

HIGGINS. But we want to find her.

PICKERING. We cant let her go like this, you know, Mrs Higgins. What were we to do?

MRS HIGGINS. You have no more sense, either of you, than two children. Why –

The parlormaid comes in and breaks off the conversation.

THE PARLORMAID. Mr Henry: a gentleman wants to see you very particular. He's been sent on from Wimpole Street.

HIGGINS. Oh, bother! I cant see anyone now. Who is it?

THE PARLORMAID. A Mr Doolittle, sir.

PICKERING. Doolittle! Do you mean the dustman?

THE PARLORMAID. Dustman! Oh no, sir: a gentleman.

HIGGINS [*springing up excitedly*] By George, Pick, it's some relative of hers that she's gone to. Somebody we know nothing about. [*To the parlormaid*] Send him up, quick.

THE PARLORMAID. Yes, sir. [*She goes*].

HIGGINS [*eagerly, going to his mother*] Genteel relatives! now we shall hear something. [*He sits down in the Chippendale chair*].

MRS HIGGINS. Do you know any of her people?

PICKERING. Only her father: the fellow we told you about.

THE PARLORMAID [*announcing*] Mr Doolittle. [*She withdraws*].

Doolittle enters. He is resplendently dressed as for a fashionable wedding, and might, in fact, be the bridegroom. A flower in his buttonhole, a dazzling silk hat, and patent leather shoes complete the effect. He is too concerned with the business he has come on to notice Mrs Higgins. He walks straight to Higgins, and accosts him with vehement reproach.

DOOLITTLE [*indicating his own person*] See here! Do you see this? You done this.

HIGGINS. Done what, man?

DOOLITTLE. This, I tell you. Look at it. Look at this hat. Look at this coat.

PICKERING. Has Eliza been buying you clothes?

DOOLITTLE. Eliza! not she. Why would she buy me clothes?

MRS HIGGINS. Good morning, Mr Doolittle. Wont you sit down?

DOOLITTLE [*taken aback as he becomes conscious that he has forgotten his hostess*] Asking your pardon, maam. [*He approaches her and shakes her proffered hand*]. Thank you. [*He sits*

down on the ottoman, on Pickering's right]. I am that full of what has happened to me that I cant think of anything else.

HIGGINS. What the dickens has happened to you?

DOOLITTLE. I shouldnt mind if it had only happened to me: anything might happen to anybody and nobody to blame but Providence, as you might say. But this is something that you done to me: yes, you, Enry Iggins.

HIGGINS. Have you found Eliza?

DOOLITTLE. Have you lost her?

HIGGINS. Yes.

DOOLITTLE. You have all the luck, you have. I aint found her; but she'll find me quick enough now after what you done to me.

MRS HIGGINS. But what has my son done to you, Mr Doolittle?

DOOLITTLE. Done to me! Ruined me. Destroyed my happiness. Tied me up and delivered me into the hands of middle class morality.

HIGGINS [*rising intolerantly and standing over Doolittle*] Youre raving. Youre drunk. Youre mad. I gave you five pounds. After that I had two conversations with you, at half-a-crown an hour. Ive never seen you since.

DOOLITTLE. Oh! Drunk am I? Mad am I? Tell me this. Did you or did you not write a letter to an old blighter in America that was giving five millions to found Moral Reform Societies all over the world, and that wanted you to invent a universal language for him?

HIGGINS. What! Ezra D. Wannafeller! He's dead. [*He sits down again carelessly*].

DOOLITTLE. Yes: he's dead; and I'm done for. Now did you or did you not write a letter to him to say that the most original moralist at present in England, to the best of your knowledge, was Alfred Doolittle, a common dustman?

HIGGINS. Oh, after your first visit I remember making some silly joke of the kind.

DOOLITTLE. Ah! You may well call it a silly joke. It put the lid on me right enough. Just give him the chance he wanted to shew that Americans is not like us: that they reckonize and respect merit in every class of life, however humble. Them words is in his blooming will, in which, Henry Higgins, thanks to your silly joking, he leaves me a share in his Pre-digested Cheese Trust worth three thousand a year on condition that I lecture for his Wannafeller Moral Reform World League as often as they ask me up to six times a year.

HIGGINS. The devil he does! Whew! [*Brightening suddenly*] What a lark!

PICKERING. A safe thing for you, Doolittle. They wont ask you twice.

DOOLITTLE. It aint the lecturing I mind. I'll lecture them blue in the face, I will, and not turn a hair. It's making a gentleman of me that I object to. Who asked him to make a gentleman of me? I was happy. I was free. I touched pretty nigh everybody for money when I wanted it, same as I touched you, Enry Iggins. Now I am worritted; tied neck and heels; and everybody touches me for money. It's a fine thing for you, says my solicitor. Is it? says I. You mean it's a good thing for you, I says. When I was a poor man and had a solicitor once when they found a pram in the dust cart, he got me off, and got shut of me and got me shut of him as quick as he could. Same with the doctors: used to shove me out of the hospital before I could hardly stand on my legs, and nothing to pay. Now they finds out that I'm not a healthy man and cant live unless they looks after me twice a day. In the house I'm not let do a hand's turn for myself: somebody else must do it and touch me for it. A year ago I hadnt a relative in the world except two or three that wouldnt speak to me. Now Ive fifty, and not a decent week's wages among the lot of them. I have to live for others and not for myself: thats middle class morality. You talk of losing Eliza. Dont you be anxious: I bet she's on my doorstep by this: she that could support herself easy by selling flowers if I wasnt respectable. And the next one to touch me will be you, Enry Iggins. I'll have to learn to speak middle class language from you, instead of speaking proper English. Thats where youll come in; and I daresay thats what you done it for.

MRS HIGGINS. But, my dear Mr Doolittle, you need not suffer all this if you are really in earnest. Nobody can force you to accept this bequest. You can repudiate it. Isnt that so, Colonel Pickering?

PICKERING. I believe so.

DOOLITTLE [*softening his manner in deference to her sex*] Thats the tragedy of it, maam. It's easy to say chuck it; but I havnt the nerve. Which of us has? We're all intimidated. Intimidated, maam: thats what we are. What is there for me if I chuck it but the workhouse in my old age? I have to dye my hair already to keep my job as a dustman. If I was one of the deserving poor, and had put by a bit, I could chuck it; but then why should I, acause the deserving poor might as well be millionaires for all the happiness they ever has. They dont know what happiness is. But I, as one of the undeserving poor, have nothing between me and the pauper's uniform but this here blasted three thousand a year that shoves me into the middle class. (Excuse the expression, maam; youd use it yourself if you had my provocation.) Theyve got you every way you turn: it's a choice between the Skilly of the workhouse and the Char Bydis of the middle class; and I havnt the nerve for the workhouse. Intimidated: thats what I am. Broke. Bought up. Happier men than me will call for my dust, and touch me for their tip; and I'll look on helpless, and envy them. And thats what your son has brought me to. [*He is overcome by emotion*].

MRS HIGGINS. Well, I'm very glad youre not going to do anything foolish, Mr Doolittle. For this solves the problem of Eliza's future. You can provide for her now.

DOOLITTLE [*with melancholy resignation*] Yes, maam: I'm expected to provide for everyone now, out of three thousand a year.

HIGGINS [*jumping up*] Nonsense! he cant provide for her. He shant provide for her. She doesnt belong to him. I paid him five pounds for her. Doolittle: either youre an honest man or a rogue.

DOOLITTLE [*tolerantly*] A little of both, Henry, like the rest of us: a little of both.

HIGGINS. Well, you took that money for the girl; and you have no right to take her as well.

MRS HIGGINS. Henry: dont be absurd. If you want to know where Eliza is, she is upstairs.

HIGGINS [*amazed*] Upstairs!!! Then I shall jolly soon fetch her downstairs. [*He makes resolutely for the door*].

MRS HIGGINS [*rising and following him*] Be quiet, Henry. Sit down.

HIGGINS. I –

MRS HIGGINS. Sit down, dear; and listen to me.

HIGGINS. Oh very well, very well, very well. [*He throws himself ungraciously on the ottoman, with his face towards the windows*]. But I think you might have told us this half an hour ago.

MRS HIGGINS. Eliza came to me this morning. She told me of the brutal way you two treated her.

HIGGINS [*bouncing up again*] What!

PICKERING [*rising also*] My dear Mrs Higgins, she's been telling you stories. We didnt treat her brutally. We hardly said a word to her; and we parted on particularly good terms. [*Turning on Higgins*] Higgins: did you bully her after I went to bed?

HIGGINS. Just the other way about. She threw my slippers in my face. She behaved in the most outrageous way. I never gave her the slightest provocation. The slippers came bang into my face the moment I entered the room – before I had uttered a word. And used perfectly awful language.

PICKERING [*astonished*] But why? What did we do to her?

MRS HIGGINS. I think I know pretty well what you did. The girl is naturally rather affectionate, I think. Isnt she, Mr Doolittle?

DOOLITTLE. Very tender-hearted, maam. Takes after me.

MRS HIGGINS. Just so. She had become attached to you both. She worked very hard for you, Henry. I dont think you quite realize what anything in the nature of brain work means to a girl of her class. Well, it seems that when the great day of trial came, and she did this wonderful thing for you without making a single mistake, you two sat there and never said a word to her, but talked together of how glad you were that it was all over and how you had been bored with the whole thing. And then you were surprised because she threw your slippers at you! *I* should have thrown the fire-irons at you.

HIGGINS. We said nothing except that we were tired and wanted to go to bed. Did we, Pick?

PICKERING [*shrugging his shoulders*] That was all.

MRS HIGGINS [*ironically*] Quite sure?

PICKERING. Absolutely. Really, that was all.

MRS HIGGINS. You didnt thank her, or pet her, or admire her, or tell her how splendid she'd been.

HIGGINS [*impatiently*] But she knew all about that. We didnt make speeches to her, if thats what you mean.

PICKERING [*conscience stricken*] Perhaps we were a little inconsiderate. Is she very angry?

MRS HIGGINS [*returning to her place at the writing-table*] Well, I'm afraid she wont go back to Wimpole Street, especially now that Mr Doolittle is able to keep up the position you have thrust on her; but she says she is quite willing to meet you on friendly terms and to let bygones be bygones.

HIGGINS [*furious*] Is she, by George? Ho!

MRS HIGGINS. If you promise to behave yourself, Henry, I'll ask her to come down. If not, go home: for you have taken up quite enough of my time.

HIGGINS. Oh, all right. Very well. Pick: you behave yourself. Let us put on our best Sunday manners for this creature that we picked out of the mud. [*He flings himself sulkily into the Elizabethan chair*].

DOOLITTLE [*remonstrating*] Now, now, Enry Iggins! Have some consideration for my feelings as a middle class man.

MRS HIGGINS. Remember your promise, Henry. [*She presses the bell-button on the writing-table*]. Mr Doolittle: will you be so good as to step out on the balcony for a moment. I dont want Eliza to have the shock of your news until she has made it up with these two gentlemen. Would you mind?

DOOLITTLE. As you wish, lady. Anything to help Henry to keep her off my hands. [*He disappears through the window*].

The parlormaid answers the bell. Pickering sits down in Doolittle's place.

MRS HIGGINS. Ask Miss Doolittle to come down, please.

THE PARLORMAID. Yes, maam. [*She goes out*].

MRS HIGGINS. Now, Henry: be good.

HIGGINS. I am behaving myself perfectly.

PICKERING. He is doing his best, Mrs Higgins.

A pause. Higgins throws back his head; stretches out his legs; and begins to whistle.

MRS HIGGINS. Henry, dearest, you dont look at all nice in that attitude.

HIGGINS [*pulling himself together*] I was not trying to look nice, mother.

MRS HIGGINS. It doesnt matter, dear. I only wanted to make you speak.

HIGGINS. Why?

MRS HIGGINS. Because you cant speak and whistle at the same time.

Higgins groans. Another very trying pause.

HIGGINS [*springing up, out of patience*] Where the devil is that girl? Are we to wait here all day?

Eliza enters, sunny, self-possessed, and giving a staggeringly convincing exhibition of ease of manner. She carries a little work-basket, and is very much at home. Pickering is too much taken aback to rise.

LIZA. How do you do, Professor Higgins? Are you quite well?

HIGGINS [*choking*] Am I – [*He can say no more*].

LIZA. But of course you are: you are never ill. So glad to see you again, Colonel Pickering. [*He rises hastily; and they shake hands*]. Quite chilly this morning, isnt it? [*She sits down on his left. He sits beside her*].

HIGGINS. Dont you dare try this game on me. I taught it to you; and it doesnt take me in. Get up and come home; and dont be a fool.

Eliza takes a piece of needlework from her basket, and begins to stitch at it, without taking the least notice of this outburst.

MRS HIGGINS. Very nicely put, indeed, Henry. No woman could resist such an invitation.

HIGGINS. You let her alone, mother. Let her speak for herself. You will jolly soon see whether she has an idea that I havnt put into her head or a word that I havnt put into her mouth. I tell you I have created this thing out of the squashed cabbage leaves of Covent Garden; and now she pretends to play the fine lady with me.

MRS HIGGINS [*placidly*] Yes, dear; but youll sit down, wont you?

   Higgins sits down again, savagely.

LIZA [*to Pickering, taking no apparent notice of Higgins, and working away deftly*] Will you drop me altogether now that the experiment is over, Colonel Pickering?

PICKERING. Oh dont. You mustnt think of it as an experiment. It shocks me, somehow.

LIZA. Oh, I'm only a squashed cabbage leaf –

PICKERING [*impulsively*] No.

LIZA [*continuing quietly*] – but I owe so much to you that I should be very unhappy if you forgot me.

PICKERING. It's very kind of you to say so, Miss Doolittle.

LIZA. It's not because you paid for my dresses. I know you are generous to everybody with money. But it was from you that I learnt really nice manners; and that is what makes one a lady, isnt it? You see it was so very difficult for me with the example of Professor Higgins always before me. I was brought up to be just like him, unable to control myself, and using bad language on the slightest provocation. And I should never have known that ladies and gentlemen didnt behave like that if you hadnt been there.

HIGGINS. Well!!

PICKERING. Oh, thats only his way, you know. He doesnt mean it.

LIZA. Oh, *I* didnt mean it either, when I was a flower girl. It was only my way. But you see I did it; and thats what makes the difference after all.

PICKERING. No doubt. Still, he taught you to speak; and I couldnt have done that, you know.

LIZA [*trivially*] Of course: that is his profession.

HIGGINS. Damnation!

LIZA [*continuing*] It was just like learning to dance in the fashionable way: there was nothing more than that in it. But do you know what began my real education?

PICKERING. What?

LIZA [*stopping her work for a moment*] Your calling me Miss Doolittle that day when I first came to Wimpole Street. That was the beginning of self-respect for me. [*She resumes her stitching*]. And there were a hundred little things you never noticed, because they came naturally to you. Things about standing up and taking off your hat and opening doors —

PICKERING. Oh, that was nothing.

LIZA. Yes: things that shewed you thought and felt about me as if I were something better than a scullery-maid; though of course I know you would have been just the same to a scullery-maid if she had been let into the drawing room. You never took off your boots in the dining room when I was there.

PICKERING. You mustnt mind that. Higgins takes off his boots all over the place.

LIZA. I know. I am not blaming him. It is his way, isnt it? But it made such a difference to me that you didnt do it. You see, really and truly, apart from the things anyone can pick up (the dressing and the proper way of speaking, and so on), the difference between a lady and a flower girl is not how she behaves, but how she's treated. I shall always be a flower girl to Professor Higgins, because he always treats me as a flower girl, and always will; but I know I can be a lady to you, because you always treat me as a lady, and always will.

MRS HIGGINS. Please dont grind your teeth, Henry.

PICKERING. Well, this is really very nice of you, Miss Doolittle.

LIZA. I should like you to call me Eliza, now, if you would.

PICKERING. Thank you. Eliza, of course.

LIZA. And I should like Professor Higgins to call me Miss Doolittle.

HIGGINS. I'll see you damned first.

MRS HIGGINS. Henry! Henry!

PICKERING [*laughing*] Why dont you slang back at him? Dont stand it. It would do him a lot of good.

LIZA. I cant. I could have done it once but now I cant go back to it. You told me, you know, that when a child is brought to a foreign country, it picks up the language in a few weeks, and forgets its own. Well, I am a child in your country. I have forgotten my own language, and can speak nothing but yours. Thats the real break-off with the corner of Tottenham Court Road. Leaving Wimpole Street finishes it.

PICKERING [*much alarmed*] Oh! but youre coming back to Wimpole Street, arnt you? Youll forgive Higgins?

HIGGINS [*rising*] Forgive! Will she, by George! Let her go. Let her find out how she can get on without us. She will relapse into the gutter in three weeks without me at her elbow.

Doolittle appears at the centre window. With a look of dignified reproach at Higgins, he comes slowly and silently to his daughter, who, with her back to the window, is unconscious of his approach.

PICKERING. He's incorrigible, Eliza. You wont relapse, will you?

LIZA. No: not now. Never again. I have learnt my lesson. I dont believe I could utter one of the old sounds if I tried. [*Doolittle touches her on her left shoulder. She drops her work, losing her self-possession utterly at the spectacle of her father's splendor*] A-a-a-a-a-ah-ow-ooh!

HIGGINS [*with a crow of triumph*] Aha! Just so. A-a-a-a-ahowooh! A-a-a-a-ahowooh! A-a-a-a-ahowooh! Victory! Victory! [*He throws himself on the divan, folding his arms, and spraddling arrogantly*].

DOOLITTLE. Can you blame the girl? Dont look at me like that, Eliza. It aint my fault. Ive come into some money.

LIZA. You must have touched a millionaire this time, dad.

DOOLITTLE. I have. But I'm dressed something special today. I'm going to St George's, Hanover Square. Your stepmother is going to marry me.

LIZA [*angrily*] Youre going to let yourself down to marry that low common woman!

PICKERING [*quietly*] He ought to, Eliza. [*To Doolittle*] Why has she changed her mind?

DOOLITTLE [*sadly*] Intimidated, Governor. Intimidated. Middle class morality claims its victim. Wont you put on your hat, Liza, and come and see me turned off?

LIZA. If the Colonel says I must, I – I'll [*almost sobbing*] I'll demean myself. And get insulted for my pains, like enough.

DOOLITTLE. Dont be afraid: she never comes to words with anyone now, poor woman! respectability has broke all the spirit out of her.

PICKERING [*squeezing Eliza's elbow gently*] Be kind to them, Eliza. Make the best of it.

LIZA [*forcing a little smile for him through her vexation*] Oh well, just to shew theres no ill feeling. I'll be back in a moment. [*She goes out*].

DOOLITTLE [*sitting down beside Pickering*] I feel uncommon nervous about the ceremony, Colonel. I wish youd come and see me through it.

PICKERING. But youve been through it before, man. You were married to Eliza's mother.

DOOLITTLE. Who told you that, Colonel?

PICKERING. Well, nobody told me. But I concluded – naturally –

DOOLITTLE. No: that aint the natural way, Colonel: it's only the middle class way. My way was always the undeserving way. But dont say nothing to Eliza. She dont know: I always had a delicacy about telling her.

PICKERING. Quite right. We'll leave it so, if you dont mind.

DOOLITTLE. And youll come to the church, Colonel, and put me through straight?

PICKERING. With pleasure. As far as a bachelor can.

MRS HIGGINS. May I come, Mr Doolittle? I should be very sorry to miss your wedding.

DOOLITTLE. I should indeed be honored by your condescension, maam; and my poor old woman would take it as a tremenjous compliment. She's been very low, thinking of the happy days that are no more.

MRS HIGGINS [*rising*] I'll order the carriage and get ready. [*The men rise, except Higgins*]. I shant be more than fifteen minutes. [*As she goes to the door Eliza comes in, hatted and buttoning her gloves*]. I'm going to the church to see your father married, Eliza. You had better come in the brougham with me. Colonel Pickering can go on with the bridegroom.

Mrs Higgins goes out. Eliza comes to the middle of the room between the centre window and the ottoman. Pickering joins her.

DOOLITTLE. Bridegroom! What a word! It makes a man realize his position, somehow. [*He takes up his hat and goes towards the door*].

PICKERING. Before I go, Eliza, do forgive Higgins and come back to us.

LIZA. I dont think dad would allow me. Would you, dad?

DOOLITTLE [*sad but magnanimous*] They played you off very cunning, Eliza, them two sportsmen. If it had been only one of them, you could have nailed him. But you see, there was two; and one of them chaperoned the other, as you might say. [*To Pickering*] It was artful of you, Colonel; but I bear no malice: I should have done the same myself. I been the victim of one woman after another all my life, and I dont grudge you two getting the better of Liza. I shant interfere. It's time for us to go, Colonel. So long, Henry. See you in St George's, Eliza. [*He goes out*].

PICKERING [*coaxing*] Do stay with us, Eliza. [*He follows Doolittle*].

Eliza goes out on the balcony to avoid being alone with Higgins. He rises and joins her there. She immediately comes back into the

room and makes for the door; but he goes along the balcony quickly and gets his back to the door before she reaches it.

HIGGINS. Well, Eliza, youve had a bit of your own back, as you call it. Have you had enough? and are you going to be reasonable? Or do you want any more?

LIZA. You want me back only to pick up your slippers and put up with your tempers and fetch and carry for you.

HIGGINS. I havnt said I wanted you back at all.

LIZA. Oh, indeed. Then what are we talking about?

HIGGINS. About you, not about me. If you come back I shall treat you just as I have always treated you. I cant change my nature; and I dont intend to change my manners. My manners are exactly the same as Colonel Pickering's.

LIZA. Thats not true. He treats a flower girl as if she was a duchess.

HIGGINS. And I treat a duchess as if she was a flower girl.

LIZA. I see. [*She turns away composedly, and sits on the ottoman, facing the window*]. The same to everybody.

HIGGINS. Just so.

LIZA. Like father.

HIGGINS [*grinning, a little taken down*] Without accepting the comparison at all points, Eliza, it's quite true that your father is not a snob, and that he will be quite at home in any station of life to which his eccentric destiny may call him. [*Seriously*] The great secret, Eliza, is not having bad manners or good manners or any other particular sort of manners, but having the same manner for all human souls: in short, behaving as if you were in Heaven, where there are no third-class carriages, and one soul is as good as another.

LIZA. Amen. You are a born preacher.

HIGGINS [*irritated*] The question is not whether I treat you rudely, but whether you ever heard me treat anyone else better.

LIZA [*with sudden sincerity*] I dont care how you treat me. I dont mind your swearing at me. I shouldnt mind a black eye: Ive had one before this. But [*standing up and facing him*] I wont be passed over.

HIGGINS. Then get out of my way; for I wont stop for you. You talk about me as if I were a motor bus.

LIZA. So you are a motor bus: all bounce and go, and no consideration for anyone. But I can do without you: dont think I cant.

HIGGINS. I know you can. I told you you could.

LIZA [*wounded, getting away from him to the other side of the ottoman with her face to the hearth*] I know you did, you brute. You wanted to get rid of me.

HIGGINS. Liar.

LIZA. Thank you. [*She sits down with dignity*].

HIGGINS. You never asked yourself, I suppose, whether *I* could do without *you*.

LIZA [*earnestly*] Dont you try to get round me. Youll have to do without me.

HIGGINS [*arrogant*] I can do without anybody. I have my own soul: my own spark of divine fire. But [*with sudden humility*] I shall miss you, Eliza. [*He sits down near her on the ottoman*]. I have learnt something from your idiotic notions: I confess that humbly and gratefully. And I have grown accustomed to your voice and appearance. I like them, rather.

LIZA. Well, you have both of them on your gramophone and in your book of photographs. When you feel lonely without me, you can turn the machine on. It's got no feelings to hurt.

HIGGINS. I cant turn your soul on. Leave me those feelings; and you can take away the voice and the face. They are not you.

LIZA. Oh, you are a devil. You can twist the heart in a girl as easy as some could twist her arms to hurt her. Mrs Pearce warned me. Time and again she has wanted to leave you; and you always got round her at the last minute. And you dont care a bit for her. And you dont care a bit for me.

HIGGINS. I care for life, for humanity; and you are a part of it that has come my way and been built into my house. What more can you or anyone ask?

LIZA. I wont care for anybody that doesnt care for me.

HIGGINS. Commercial principles, Eliza. Like [*reproducing her*

127

Covent Garden pronunciation with professional exactness]
s'yollin voylets [selling violets], isnt it?

LIZA. Dont sneer at me. It's mean to sneer at me.

HIGGINS. I have never sneered in my life. Sneering doesnt become either the human face or the human soul. I am expressing my righteous contempt for Commercialism. I dont and wont trade in affection. You call me a brute because you couldnt buy a claim on me by fetching my slippers and finding my spectacles. You were a fool: I think a woman fetching a man's slippers is a disgusting sight: did I ever fetch your slippers? I think a good deal more of you for throwing them in my face. No use slaving for me and then saying you want to be cared for: who cares for a slave? If you come back, come back for the sake of good fellowship; for youll get nothing else. Youve had a thousand times as much out of me as I have out of you; and if you dare to set up your little dog's tricks of fetching and carrying slippers against my creation of a Duchess Eliza, I'll slam the door in your silly face.

LIZA. What did you do it for if you didnt care for me?

HIGGINS [*heartily*] Why, because it was my job.

LIZA. You never thought of the trouble it would make for me.

HIGGINS. Would the world ever have been made if its maker had been afraid of making trouble? Making life means making trouble. Theres only one way of escaping trouble; and thats killing things. Cowards, you notice, are always shrieking to have troublesome people killed.

LIZA. I'm no preacher: I dont notice things like that. I notice that you dont notice me.

HIGGINS [*jumping up and walking about intolerantly*] Eliza: youre an idiot. I waste the treasures of my Miltonic mind by spreading them before you. Once for all, understand that I go my way and do my work without caring twopence what happens to either of us. I am not intimidated, like your father and your stepmother. So you can come back or go to the devil: which you please.

LIZA. What am I to come back for?

HIGGINS [*bouncing up on his knees on the ottoman and leaning over it to her*] For the fun of it. Thats why I took you on.

LIZA [*with averted face*] And you may throw me out tomorrow if I dont do everything you want me to?

HIGGINS. Yes; and you may walk out tomorrow if I dont do everything you want me to.

LIZA. And live with my stepmother?

HIGGINS. Yes, or sell flowers.

LIZA. Oh! If I only could go back to my flower basket! I should be independent of both you and father and all the world! Why did you take my independence from me? Why did I give it up? I'm a slave now, for all my fine clothes.

HIGGINS. Not a bit. I'll adopt you as my daughter and settle money on you if you like. Or would you rather marry Pickering?

LIZA [*looking fiercely round at him*] I wouldnt marry you if you asked me; and youre nearer my age than what he is.

HIGGINS [*gently*] Than he is: not 'than what he is'.

LIZA [*losing her temper and rising*] I'll talk as I like. Youre not my teacher now.

HIGGINS [*reflectively*] I dont suppose Pickering would, though. He's as confirmed an old bachelor as I am.

LIZA. Thats not what I want; and dont you think it. Ive always had chaps enough wanting me that way. Freddy Hill writes to me twice and three times a day, sheets and sheets.

HIGGINS [*disagreeably surprised*] Damn his impudence! [*He recoils and finds himself sitting on his heels*].

LIZA. He has a right to if he likes, poor lad. And he does love me.

HIGGINS [*getting off the ottoman*] You have no right to encourage him.

LIZA. Every girl has a right to be loved.

HIGGINS. What! By fools like that?

LIZA. Freddy's not a fool. And if he's weak and poor and wants me, may be he'd make me happier than my betters that bully me and dont want me.

HIGGINS. Can he make anything of you? Thats the point.

LIZA. Perhaps I could make something of him. But I never thought of us making anything of one another; and you never think of anything else. I only want to be natural.

HIGGINS. In short, you want me to be as infatuated about you as Freddy? Is that it?

LIZA. No I dont. Thats not the sort of feeling I want from you. And dont you be too sure of yourself or of me. I could have been a bad girl if I'd liked. Ive seen more of some things than you, for all your learning. Girls like me can drag gentlemen down to make love to them easy enough. And they wish each other dead the next minute.

HIGGINS. Of course they do. Then what in thunder are we quarrelling about?

LIZA [much troubled] I want a little kindness. I know I'm a common ignorant girl, and you a book-learned gentleman; but I'm not dirt under your feet. What I done [correcting herself] what I did was not for the dresses and the taxis: I did it because we were pleasant together and I come – came – to care for you; not to want you to make love to me, and not forgetting the difference between us, but more friendly like.

HIGGINS. Well, of course. Thats just how I feel. And how Pickering feels. Eliza: youre a fool.

LIZA. Thats not a proper answer to give me [she sinks on the chair at the writing-table in tears].

HIGGINS. It's all youll get until you stop being a common idiot. If youre going to be a lady, youll have to give up feeling neglected if the men you know dont spend half their time snivelling over you and the other half giving you black eyes. If you cant stand the coldness of my sort of life, and the strain of it, go back to the gutter. Work til youre more a brute than a human being; and then cuddle and squabble and drink til you fall asleep. Oh, it's a fine life, the life of the gutter. It's real: it's warm: it's violent: you can feel it through the thickest skin: you can taste it and smell it without any training or any work. Not like Science and Literature and Classical Music and Philosophy and Art. You find me cold, unfeeling, selfish, dont you? Very well: be off with you to the sort of people you like. Marry some sentimental hog or other with lots of money, and a thick pair of lips to kiss you with and a thick pair of boots to kick you with. If you cant appreciate what youve got, youd better get what you can appreciate.

LIZA [*desperate*] Oh, you are a cruel tyrant. I cant talk to you: you turn everything against me: I'm always in the wrong. But you know very well all the time that youre nothing but a bully. You know I cant go back to the gutter, as you call it, and that I have no real friends in the world but you and the Colonel. You know well I couldnt bear to live with a low common man after you two; and it's wicked and cruel of you to insult me by pretending I could. You think I must go back to Wimpole Street because I have nowhere else to go but father's. But dont you be too sure that you have me under your feet to be trampled on and talked down. I'll marry Freddy, I will, as soon as I'm able to support him.

HIGGINS [*thunderstruck*] Freddy!!! that young fool! That poor devil who couldnt get a job as an errand boy even if he had the guts to try for it! Woman: do you not understand that I have made you a consort for a king?

LIZA. Freddy loves me: that makes him king enough for me. I dont want him to work: he wasnt brought up to it as I was. I'll go and be a teacher.

HIGGINS. Whatll you teach, in heaven's name?

LIZA. What you taught me. I'll teach phonetics.

HIGGINS. Ha! ha! ha!

LIZA. I'll offer myself as an assistant to that hairyfaced Hungarian.

HIGGINS [*rising in a fury*] What! That impostor! that humbug! that toadying ignoramus! Teach him my methods! my discoveries! You take one step in his direction and I'll wring your neck. [*He lays hands on her*]. Do you hear?

LIZA [*defiantly non-resistant*] Wring away. What do I care? I knew youd strike me some day. [*He lets her go, stamping with rage at having forgotten himself, and recoils so hastily that he stumbles back into his seat on the ottoman*]. Aha! Now I know how to deal with you. What a fool I was not to think of it before! You cant take away the knowledge you gave me. You said I had a finer ear than you. And I can be civil and kind to people, which is more than you can. Aha! [*Purposely dropping her aitches to annoy him*] Thats done you, Enry Iggins, it az. Now I dont care that [*snapping her fingers*] for your bullying and your big talk. I'll advertize it in the papers that your duchess is only a flower girl that you taught, and that she'll teach anybody to be a duchess just the same in six months for a thousand guineas. Oh, when I think of myself crawling under your feet and being trampled on and called names, when all the time I had only to lift up my finger to be as good as you, I could just kick myself.

HIGGINS [*wondering at her*] You damned impudent slut, you! But it's better than snivelling; better than fetching slippers and finding spectacles, isnt it? [*Rising*] By George, Eliza, I said I'd make a woman of you; and I have. I like you like this.

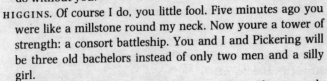

LIZA. Yes: you can turn round and make up to me now that I'm not afraid of you, and can do without you.

HIGGINS. Of course I do, you little fool. Five minutes ago you were like a millstone round my neck. Now youre a tower of strength: a consort battleship. You and I and Pickering will be three old bachelors instead of only two men and a silly girl.

Mrs Higgins returns, dressed for the wedding. Eliza instantly becomes cool and elegant.

MRS HIGGINS. The carriage is waiting, Eliza. Are you ready?

LIZA. Quite. Is the Professor coming?

MRS HIGGINS. Certainly not. He cant behave himself in church. He makes remarks out loud all the time on the clergyman's pronunciation.

LIZA. Then I shall not see you again, Professor. Goodbye. [*She goes to the door*].

MRS HIGGINS [*coming to Higgins*] Goodbye, dear.

HIGGINS. Goodbye, mother. [*He is about to kiss her, when he recollects something*]. Oh, by the way, Eliza, order a ham and a Stilton cheese, will you? And buy me a pair of reindeer gloves, number eights, and a tie to match that new suit of mine. You can choose the color. [*His cheerful, careless, vigorous voice shews that he is incorrigible*].

LIZA [*disdainfully*] Number eights are too small for you if you want them lined with lamb's wool. You have three new ties that you have forgotten in the drawer of your washstand. Colonel Pickering prefers double Gloucester to Stilton; and you dont notice the difference. I telephoned Mrs Pearce this morning not to forget the ham. What you are to do without me I cannot imagine. [*She sweeps out*].

MRS HIGGINS. I'm afraid youve spoilt that girl, Henry. I should be uneasy about you and her if she were less fond of Colonel Pickering.

HIGGINS. Pickering! Nonsense: she's going to marry Freddy. Ha ha! Freddy! Freddy!! Ha ha ha ha ha!!!!!

[*He roars with laughter as the play ends*].

The rest of the story need not be shewn in action, and indeed, would hardly need telling if our imaginations were not so enfeebled by their lazy dependence on the ready-mades and reach-me-downs of the ragshop in which Romance keeps its stock of 'happy endings' to misfit all stories. Now, the history of Eliza Doolittle, though called a romance because the transfiguration it records seems exceedingly improbable, is common enough. Such transfigurations have been achieved by hundreds of resolutely ambitious young women since Nell Gwynne set them the example by playing queens and fascinating kings in the theatre in which she began by selling oranges. Nevertheless, people in all directions have assumed, for no other reason than that she became the heroine of a romance, that she must have married the hero of it. This is unbearable, not only because her little drama, if acted on such a thoughtless assumption, must be spoiled, but because the true sequel is patent to anyone with a sense of human nature in general, and of feminine instinct in particular.

Eliza, in telling Higgins she would not marry him if he asked, was not coquetting: she was announcing a well-considered decision. When a bachelor interests, and dominates, and teaches, and becomes important to a spinster, as Higgins with Eliza, she always, if she has character enough to be capable of it, considers very seriously indeed whether she will play for becoming that bachelor's wife, especially if he is so little interested in marriage that a determined and devoted woman might capture him if she set herself resolutely to do it. Her decision will depend a good deal on whether she is really free to choose; and that, again, will depend on her age and income. If she is at the end of her youth, and has no security for her livelihood, she will marry him because she must marry anybody who will provide for her. But at Eliza's age a good-looking girl does not feel that pressure: she feels free to pick and choose. She is therefore guided by her instinct in the matter. Eliza's instinct tells her not to marry Higgins. It does not tell her to give him up. It is not in the slightest doubt as to his remaining one of the strongest personal interests in her life. It would be very sorely strained if there was another woman likely to supplant her with him. But as she feels sure of him on that last point, she has no doubt at all as to her course, and would not have any, even if the difference of twenty years in age, which seems so great to youth, did not exist between them.

As our own instincts are not appealed to by her conclusion, let us see whether we cannot discover some reason in it. When Higgins excused his indifference to young women on the ground that they had an irresistible rival in his mother, he gave the clue to his inveterate old-bachelordom. The case is uncommon only to the extent that remarkable mothers are uncommon. If an imaginative boy has a sufficiently rich mother who has intelligence, personal grace, dignity of character without harshness, and a cultivated sense of the best art of her time to enable her to make her house beautiful, she sets a standard for him against which very few women can struggle, besides effecting for him a disengagement of his affections, his sense of beauty, and his idealism from his specifically sexual impulses. This makes him a standing puzzle to the huge number of uncultivated people who have been brought up in tasteless homes by commonplace or disagreeable parents, and to whom, consequently, literature, painting, sculpture, music, and affectionate personal relations come as modes of sex if they come at all. The word passion means nothing else to them; and that Higgins could have a passion for phonetics and idealize his mother instead of Eliza, would seem to them absurd and unnatural. Nevertheless, when we look round and see that hardly anyone is too ugly or disagreeable to find a wife or a husband if he or she wants one, whilst many old maids and bachelors are above the average in quality and culture, we cannot help suspecting that the disentanglement of sex from the associations with which it is commonly confused, a disentanglement which persons of genius achieve by sheer intellectual analysis, is sometimes produced or aided by parental fascination.

Now, though Eliza was incapable of thus explaining to herself Higgins's formidable powers of resistance to the charm that prostrated Freddy at the first glance, she was instinctively aware that she could never obtain a complete grip of him, or come between him and his mother (the first necessity of the married woman). To put it shortly, she knew that for some mysterious reason he had not the makings of a married man in him, according to her conception of a husband as one to whom she would be his nearest and fondest and warmest interest. Even had there been no mother-rival, she would still have refused to accept an interest in herself that was secondary to philosophic interests. Had Mrs Higgins died, there would still have been Milton and the Universal Alphabet. Landor's remark that to those who have the greatest power of loving, love is a secondary affair, would not have recommended Landor to Eliza. Put that along with her resentment of Higgins's domineering superiority, and her mistrust of his coaxing cleverness in getting round her and evading her wrath when he had gone too far with his impetuous bullying, and you will see that Eliza's instinct had good grounds for warning her not to marry her Pygmalion.

And now, whom did Eliza marry? For if Higgins was a predestinate old bachelor, she was most certainly not a predestinate old maid. Well, that can be told very shortly to those who have not guessed it from the indications she has herself given them.

Almost immediately after Eliza is stung into proclaiming her considered determination not to marry Higgins, she mentions the fact that young Mr Frederick Eynsford Hill is pouring out his love for her daily through the post. Now Freddy is young, practically twenty years younger than Higgins: he is a gentleman (or, as Eliza would qualify him, a toff), and speaks like one. He is nicely dressed, is treated by the Colonel as an equal, loves her unaffectedly, and is not her master, nor ever likely to dominate her in spite of his advantage of social standing. Eliza has no use for the foolish romantic tradition that all women love to be mastered, if not actually bullied and beaten. 'When you go to women' says Nietzsche 'take your whip with you.' Sensible despots have never confined that precaution to women: they have taken their whips with them when they have dealt with men, and been slavishly idealized by the men over whom they have flourished the whip much more than by women. No doubt there are slavish women as well as slavish men; and women, like men, admire those that are  stronger than themselves. But to admire a strong person and to live under that strong person's thumb are two different things. The weak may not be admired and hero-worshipped; but they are by no means disliked or shunned; and they never seem to have the least difficulty in marrying people who are too good for them. They may fail in emergencies; but life is not one long emergency: it is mostly a string of situations for which no exceptional strength is needed, and with which even rather weak people can cope if they have a stronger partner to help them out. Accordingly, it is a truth everywhere in evidence that strong people, masculine or feminine, not only do not marry stronger people, but do not shew any preference for them in selecting their friends. When a lion meets another with a louder roar 'the first lion thinks the last a bore'. The man or woman who feels strong enough for two, seeks for every other quality in a partner than strength.

The converse is also true. Weak people want to marry strong people who do not frighten them too much; and this often leads them to make the mistake we describe metaphorically as 'biting off more than they can chew'. They want too much for too little; and when the bargain is unreasonable beyond all bearing, the union becomes impossible: it ends in the weaker party being either discarded or borne as a cross, which is worse. People who are not only weak, but silly or obtuse as well, are often in these difficulties.

This being the state of human affairs, what is Eliza fairly sure to do when she is placed between Freddy and Higgins? Will she look forward to a lifetime of fetching Higgins's slippers or to a lifetime of Freddy fetching hers? There can be no doubt about the answer. Unless Freddy is biologically repulsive to her, and Higgins biologically attractive to a degree that overwhelms all her other instincts, she will, if she marries either of them, marry Freddy.

And that is just what Eliza did.

Complications ensued; but they were economic, not romantic. Freddy had no money and no occupation. His mother's jointure, a last relic of the opulence of Largelady Park, had enabled her to struggle along in Earlscourt with an air of gentility, but not to procure any serious secondary education for her children, much less give the boy a profession. A clerkship at thirty shillings a week was beneath Freddy's dignity, and extremely distasteful to him besides. His prospects consisted of a hope that if he kept up appearances somebody would do something for him. The something appeared vaguely to his imagination as a private secretary-ship or a sinecure of some sort. To his mother it perhaps appeared as a marriage to some lady of means who could not resist her boy's niceness. Fancy her feelings when he married a flower girl who had become disclassed under extraordinary circumstances which were now notorious!

It is true that Eliza's situation did not seem wholly ineligible. Her father, though formerly a dustman, and now fantastically disclassed, had become extremely popular in the smartest society by a social talent which triumphed over every prejudice and every disadvantage. Rejected by the middle class, which he loathed, he had shot up at once into the highest circles by his wit, his dustmanship (which he carried like a banner), and his Nietzschean transcendence of good and evil. At intimate ducal dinners he sat on the right-hand of the Duchess; and in country houses he smoked in the pantry and was made much of by the butler when he was not feeding in the dining room and being consulted by cabinet ministers. But he found it almost as hard to do all this on four thousand a year as Mrs Eynsford Hill to live in Earlscourt on an income so pitiably smaller that I have not the heart to disclose its exact figure. He absolutely refused to add the last straw to his burden by contributing to Eliza's support.

Thus Freddy and Eliza, now Mr and Mrs Eynsford Hill, would have spent a penniless honeymoon but for a wedding present of £500 from the Colonel to Eliza. It lasted a long time because

Freddy did not know how to spend money, never having had any to spend, and Eliza, socially trained by a pair of old bachelors, wore her clothes as long as they held together and looked pretty, without the least regard to their being many months out of fashion. Still, £500 will not last two young people for ever; and they both knew, and Eliza felt as well, that they must shift themselves in the end. She could quarter herself on Wimpole Street because it had come to be her home; but she was quite aware that she ought not to quarter Freddy there, and that it would not be good for his character if she did.

Not that the Wimpole Street bachelors objected. When she consulted them, Higgins declined to be bothered about her housing problem when that solution was so simple. Eliza's desire to have Freddy in the house with her seemed of no more importance than if she had wanted an extra piece of bedroom furniture. Pleas as to Freddy's character, and the moral obligation on him to earn his own living, were lost on Higgins. He denied that Freddy had any character, and declared that if he tried to do any useful work some competent person would have the trouble of undoing it: a procedure involving a net loss to the community, and great unhappiness to Freddy himself, who was obviously intended by Nature for such light work as amusing Eliza, which, Higgins declared, was a much more useful and honorable occupation than working in the city. When Eliza referred again to her project of teaching phonetics, Higgins abated not a jot of his violent opposition to it. He said she was not within ten years of being qualified to meddle with his pet subject; and as it was evident that the Colonel agreed with him, she felt she could not go against them in this grave matter, and that she had no right, without Higgins's consent, to exploit the knowledge he had given her; for his knowledge seemed to her as much his private property as his watch: Eliza was no communist. Besides, she was superstitiously devoted to them both, more entirely and frankly after her marriage than before it.

It was the Colonel who finally solved the problem, which had cost him much perplexed cogitation. He one day asked Eliza, rather shyly, whether she had quite given up her notion of keeping a flower shop. She replied that she had thought of it, but had put it out of her head, because the Colonel had said, that day at Mrs Higgins's, that it would never do. The Colonel confessed that when he said that, he had not quite recovered from the dazzling impression of the day before. They broke the matter to Higgins that evening. The sole comment vouchsafed by him very nearly led to a serious quarrel with Eliza. It was to the effect that she would have in Freddy an ideal errand boy.

Freddy himself was next sounded on the subject. He said he had been thinking of a shop himself; though it had presented itself to his pennilessness as a small place in which Eliza should sell tobacco at one counter whilst he sold newspapers at the opposite one. But he agreed that it would be extraordinarily jolly to go early every morning with Eliza to Covent Garden and buy flowers on the scene of their first meeting: a sentiment which earned him many kisses from his wife. He added that he had always been afraid to propose anything of the sort, because Clara would make an awful row about a step that must damage her matrimonial chances, and his mother could not be expected to like it after clinging for so many years to that step of the social ladder on which retail trade is impossible.

This difficulty was removed by an event highly unexpected by Freddy's mother. Clara, in the course of her incursions into those artistic circles which were the highest within her reach, discovered that her conversational qualifications were expected to include a grounding in the novels of Mr H. G. Wells. She borrowed them in various directions so energetically that she swallowed them all within two months. The result was a conversion of a kind quite common today. A modern Acts of the Apostles would fill fifty whole Bibles if anyone were capable of writing it.

Poor Clara, who appeared to Higgins and his mother as a disagreeable and ridiculous person, and to her own mother as in some inexplicable way a social failure, had never seen herself in either light; for, though to some extent ridiculed and mimicked in West Kensington like everybody else there, she was accepted as a rational and normal – or shall we say inevitable? – sort of human being. At worst they called her The Pusher; but to them no more than to herself had it ever occurred that she was pushing the air, and pushing it in a wrong direction. Still, she was not happy. She was growing desperate. Her one asset, the fact that her mother was what the Epsom greengrocer called a carriage lady, had no exchange value, apparently. It had prevented her from getting educated, because the only education she could have afforded was education with the Earlscourt greengrocer's daughter. It had led her to seek the society of  her mother's class; and that class simply would not have her, because she was much poorer than the greengrocer, and, far from being able to afford a maid, could not afford even a housemaid, and had to scrape along at home with an illiberally treated general servant. Under such circumstances nothing could give her an air of being a genuine product of Largelady Park. And yet its tradition made her regard a marriage with anyone within her reach as an unbearable humiliation. Commercial people and professional people in a small way were odious to her. She ran after painters and novelists; but she did not charm them; and her bold attempts to pick up and practise artistic and literary talk irritated them. She was, in short, an utter failure, an ignorant, incompetent, pretentious, unwelcome, penniless, useless little snob; and though she did not admit these disqualifications (for nobody ever faces unpleasant truths of this kind until the possibility of a way out dawns on them) she felt their effects too keenly to be satisfied with her position.

Clara had a startling eyeopener when, on being suddenly wakened to enthusiasm by a girl of her own age who dazzled her and produced in her a gushing desire to take her for a model, and gain her friendship, she discovered that this exquisite apparition had graduated from the gutter in a few months time. It shook her so violently, that when Mr H. G. Wells lifted her on the point of his puissant pen, and placed her at the angle of view from which the life she was leading and the society to which she clung appeared in its true relation to real human needs and worthy social structure, he effected a conversion and a conviction of sin comparable to the most sensational feats of General Booth or Gypsy Smith. Clara's snobbery went bang. Life suddenly began to move with her. Without knowing how or why, she began to make friends and enemies. Some of the acquaintances to whom she had been a tedious or indifferent or ridiculous affliction, dropped her: others became cordial. To her amazement she found that some 'quite nice' people were saturated with Wells, and that this accessibility to ideas was the secret of their niceness. People she had thought deeply religious and had tried to conciliate on that tack with disastrous results, suddenly took an interest in her, and revealed a hostility to conventional religion which she had never conceived possible except among the most desperate characters. They made her read Galsworthy; and Galsworthy exposed the vanity of Largelady Park and finished her. It exasperated her to think that the dungeon in which she had languished for so many unhappy years had been unlocked all the time, and that the im-

pulses she had so carefully struggled with and stifled for the sake of keeping well with society, were precisely those by which alone she could have come into any sort of sincere human contact. In the radiance of these discoveries, and the tumult of their reaction, she made a fool of herself as freely and conspicuously as when she so rashly adopted Eliza's expletive in Mrs Higgins's drawing room; for the new-born Wellsian had to find her bearings almost as ridiculously as a baby; but nobody hates a baby for its ineptitudes, or thinks the worse of it for trying to eat the matches; and Clara lost no friends by her follies. They laughed at her to her face this time; and she had to defend herself and fight it out as best she could.

When Freddy paid a visit to Earlscourt (which he never did when he could possibly help it) to make the desolating announcement that he and his Eliza were thinking of blackening the Largelady scutcheon by opening a shop, he found the little household already convulsed by a prior announcement from Clara that she also was going to work in an old furniture shop in Dover Street, which had been started by a fellow Wellsian. This appointment Clara owed, after all, to her old social accomplishment of Push. She had made up her mind that, cost what it might, she would see Mr Wells in the flesh; and she had achieved her end at a garden party. She had better luck than so rash an enterprise deserved. Mr Wells came up to her expectations. Age had not withered him, nor could custom stale his

infinite variety in half an hour. His pleasant neatness and compactness, his small hands and feet, his teeming ready brain, his unaffected accessibility, and a certain fine apprehensiveness which stamped him as susceptible from his topmost hair to his tipmost toe, proved irresistible. Clara talked of nothing else for weeks and weeks afterwards. And as she happened to talk to the lady of the furniture shop, and that lady also desired above all things to know Mr Wells and sell pretty things to him, she offered Clara a job on the chance of achieving that end through her.

And so it came about that Eliza's luck held, and the expected opposition to the flower shop melted away. The shop is in the arcade of a railway station not very far from the Victoria and Albert Museum; and if you live in that neighborhood you may go there any day and buy a buttonhole from Eliza.

Now here is a last opportunity for romance. Would you not like to be assured that the shop was an immense success, thanks to Eliza's charms and her early business experience in Covent Garden? Alas! the truth is the truth: the shop did not pay for a long time, simply because Eliza and her Freddy did not know how to keep it. True, Eliza had not to begin at the very beginning: she knew the names and prices of the cheaper flowers; and her elation was unbounded when she found that Freddy, like all youths educated at cheap, pretentious, and thoroughly inefficient schools, knew a little Latin. It was very little, but enough to make him appear to her a Porson or Bentley, and to put him at his ease with botanical nomenclature. Unfortunately he knew nothing else; and Eliza, though she could count money up to eighteen shillings or so, and had acquired a certain familiarity with the language of Milton from her struggles to qualify herself for winning Higgins's bet, could not write out a bill without utterly disgracing the establishment. Freddy's power of stating in Latin that Balbus built a wall and that Gaul was divided into three parts did not carry with it the slightest knowledge of accounts or business: Colonel Pickering had to explain to him what a cheque book and a bank account meant. And the pair were by no means easily teachable. Freddy backed up Eliza in her obstinate refusal to believe that they could save money by engaging a bookkeeper with some knowledge of the business. How, they argued, could you possibly save money by going to extra expense when you already could not make both ends meet? But the Colonel, after making the ends meet over and over again, at last gently insisted; and Eliza, humbled to the dust by having to beg from him so often, and stung by the uproarious derision of Higgins, to whom the notion of Freddy succeeding at anything was a joke that never palled, grasped the fact that business, like phonetics, has to be learned.

On the piteous spectacle of the pair spending their evenings in shorthand schools and polytechnic classes, learning book-keeping and typewriting with incipient junior clerks, male and female, from the elementary schools, let me not dwell. There were even classes at the London School of Economics, and a humble personal appeal to the director of that institution to recommend a course bearing on the flower business. He, being a humorist, explained to them the method of the celebrated Dickensian essay on Chinese Metaphysics by the gentleman who read an article on China and an article on Metaphysics and combined the information. He suggested that they should combine the London School with Kew Gardens. Eliza, to whom the procedure of the Dickensian gentleman seemed perfectly correct (as in fact it was) and not in the least funny (which was only her ignorance), took the advice with entire gravity. But the effort that cost her the deepest humiliation was a request to Higgins, whose pet artistic fancy, next to Milton's verse, was calligraphy, and who himself wrote a most beautiful Italian hand, that he would teach her to write. He declared that she was congenitally incapable of forming a single letter worthy of the least of Milton's words; but she persisted; and again he suddenly threw himself into the task of teaching her with a combination of stormy intensity, concentrated patience, and occasional bursts of interesting disquisition on the beauty and nobility, the august mission and destiny, of human handwriting. Eliza ended by acquiring an extremely uncommercial script which was a positive extension of her personal beauty, and spending three times as much on stationery as anyone else because certain qualities and shapes of paper became indispensable to her. She could not even address an envelope in the usual way because it made the margins all wrong.

Their commercial schooldays were a period of disgrace and despair for the young couple. They seemed to be learning nothing about flower shops. At last they gave it up as hopeless, and shook the dust of the shorthand schools, and the polytechnics, and the London School of Economics from their feet for ever. Besides, the business was in some mysterious way beginning to take care of itself. They had somehow forgotten their objections to employing other people. They came to the

conclusion that their own way was the best, and that they had really a remarkable talent for business. The Colonel, who had been compelled for some years to keep a sufficient sum on current account at his bankers to make up their deficits, found that the provision was unnecessary: the young people were prospering. It is true that there was not quite fair play between them and their competitors in trade. Their week-ends in the country cost them nothing, and saved them the price of their Sunday dinners; for the motor car was the Colonel's; and he and Higgins paid the hotel bills. Mr F. Hill, florist and greengrocer (they soon discovered that there was money in asparagus; and asparagus led to other vegetables), had an air which stamped the business as classy; and in private life he was still Frederick Eynsford Hill, Esquire. Not that there was any swank about him: nobody but Eliza knew that he had been christened Frederick Challoner. Eliza herself swanked like anything.

That is all. That is how it has turned out. It is astonishing how much Eliza still manages to meddle in the housekeeping at Wimpole Street in spite of the shop and her own family. And it is notable that though she never nags her husband, and frankly loves the Colonel as if she were his favorite daughter, she has never got out of the habit of nagging Higgins that was established on the fatal night when she won his bet for him. She snaps his head off on the faintest provocation, or on none. He no longer dares to tease her by as-

suming an abysmal inferiority of Freddy's mind to his own. He storms and bullies and derides; but she stands up to him so ruthlessly that the Colonel has to ask her from time to time to be kinder to Higgins; and it is the only request of his that brings a mulish expression into her face. Nothing but some emergency or calamity great enough to break down all likes and dislikes, and throw them both back on their common humanity – and may they be spared any such trial! – will ever alter this. She knows that Higgins does not need her, just as her father did not need her. The very scrupulousness with which he told her that day that he had become used to having her there, and dependent on her for all sorts of little services, and that he should miss her if she went away (it would never have occurred to Freddy or the Colonel to say anything of the sort) deepens her inner certainty that she is 'no more to him than them slippers'; yet she has a sense, too, that his indifference is deeper than the infatuation of commoner souls. She is immensely interested in him. She has even secret mischievous moments in which she wishes she could get him alone, on a desert island, away from all ties and with nobody else in the world to consider, and just drag him off his pedestal and see him making love like any common man. We all have private imaginations of that sort. But when it comes to business, to the life that she really leads as distinguished from the life of dreams and fancies, she likes Freddy and she likes the Colonel; and she does not like Higgins and Mr Doolittle. Galatea never does quite like Pygmalion: his relation to her is too godlike to be altogether agreeable.

PYGMALION

Composition begun 7 March 1912; completed early June 1912. First published in German translation, 1913. Published in *Everybody's Magazine* (New York), November 1914, and in *Nash's Magazine*, November–December 1914. First collected in *Androcles and the Lion, Overruled, Pygmalion*, 1916. Revised 1941 for separate printing of *Pygmalion* in Standard Edition text, also incorporating several revised sequences from the film scenario. This revision was followed for the Penguin Books edition later in 1941. First presented in German at the Hofburg Theater, Vienna, on 16 October 1913. First presented in English at His Majesty's Theatre, London, on 11 April 1914.

Clara Eynsford-Hill   *Margaret Bussé*
Mrs Eynsford-Hill   *Carlotta Addison*
A Bystander   *Roy Byford*
Freddy Eynsford-Hill   *Algernon Greig*
Eliza Doolittle   *Mrs Patrick Campbell*
Colonel Pickering   *Philip Merivale*
Henry Higgins   *Herbert Tree*
A Sarcastic Bystander   *Alexander Sarner*
Mrs Pearce   *Geraldine Olliffe*
Alfred Doolittle   *Edmund Gurney*
Mrs Higgins   *Rosamond Mayne-Young*
Parlormaid   *Irene Delisse*

Period—The Present

READ MORE IN PENGUIN

In every corner of the world, on every subject under the sun, Penguin represents quality and variety – the very best in publishing today.

For complete information about books available from Penguin – including Puffins, Penguin Classics and Arkana – and how to order them, write to us at the appropriate address below. Please note that for copyright reasons the selection of books varies from country to country.

In the United Kingdom: Please write to *Dept. JC, Penguin Books Ltd, FREEPOST, West Drayton, Middlesex UB7 0BR*

If you have any difficulty in obtaining a title, please send your order with the correct money, plus ten per cent for postage and packaging, to *PO Box No. 11, West Drayton, Middlesex UB7 0BR*

In the United States: Please write to *Penguin USA Inc., 375 Hudson Street, New York, NY 10014*

In Canada: Please write to *Penguin Books Canada Ltd, 10 Alcorn Avenue, Suite 300, Toronto, Ontario M4V 3B2*

In Australia: Please write to *Penguin Books Australia Ltd, 487 Maroondah Highway, Ringwood, Victoria 3134*

In New Zealand: Please write to *Penguin Books (NZ) Ltd, 182–190 Wairau Road, Private Bag, Takapuna, Auckland 9*

In India: Please write to *Penguin Books India Pvt Ltd, 706 Eros Apartments, 56 Nehru Place, New Delhi 110 019*

In the Netherlands: Please write to *Penguin Books Netherlands B.V., Keizersgracht 231 NL–1016 DV Amsterdam*

In Germany: Please write to *Penguin Books Deutschland GmbH, Friedrichstrasse 10–12, W–6000 Frankfurt/Main 1*

In Spain: Please write to *Penguin Books S. A., C. San Bernardo 117–6° E–28015 Madrid*

In Italy: Please write to *Penguin Italia s.r.l., Via Felice Casati 20, I–20124 Milano*

In France: Please write to *Penguin France S. A., 17 rue Lejeune, F–31000 Toulouse*

In Japan: Please write to *Penguin Books Japan, Ishikiribashi Building, 2–5–4, Suido, Tokyo 112*

In Greece: Please write to *Penguin Hellas Ltd, Dimocritou 3, GR–106 71 Athens*

In South Africa: Please write to *Longman Penguin Southern Africa (Pty) Ltd, Private Bag X08, Bertsham 2013*

READ MORE IN PENGUIN

A CHOICE OF TWENTIETH - CENTURY CLASSICS

Ulysses James Joyce

Ulysses is unquestionably one of the supreme masterpieces, in any artistic form, of the twentieth century. A modernist classic, its ceaseless verbal inventiveness and astonishingly wide-ranging allusions confirm its standing as an imperishable monument to the human condition. 'It is the book to which we are all indebted and from which none of us can escape' – T. S. Eliot

The End of the Affair Graham Greene

'One of the most personal and most interesting of Greene's stories, containing not only his mature thoughts on the literary life and the dubious fame it brings, but also on the nature of an adulterous love affair, the joy and guilt it generates in roughly equal proportions' – Anthony Curtis in the *Financial Times*

Tigers are Better-Looking Jean Rhys

Jean Rhys wrote about women – society's victims – with all the passion and despair of a loser. Set in Paris, London and the Caribbean, her bitter-sweet, tantalizingly evocative stories conjure up the loneliness of a rented room, the regrets of a failed love affair and the temporary oblivion of alcohol with astonishing power and poignancy.

Babbitt Sinclair Lewis

In chronicling the follies, ambitions and fantasies of Babbitt, Sinclair Lewis captures with superb realism and biting satire the small-town mentality of America in the twenties. 'One of the greatest novels I have read for a long time' – H. G. Wells

The End of the Chapter John Galsworthy

Here Galsworthy writes about the lives and loves of the Cherrells, cousins of the Forsytes. Galsworthy's grasp of political and social change and its effect on a family, as well as his incisive sense of character, make this a fine trilogy with which to end The Forsyte Saga.

READ MORE IN PENGUIN

A CHOICE OF TWENTIETH - CENTURY CLASSICS

Between the Acts Virginia Woolf

'Her posthumous novel ... suggests several new directions ... Its weave of past and present, quotidian reality and imminent catastrophe, the thin line between civilization and barbarism, its erotic overtones and continual humour make a powerful and prophetic statement' – *The Times*

Gentlemen Prefer Blondes Anita Loos

Gentlemen Prefer Blondes had its first acclaimed appearance in *Harpers Bazaar* and was later made famous on stage and screen. In this brilliant satire of the Jazz Age Anita Loos has created the funniest Bad Blonde in American literature.

The Living and the Dead Patrick White

To hesitate on the edge of life or to plunge in and risk change – this is the dilemma explored in *The Living and the Dead*. 'Scene after scene is worked out with an exactness and subtlety which no second-string novelist can scent, far less nail to paper' – *Time*. 'He is, in the finest sense, a world novelist' – *Guardian*

Go Tell It on the Mountain James Baldwin

'*Mountain* is the book I had to write if I was ever going to write anything else. I had to deal with what hurt me most. I had to deal with my father' – James Baldwin. 'Passionately eloquent' – *The Times*

Memories of a Catholic Girlhood Mary McCarthy

Blending memories and family myths, Mary McCarthy takes us back to the twenties, when she was orphaned in a world of relations as colourful, potent and mysterious as the Catholic religion. 'Superb ... so heartbreaking that in comparison Jane Eyre seems to have got off lightly' – Anita Brookner

READ MORE IN PENGUIN

A CHOICE OF TWENTIETH - CENTURY CLASSICS

The Sea of Fertility   Yukio Mishima

'Mishima's thrilling storytelling is unique; there is nothing like it. His flashing style is perfect for his dark motives and there are times when his words are so splendid, and his concepts so tragic, that reading him becomes a profound experience' – Ronald Blythe in the *Sunday Times*

Nineteen Eighty-Four   George Orwell

'It is a volley against the authoritarian in every personality, a polemic against every orthodoxy, an anarchistic blast against every unquestioning conformist ... *Nineteen Eighty-Four* is a great novel and a great tract because of the clarity of its call, and it will endure because its message is a permanent one: erroneous thought is the stuff of freedom' – Ben Pimlott

The Outsider   Albert Camus

Meursault leads an apparently unremarkable bachelor life in Algiers, until his involvement in a violent incident calls into question the fundamental values of society. 'Few French writers of this century have been more versatile or more influential than Camus ... No one in his lifetime wrote better prose than he, no one better blended conviction and grace of style' – *The Times*

Mittee   Daphne Rooke

Daphne Rooke is one of South Africa's finest post-war novelists and *Mittee*, set in nineteenth-century Transvaal, remains her masterpiece. Juxtaposing violence and sexuality, the novel is a searing indictment of the alienation created by the excesses of Afrikaaner nationalism.

The Home and the World   Rabindranath Tagore

Rabindranath Tagore's powerful novel, set on a Bengali noble's estate in 1908, is both a love story and a novel of political awakening. 'It has the complexity and tragic dimensions of Tagore's own time, and ours' – Anita Desai

READ MORE IN PENGUIN

A SELECTION OF PLAYS

READ MORE IN PENGUIN

THE PLAYS OF BERNARD SHAW

'Shaw has redeemed and embellished our fantasies' – Raymond Williams. The complete dramatic works of Bernard Shaw are now published in paperback for the first time, definitive texts under the editorial supervision of Dan H. Laurence.

THE BERNARD SHAW LIBRARY

Androcles and the Lion
The Apple Cart
Back to Methuselah
The Doctor's Dilemma
Getting Married/Press Cuttings
Heartbreak House
Major Barbara
Man and Superman
Plays Extravagant
(The Millionairess, Too True to be Good, The Simpleton of the Unexpected Isles)
Plays Pleasant
(Arms and the Man, Candida, The Man of Destiny, You Never Can Tell)
Plays Political
(The Apple Cart, On the Rocks, Geneva)
Plays Unpleasant
(Widowers' Houses, The Philanderer, Mrs Warren's Profession)
Pygmalion
Saint Joan
Selected Short Plays
(including The Admirable Bashville and Great Catherine)
The Shewing-Up of Blanco Posnet and **Fanny's First Play**
Three Plays for Puritans
(The Devil's Disciple, Caesar and Cleopatra, Captain Brassbound's Conversion)

PUBLISHED IN PENGUIN PLAYS

John Bull's Other Island
Misalliance and the Fascinating Foundling